# The Book of Mormon and DNA Research

THE BEST OF THE
MAXWELL INSTITUTE

# THE
# BOOK
## OF
# MORMON
# —AND—
# DNA RESEARCH

Essays from *The FARMS Review*
and the *Journal of Book of Mormon Studies*

Edited by Daniel C. Peterson

The Neal A. Maxwell Institute for Religious Scholarship
Brigham Young University
Provo, Utah

Cover design by Jacob D. Rawlins

The Neal A. Maxwell Institute for Religious Scholarship
Brigham Young University
200 WAIH
Provo, UT 84602

### Library of Congress Cataloging-in-Publication Data

The Book of Mormon and DNA research : essays from the Farms review and the
Journal of Book of Mormon studies / edited by Daniel C. Peterson.
    p. cm.
Includes bibliographical references and index.
ISBN 978-0-8425-2706-4 (alk. paper)
1. Book of Mormon. 2. DNA—Analysis. 3. Lehi (Book of Mormon figure) 4. Nephi
(Book of Mormon figure) 5. Indians—Origin. I. Peterson, Daniel C.
BX8627.B62733 2008
289.3'22—dc22
                      2008017034

# Contents

# About the Contributors

John M. Butler holds a doctoral degree in chemistry from the University of Virginia and is the author of eighty research articles and book chapters on human DNA, including essays on Y-chromosome and mitochondrial DNA as applied to human-identity testing. He has received a number of awards in the field of forensic genetics and is the author of the award-winning textbook *Forensic DNA Typing*, now in its second edition. In July 2002, Butler received the Presidential Early Career Award for Scientists and Engineers from President George W. Bush in a White House ceremony for his work in pioneering modern forensic DNA testing. He is currently employed as a research chemist in the Biochemical Science Division at the U.S. National Institute of Standards and Technology, where he directs a project team developing new DNA technologies for forensic and human-identity applications.

David A. McClellan earned a PhD from Louisiana State University. He is an assistant professor of integrative biology at Brigham Young University, where he researches the theoretical aspects of protein and DNA molecular evolution. This includes mathematical and statistical modeling, software and other methodology development, and empirical analysis of protein-coding gene sequences.

D. Jeffrey Meldrum holds a PhD in anatomical sciences with an emphasis in physical anthropology from SUNY at Stony Brook. As an associate professor of biology at Idaho State University, he teaches human anatomy and evolution. His research in evolutionary morphology and paleontology centers on primate and human locomotion.

Matthew Roper, who received a master's degree from Brigham Young University, is a resident scholar at the Neal A. Maxwell Institute for Religious Scholarship.

John L. Sorenson, who earned his PhD at UCLA, is emeritus professor of anthropology at Brigham Young University. His major interest has been in applied sociocultural anthropology. He served as head social scientist at General Research Corporation in Santa Barbara, California, and was founder and president of Bonneville Research Corporation in Provo, Utah. He has published extensively in Mesoamerican archaeology.

Trent D. Stephens holds a PhD in anatomy and embryology from the University of Pennsylvania. He is a professor of biology at Idaho State University, and his research in embryology and teratology focuses on the mechanisms of limb development.

Brian D. Stubbs earned a PhD from the University of Utah and now teaches English, Spanish, and ESL at the College of Eastern Utah–San Juan Campus, where he also does research on the Ute, Hopi, and Tewa languages spoken in the region.

Michael F. Whiting holds a PhD in entomology from Cornell University. He has received multiple National Science Foundation (NSF) grants (including the prestigious NSF CAREER award), regularly serves on review panels for NSF, and is director of Brigham Young University's DNA Sequencing Center and an associate professor in Brigham Young University's Department of Integrative Biology.

# Introduction

*Daniel C. Peterson*

"The normal way of dealing with the Book of Mormon 'scientifically,'" wrote Hugh Nibley in 1967, "has been first to attribute to the Book of Mormon something it did not say, and then to refute the claim by scientific statements that have not been proven."[1]

More than forty years later, Professor Nibley's words still ring true.

In this volume, the first in the series The Best of the Maxwell Institute, we present articles written by contributors to both the *Journal of Book of Mormon Studies* and *The FARMS Review* that deal specifically with the subject of DNA and the Book of Mormon. Where applicable, we have updated the references to reflect later publications. Although the question of limited geography is strongly linked to DNA and the Book of Mormon, we will not be dealing with that in this volume. It will appear in a volume on approaches to the Book of Mormon. However, a comprehensive survey of the literature by Matthew Roper can be found in *The FARMS Review* 16/2 (2004) 225–74, and on the Maxwell Institute Web site.

The first article, John L. Sorenson's "The Problematic Role of DNA Testing in Unraveling Human History," was published before the so-called controversy about DNA and the Book of Mormon had drawn much attention among the general public. Sorenson's article serves as an introduction to the subject, highlighting the complexity of the research and the tools used to conduct it. In a short piece, John M. Butler, the lead scientist in developing DNA tests that identify the victims of the attacks on the World Trade Center on September 11, 2001, points to the insurmountable difficulties in identifying the genetic heritage of the chief ancestors of the Lehite peoples. One of his points is that the females in the Lehite colonies all inherited their mitochondrial DNA from Ishmael's wife, about whom we know almost nothing, including whether she was a full-blooded Israelite.

"Before DNA," by John L. Sorenson and Matthew Roper, sets out the major cultural, historical, and theological questions that a person must attempt to answer before turning to science. Though necessarily brief, their answers to fourteen questions bring us inside what scholars have learned during the past century about ancient America. John Butler's second piece in this collection, "Addressing Questions surrounding the Book of Mormon and DNA Research," gives an in-depth study of DNA with regard to ancestry studies. He insightfully addresses the tension between science and religion as he turns the question of DNA ancestry studies to the Book of Mormon.

Michael F. Whiting's DNA-related work on walking sticks that re-evolved the ability to fly 50 million years after losing it was featured in the 16 January 2003 issue of the journal *Nature*. In "DNA and the Book of Mormon: A Phylogenetic Perspective," Whiting, a BYU professor of biology, frames the challenges of creating an experiment that could determine scientifically which Native Americans are descendants of any of the three known colonizing groups mentioned in the Book of Mormon. He concludes that, given the present state of science, such an experiment is impossible to design and would not be taken seriously by the scientific community.

In "Detecting Lehi's Genetic Signature: Possible, Probable, or Not?" David A. McClellan, who differs from the most prominent critics on this issue in being an actual scientist actually specializing in human genetics, offers a challenging but essential basic overview of the biology relevant to serious discussion of questions involving DNA. But he does *not* expect to find "an Israelite genetic presence in Central America and perhaps as far away as Arizona to the north and Colombia to the south." McClellan points out that proper interpretation of Native American population genetic data in the context of Latter-day Saint claims about ancient migrations to the Americas by a few families from the Middle East requires a preliminary understanding of several fairly complex concepts, including scientific method, basic genomics and genetics, molecular evolution, population genetics, and genealogical inference from molecular data. His essay seeks to outline these concepts in layman's terms and to evaluate the current status of Native American genetic data in light of these concepts in order to evaluate the plausibility of the Book of Mormon story line. McClellan's general conclusion is that, although it may be possible to recover the genetic signature of a few migrating families from 2,600 years ago, it is not probable. However, the data suggest that there has been a trickle of gene flow to the Americas from non-Asiatic source populations. Though far from verifying or proving the Book of Mormon, these data do allow for the plausibility of its story line.

Two biologists from Idaho State University, D. Jeffrey Meldrum and Trent D. Stephens, focus on DNA questions touching on the descendants of Lehi and Sariah in their essay entitled "Who Are the Children of Lehi?" One of their chief points has to do with the traceable genetic characteristics that a person inherits from distant ancestors. By appealing to straightforward genealogical research, they show that the chance of scientifically tracing a person's genetic heritage by DNA alone is highly remote. This observation has important consequences for any DNA research that seeks to identify descendants of the Lamanite survivors from the devastating wars of the fourth century AD.

In "Nephi's Neighbors: Book of Mormon Peoples and Pre-Columbian Populations," Matthew Roper addresses the assumption that the peoples of the Book of Mormon were the only inhabitants of the pre-Columbian New World and, thus, inescapably the sole ancestors of the Amerindians. Many close students of latter-day scripture have long recognized the overwhelming likelihood that contemporary Native American peoples represent a blending of various groups descended from a variety of ancestors in addition to Lehi and Sariah. Given this complexity and the extremely limited picture that contemporary genetics offers of our distant ancestral tree, it is unreasonable to insist that DNA studies alone can prove or disprove an Israelite connection.

Roper follows this study with "Swimming in the Gene Pool: Israelite Kinship Relations, Genes, and Genealogy," in which he investigates the nature of the people of ancient Near Eastern Israel and of Lehite Israel as described in the Book of Mormon, illustrating the complexity of kinship and tribal lineage terminology among the Israelites and those who were affiliated with them.

"Elusive Israel and the Numerical Dynamics of Population Mixing," by Brian D. Stubbs, offers an independent discussion of the complex nature of population dynamics and the factors that lead, surprisingly quickly, to extensive literal kinships among large populations and the dissemination of a distinct group into the mainstream population. Even a fairly low rate of intermarriage can transform a once homogenous group within relatively few generations.

In a very real sense, this debate is (or should be) over. Just two or three years ago, the Signature Books Web page still featured an admission from Simon Southerton, an Australian plant geneticist and former Latter-day Saint who is now the most vocal critic of the Book of Mormon on DNA grounds, that "In 600 BC there were probably several million American Indians living in the Americas. If a small group of Israelites, say less than thirty, entered such a massive native population, it would be very hard to detect their genes today."[2] This confession effectively concedes a major portion of what several in this volume argue regarding Amerindian DNA and the Book of Mormon. Strikingly, though, so far as I can determine, it has now utterly disappeared from the Signature Web page.

So the controversy continues, albeit at a lower level of intensity and media attention than it once enjoyed. (As we go to press, an essay by Terryl Givens has just been published which offers a brief but superb summary statement about the DNA issue.[3]) Significantly, it now seems to have little to do with genetics as such—the articles collected in this book will illustrate why the critics' hoped-for magic DNA bullet has notably failed to give them the clean kill they sought—but has shifted to how the Book of Mormon should be interpreted.

Desperate Latter-day Saint scholars, we are told, have retreated to a limited Mesoamerican geography for the Book of Mormon in a forlorn last ditch effort to cope with mounting challenges from archaeology and genetic science. But this is demonstrably false. Limited Mesoamerican models were indisputably circulating before Watson and Crick's 1953 discovery of the structure of the DNA molecule, and, as even a cursory reading of John L. Sorenson's seminal *An Ancient American Setting for the Book of Mormon*[4] confirms, a limited geography flows inescapably from close and careful reading of the Nephite text.

Latter-day Saint scholars are also said to be in utter, despairing disarray—literally all over the map—with some, yes, holding to a limited Mesoamerican model but others insisting that the Book of Mormon narrative covers both North and South America, or simply the vicinity of New York State, or the Upper Midwest of the United States, or, even, the Malay Peninsula.

"It may come as a surprise to some readers," writes one vocal internet critic, "that there are many apologists who see the Book of Mormon events as having occurred outside the Americas. The weight of scientific evidence against the possibility of an American setting has been sufficiently compelling, and their faith in the historical claims of the Book of Mormon sufficiently rigid, that they have looked elsewhere." In support of his assertion that there are "many" such apologists, he cites a single author's self-published book.

The broad consensus of serious Book of Mormon researchers, however, remains today what it has been for many decades: Book of Mormon events took place chiefly within a relatively small area in Mesoamerica. This consensus, reflected in a large number of scholarly publications, is scarcely to be overturned by the appearance of a handful of self-produced books and videos or an engaging fireside speaker or two.

It will be obvious, after serious engagement with the essays re-published here, that simplistic claims that the Book of Mormon has been "proven false" by contemporary genetic research reflect wishful thinking and propaganda rather than science. Of course, studies of Amerindian DNA haven't proven the Book of Mormon true, either. Which leaves the matter where, on the whole, it has always been, and where, it would seem, it was always intended to be: Opinions regarding the claims of the Restoration in general must go beyond what the evidence strictly requires into the territory of religious faith. Fancy that.

As usual, the efforts of many people went into the production of the materials included here. Louis Midgley, George Mitton, Shirley Ricks, S. Kent Brown, and Don Brugger edited the articles for their original publication. Alison V. P. Coutts and Jacob Rawlins put this particular volume together and typeset it. Alison Coutts created the index and updated the articles where necessary. Jacob Rawlins designed the cover, and Brette Jones helped him to secure input and permissions from the authors. Paula Hicken proofread the text, while Shirley Ricks proofread the index. We are grateful to all of them, and, most especially of course, to the authors themselves for creating the articles in the first place.

## Notes

1.  Hugh Nibley, *Since Cumorah*, 2nd ed. (Salt Lake City: Deseret Book and FARMS, 1988), 214. The first edition appeared in 1967.

2.  Blake Ostler called attention to Southerton's confession in a superb and substantive letter published in *Sunstone*. See Blake T. Ostler, "Simon Says, But That Doesn't Make It so," *Sunstone* (November 2005), 4–8.

3.  Terryl L. Givens, "Common Sense Meets the Book of Mormon," in *Revisiting Thomas F. O'Dea's "The Mormons": Contemporary Perspectives*, ed. Cardell K. Jacobson, John P. Hoffmann, and Tim B. Heaton (Salt Lake City: University of Utah Press, 2008).

4.  John L. Sorenson, An Ancient American Setting for the Book of Mormon (Salt Lake City: Deseret Book, 1985).

# The Problematic Role of DNA Testing in Unraveling Human History

*John L. Sorenson*

Much in the news these days is the "DNA method" for calculating affinities of individuals or populations. A general characterization and evaluation of the use of this source of "new light" is given here.

### New Tools, New Zeal

From time to time over the last century, new techniques of scientific analysis have been developed that have been applied with the intent to clarify the course of human history. These techniques characteristically exhibit a life cycle consisting of six stages.

First, the technique is applied experimentally and produces certain results that seem to sharply modify the conventional picture. Second, these preliminary findings lead developers or proponents of the new tool to loudly proclaim that their technique will revolutionize the interpretation of history once it is widely applied. Third, it is announced that sweeping modifications must be made to established views, while in quieter tones the qualification is added, "although further research is needed." Fourth, basing their views especially on apparent flaws in logic and methods used in the early studies, critics point out problems with the claims that have been made. Fifth, more critics join the counterattack, and some of the early enthusiasts grant that they may have overstated their case. Sixth, expectations and use of the "new" technique gradually sink until it occupies a specific, highly qualified place in the kit of previously developed tools for the study of history, or it may even drop out of use altogether because seemingly superior tools have been developed.

Two past cases exhibit this pattern. In the late 1950s linguist Morris Swadesh announced the development of "glottochronology," a special version of "lexicostatistics."[1] He claimed that the basic vocabulary (defined as a standard list of 100 or 200 everyday words, like *hand, water,* or *night*) evolves at a constant rate of about 13 percent of the terms changing per 1,000 years; the rate was calculated from historical cases like Latin. So if two languages share a certain percentage of the basic vocabulary, the elapsed time since they split from their common ancestral tongue could be approximated in years. A flurry of excitement and reinterpretation of linguistic history followed;[2] then critiques began appearing on the heels of the enthusiasm.[3] Before long it became clear that the method, which had appeared to be quite objective, actually involved subjective steps (when are words "the same"?) that rendered the result far more uncertain than it had first appeared.[4] Nowadays the scheme is rarely used, because the resulting dates are not generally seen as trustworthy or significant.

A parallel case in the development of a technique involved the identification of human blood groups. All of us are acquainted with the fact that the blood of any human falls into one of four broad classes or groups, AB, A, B, or O, according to the specific substances contained in the blood that cause clumping of the cells when blood serum from a person of one type is injected into a sample of blood of a different type. These groups become significant in a practical sense since the differences prevent successful blood transfusions between groups. The four classes are inherited by simple (Mendelian) rules of heredity. Early in the 20th century it was noted that different population or ethnic groups were characterized by the frequencies with which the blood types occur among their members (e.g., one people might show 13 percent having type B and 67 percent with type O, while a second people has 41 percent B and only 9 percent O). Subsequently, the frequencies of other factors—M, N, and S as well as numerous Rh features—were found to distinguish the blood of various groups.

For a couple of decades immediately after World War II, blood group data seemed to provide a magic key to open up the history of the world's populations. To illustrate, in the wake of Thor Heyerdahl's Kon Tiki voyage, much attention went to the question of possible relationships between American Indians and Polynesians based on blood group frequencies. J. J. Graydon in 1952 claimed that the blood group systems in the eastern Pacific "are all consistent with Heyerdahl's theory." "A large part of the genetic constitution of the Polynesians can be accounted for on the basis of . . . especially a North-West Coast (of North America) origin."[5] A. E. Mourant (1954) used not only ABO data but that from MNS and Rh systems in concurring that all were "consistent with the theory of Heyerdahl."[6] R. T. Simmons and his colleagues in 1955 reached a similar conclusion—that further data did not invalidate the position that there was a close blood genetic relationship between American Indians and Polynesians, but not between Polynesia and the islands in the western Pacific.[7]

But critics soon gave reasons to backtrack from those hasty conclusions. By 1962 Mourant had decided that the blood group evidence did *not* support Heyerdahl's thesis.[8] R. I. Murrill in 1965 explained at length the difficulty, exhibited in most previous studies, of drawing a sample of "pure" natives unmixed with Europeans.[9] Further, it was increasingly recognized that during the period of European expansion and colonization throughout much of the world, the blood group composition of surviving populations changed by a process of, apparently, natural selection because of exposure to new diseases.[10] Furthermore, the notion had been held that scientists could draw their sample for blood group studies from all who spoke a particular "native" language, on the assumption that common language would mean common biology.[11] Eventually this assumption was recognized as unrealistic and misleading.[12] In fact, this criticism called into question the whole concept of trying to compare the biology of, say, "Polynesians" with "American Indians." In this case the former "group" was defined only in linguistic or geographical (not biological) terms while the genetic makeup of speakers of the same language turned out to be highly variable[13] and the basis for an American Indian sample might be as much geographical as biological.[14]

So doing historical reconstruction today using blood group comparisons is essentially passé. D. Allbrook felt that studies have shown but little historically sensible patterning when viewed against linguistic and archaeological data.[15] Rubén Lisker decided that only an integrated analysis of all the known blood group systems would serve to justify statements as to the origins and relationships of New World populations.[16] This has not yet been attempted on a comprehensive scale. L. Cavalli-Sforza and associates[17] tried something of the sort in 1994; however, much of their synthesis has proved to be tentative and flawed by numerous qualifications about the use of outdated archaeology, contradictions in their explanations, and gaps in the data.

These two cases suggest that adopting a fashionable new scientific technique is something like a youth receiving a telescope for Christmas. At first it is enthusiastically turned in all directions, until the owner finds that effective use of the instrument actually requires investing heavily in an increased study of astronomy and mathematics and a discomforting exercise of critical judgment in interpreting what is observed. At that point the initial fervor to apply the tool indiscriminately palls, particularly if some new "toy" comes on the scene to divert attention.

The new toy in human biology and anthropology is DNA analysis. Despite cautions from the best scientists about the limits the new findings have for interpreting human history, some enthusiasts without adequate critical acumen claim too much for DNA study. DNA is usually obtained from a sample of body fluids in a population. It occurs in the nuclei of all cells. Examination of the DNA sequence from a person shows the presence or absence of certain mutations at particular identified points in the coded gene sequence. If another population group has the same mutation record in its members' DNA, it is certain that the two groups shared a common ancestor. Or, in general terms, the number of mutations by which samples differ allow estimation of the approximate time since the two populations separated.

### The Trend from Simple Interpretive Schemes to Complex Puzzles

But DNA information never interprets itself. The meaning or significance of—the story behind—the data is necessarily furnished by the minds of the scientists who examine the information.

The temporary, even faddish, nature of historical reconstructions based on DNA analysis is illustrated by what happened with one widely publicized interpretation early in the development of present methods. The proposition was put forward that an ancestral human female, dubbed "Eve" for journalistic pizzazz, must have lived in Africa very long ago. Here is how the notion came about. Unlike most DNA, which occurs in the nuclei of all cells, DNA found in cellular structures called mitochondria acts somewhat differently. Mitochondria are special bodies within a cell that serve as power sources for the cell's contents. DNA in the mitochondria (mtDNA) were involved in the analysis that led to the idea of "Eve." That DNA passed to the next generation only from mother to daughter. All mtDNA is reproduced in a daughter unchanged, except for rare random mutations that may occur. If a female suffers a mutation, she will pass on that disruption in her DNA to her daughters. Thus the daughters' DNA sequence provides a kind of biological record of their entire female ancestry.

In 1989 an analysis of samples of mtDNA from 147 women from diverse parts of the world was interpreted by Dr. Rebecca Cann and colleagues as indicating that all the present-day women tested descended from the same ancestress, for they all shared certain mtDNA features that they could have received only from a common female ancestor. Using estimates of the rate of mutations in mtDNA as a basis, the investigators reasoned that this hypothetical common ancestor of the women from four continents had lived about 200,000 years ago in sub-Saharan Africa.[18] This postulation, fertilized by journalistic simplification and hype, was parlayed into unhesitating statements in the press to the effect that "all human beings alive today shared one female ancestor—a kind of 'Eve'—in Africa 200,000 years ago."

Before long, however, another investigator, Alan Templeton, pointed out serious problems with this "Eve Hypothesis." He argued that the analysis was invalid because it used improper statistical tests and sampling methods biased in favor of an African origin. Its results, he said, were actually dictated by the order in which the information was fed into the computer! When the same mtDNA data was treated according to different procedural rules, instead of producing one family tree pointing back to ancient Africa, that data could produce thousands of simpler descent trees, some of which did not have African roots.[19] Others compounded the criticism. Today the only correct answer to the question, "Does mtDNA analysis demonstrate that there was a shared common ancestress in Africa for all human beings?" is, for the moment, "We don't know." And the chances are slim that we will ever know.

Another highly publicized reconstruction of the past involving genetics, this time for the settling of the Americas, was put forward in 1985 by a trio of anthropologists. Joseph Greenberg, a prominent linguistic anthropologist at Stanford, argued that there were three, and only three, language groups who entered the New World via the Bering Strait (later he softened to say "at least" three). Christy G. Turner cited studies of unique tooth forms to support Greenberg's three-group theory. Stephen Zegura interpreted blood group and related genetic studies based on blood groups (though none was on DNA) to come to the same conclusion: there were three distinct peoples who entered the northwestern gateway to America and all American Indians descended from them.[20] A subsequent small-scale

DNA analysis also claimed to find "three distinct migrations across the Bering land bridge."[21] Such follow-the-leader studies soon provided the basis for sweeping popularized statements like, "Recent genetic research . . . has helped to reconstruct native American population history, and to confirm the hitherto controversial classification of the native American languages into just three major macrofamilies."[22] But other scientists were much less kind to the proposition. Many commentators on Greenberg, Turner, and Zegura's major article were mostly unsupportive verging upward to outraged.[23] By 1998 Michael H. Crawford concluded that the triple-migration hypothesis had "slowly unravel[ed]."[24]

What had happened is that the early work was followed with more comprehensive sampling and more sophisticated analysis that have yielded results far more complicated than anything Greenberg and his associates detected. M. S. Schanfield and fellow workers found significant markers that genetically distinguished four Amerindian groups that they considered to represent four migrations, not three, and Joseph G. Lorenz and David G. Smith found a broadly comparable fourfold grouping.[25] Yet another group of scientists was led to conclude that there were nine founding mtDNA sequences behind native American peoples.[26] A more elaborate study went on to sequence 403 nucleotides in the mitochondrial control region that were drawn from seven tribes and that omitted South America from consideration at all. They identified "30 distinct lineages," from which they inferred that "mitochondrial variability within Amerindian populations" is greater than many researchers had previously claimed.[27]

For the moment many geneticists choose to simplify the confusion by talking about four Amerindian haplogroups—A, B, C, and D. (A haplogroup is composed of those descent lines that share the major characteristics in their mtDNA sequences.) Yet a significant "other" category remains beyond the accepted A-to-D set. A miscellany of odd mtDNA haplotypes have been dumped into this vague category, often because their presence in America is suspected to be due to the intrusion of European or black slave genes among American Indians in the last few generations. But that assumption may be wrong. From the "other" rubric a fifth haplogroup has now been extracted, called X. Haplogroup X has been found in the DNA of certain North American groups such as the Ojibwa of eastern Canada as well as in some very early American skeletons on this continent. But the more interesting development is the discovery that X is also found in scattered populations in the Old World—in Italy, Finland, and especially Israel, and probably nearby areas. (Some have suggested that the "European-like" characteristics exhibited by the notorious skull from Kennewick, Washington, and related ancient remains from western North America could be due to haplogroup X people from Europe who reached America, perhaps across the ice-covered North Atlantic Ocean, tens of thousands of years ago. At least T. Schurr is confident that "haplogroup X was brought to the New World by an ancient Eurasian population in a migratory event distinct from those bringing the other four lineages to the Americas.")[28] Yet X may not be the last new haplogroup to be winnowed from the residual "other" category. A haplotype among the Maya Indians has already been noted that appears to be the same as European haplogroup H, the most commonly observed mtDNA lineage in populations of Europe and the Caucasus.[29]

Thus so many disagreements have arisen as new discoveries have complicated previously simpler interpretations that linguist Greenberg now chooses simply to ignore the new genetic data: "Every time, it [mtDNA research] seems to come to a different conclusion. I've just tended to set aside the mtDNA evidence. I'll wait until they get their act together."[30] But it is in the nature of scientific research that new discoveries will continue; who knows if a time will come when "they get their act together" to his satisfaction? Rather, what we can look forward to is reiteration of that catchall slogan of the scientist—"More research is needed"—rather than final consensus. A recent assessment of "progress and perspectives" in DNA studies concluded that any comprehensive solution to questions about the relationships among and origins of the American Indians must await a substantially larger, and more costly, suite of tests on DNA than those now in use.[31]

Clearly the DNA technique is not the ultimate answer to the problems of ancient population movements that lay people (and some experts) have hoped it might be. In general, we have seen, the advent of new tools or techniques in a scientific field leads to overexpectation. That has certainly been so with DNA study. Yet short of any full consensus, fascinating new information of value in untangling the threads of history has come forth when research has been done right.

A case in point is the surprising identification of a group of black South Africans as descendants of Jewish priests, a development that press and television coverage has brought to the attention of many. Oral tradition among the Lemba people had long maintained that they were of Jewish origin. A few years ago a unique genetic signature was discovered by a group of Jewish geneticists; it occurs in the Y chromosome (which passes only from male to male) and has been identified in a majority (about 53 percent) of Jewish Cohanim, or holders of the priesthood that is passed on from father to son in certain families. Researchers set out to determine if the Cohen-line genes showed up among the Lemba. They did indeed! Lemba males carried the unique Y-cell haplotype previously shown to have been possessed only by traditional Jewish priests. Interpretation of documented Jewish history and of Lemba tribal traditions, combined with the biological findings, led to the conclusion that a group of Jews that included Cohen priests migrated to Yemen in southern Arabia some 2,700 years ago, then moved to southern Africa more than 20 centuries ago. Although the members of this group have lost most of their Jewish cultural characteristics and have taken on the external characteristics (the racial or biological features and language) of surrounding black groups, they still identify themselves as of Israelite origin, and the DNA data has decisively confirmed their tradition.[32]

All genetic data does not come from tests on living persons. The ability to recover substances from mummies and skeletons has opened new vistas for the exploration of the human past. For instance, a quarter century ago Marvin Allison and fellow researchers working in Peru found that all four ABO blood groups occurred in mummies dated from 3000 BC to AD 1450, while in the last 500 years only A and O were seen. But mummies from present-day Chile as early as the second century AD showed no B or AB, although in modern times those groups often show up in that area. Meanwhile, studies of mummies from Peru contrast sharply with those from Chile; that is, prior to the Spanish conquest the natives who lived in Peru were genetically different from those living in the territory of today's Chile.[33] DNA samples have also been taken from remains of the dead in other areas, including Egypt, and may prove equally instructive about unsuspected relationships.[34]

It begins to look like a great deal of previously undetected travel, migration, and gene mixing must have been going on throughout the world in the past. For instance, studies of Polynesians have recently shown that those included under that ethnic label actually fall into at least three descent groups. Group I includes about 95 percent of Hawaiians, 90 percent of Samoans, and 100 percent of the Tongans sampled. This group's characteristic pattern of mutations first appeared in Taiwan many generations before Polynesia was settled. A second group among nominal Polynesians includes a small minority in Hawaii, Samoa, and the Cook Islands that shows "an interesting possible phylogenetic connection between Group II and a group of African pygmy sequences from central Africa" (possibly transmitted by way of New Guinea)![35] Group III links some Samoans to Indonesia.[36] Still, some 2 percent of the "Polynesians" studied do not fit any of the three recognized groups; they belong to 14 other distinct DNA lineages, each represented by a single individual. The 14 individuals display remarkable diversity, some, though probably not all, possibly springing from mixture with Europeans in the islands in recent generations (much care was taken in drawing the sample to try to avoid such cases).[37] Two of the 14, for instance, have genetic markers that closely compare with those in American Indians ("which may be the first genetic evidence of prehistoric human contact between Polynesia and South America").[38] Another study found one Samoan who shared the same DNA sequence as a Native American.[39]

The possibility of an Amerindian-Polynesian connection is of unusual interest to some of our readers. Regarding the two persons in the Polynesian study whose DNA patterns match that of American Indians, the researchers held open the possibility that the pair represented survivors of ancestors who "came into the Pacific as a result of secondary contact [from America] of the kind that also introduced the Andean sweet potato."[40] Dr. Rebecca Cann recently observed: "More and more people are thinking there's a group of native Americans that may have closer genetic ties to Pacific Islanders. That would make a lot of sense. Why would the Polynesians get to Easter Island [from the west] and [just] stop [there]?" Evidence has surfaced that Polynesians may have sailed to Chile or Peru and returned home, she continued. Genetic studies of Indians in both North and South America show that some are linked to certain Polynesians. "The related tribes include the Cayapa, Mapuche, Huillichi, and Atacameño in South America and the Nuuchal Nulth [Nootka] of Vancouver Island, British Columbia." These findings are "consistent with direct but low levels of gene flow across the entire Pacific Ocean [to America],"[41] as well as with the likelihood of some westbound voyages that brought a few Amerindians into Polynesia.

Unexplained gene connections are not as rare as one might think. They reflect the historical potpourri of gene mixing that apparently was more characteristic of prehistoric peoples than is acknowledged by our normal supposition that "a people" are biologically homogeneous.[42] For example, Sykes and his colleagues found that one person in their Polynesian sample showed a DNA mutation history that was closely related to that of Basques of western Europe! How does history as we know it handle that? James L. Guthrie, not a geneticist but a careful scientist nonetheless, has reexamined the data in the massive work by Cavalli-Sforza[43] and associates, *The History and Geography of Human Genes* (1994), in the light of accumulated cultural data that suggests specific ancient migrations. In an unpublished monograph Guthrie has identified a substantial number of cases in which unexpected Old World gene features show up about where and when some of the migrations indicated by cultural evidences also occurred.[44] More sophisticated studies of this type could at least multiply the number of interesting questions still facing geneticists as they try to interpret human history through the lens of DNA/molecular studies.

## DNA Studies and the Book of Mormon

The interest of most readers of this journal will be on the relation that DNA analysis might have for the Book of Mormon. Is there a way in which sound DNA research could shed new light on the peoples and history described in the Book of Mormon? This ancient record, which Latter-day Saints hold sacred, reports the arrival by sea, apparently to Mesoamerica, of three different Near Eastern groups, one in the third or second millennium BC and the other two soon after 600 BC. So is there evidence from DNA studies of populations in America having Near Eastern/ Jewish characteristics?

It may be helpful to shift to a dialogue format at this point. Suppose that a DNA scientist were talking with a wealthy person anxious to fund a study of "DNA and the Book of Mormon." Their hypothetical conversation can bring out important issues.

**DNA expert:** I appreciate your anxiety and enthusiasm to have a study carried out, but we have to get some things straight before I can seriously consider being involved. First, what result would you expect to see for the money you put out?

**Donor:** I'd like to see you get in there and prove that the genes of the Nephites and maybe the Lamanites were like those of the Jews. That ought to prove that the Book of Mormon is true.

**DNA expert:** I see. But, hold on a minute. Lehi and his folks left Jerusalem about 2,600 years ago. Over that period of time the biological characteristics of both the Jews Lehi left behind and those of his own party would have changed, possibly dramatically. If Lehi, Ishmael, their wives, and Zoram were not genetically "typical" of the Jews in Jerusalem in his day—and five people could never be "typical" of a gene pool of thousands—then the unique features in those Lehites would skew the characteristics of all their descendents in unknown ways. We call that "founder effect." Adaptation to conditions in the new promised land as well as mutations would further shift their gene patterns away from whatever had been Jewish in their day.

**Donor:** Well, I see that. But "the Jews" continued on as a group, didn't they?

**DNA expert:** Many were killed in the Babylonian conquest and captivity that followed on the heels of Lehi's departure. Others surely died off in captivity. There is a good chance that the demographic crisis of the Babylonian conquest was also a genetic crisis for "the Jews." We can't tell how those massive deaths may have varied the pattern of biology in those who came back from Babylon with Ezra and Nehemiah.

You see, just because a group keeps its ethnic name over centuries does not mean that its biology has stayed anywhere near constant. The later history of the Jews offers a lesson on this point. The Ashkenazim, those Jews from eastern Europe who constitute the largest proportion of the identifiable Jewish people existing today, have actually descended from a group of only a few thousand ancestors who lived in and around the territory of Poland about five centuries ago.[45] The characteristics of those few thousand have come to define the biology of "the Jews" of today—far out of proportion to their number in relation to all Jews before AD 1500. The Lembas, the "Black Jews" of southern Africa, show "thoroughly Negroid blood groups."[46] The Falasha Jews from Ethiopia also differ little from their neighbors in their blood groups.[47] Likewise, the Bene-Israel group of Jews that developed in the Bombay area of India descended from a mere seven founding families settled there hundreds of years ago. By early in the 20th century their descendants numbered in the tens of thousands, and some of them were absorbed into the population of the state of Israel. But in Bombay they were essentially similar in biological features and speech to their non-Jewish neighbors.[48] The modern Jewish population as a whole will show a mix of the genes of various subgroups like the Ashkenazim, Lemba, Falashas, and so on that developed historically and biologically in different regions of the world. We have no way to tell how any sample of modern Jews we might select would relate to the Jews of Lehi's day, except that there is no reason to think today's sample would be very similar.[49]

**Donor:** But I understand that you can get DNA from old bones. Couldn't you get some of those from tombs of about 600 BC? Their DNA would give you approximately what Lehi's DNA was, wouldn't it?

**DNA expert:** Unfortunately, tombs or burials from that date in the land of Israel are very scarce, and those that have been found almost never contain bones, for whatever reasons. Besides, just imagine the problems involved in overcoming the objections of orthodox Jews to having a scientist meddling with the bones of their ancestors!

**Donor:** Hmmm.

**DNA expert:** From what I have been told about the American side of the equation, the problem of getting a useful sample is just as much a problem, if not worse. The Book of Mormon text does not make clear just how and when Lehi's descendants got mixed up with other peoples in their new land of promise, but it is clear that they did.[50] That complicates terribly our forming any idea of what they became genetically over the thousand-year history recorded in

Mormon's account. After AD 400 the problem would be still more complicated.

Tell me, do you have any idea where I would go to get a DNA sample of Lehi's direct descendants? No one I know seems to have a specific idea.

**Donor:** Haven't LDS archaeologists found evidence among some tribes in Mexico that they descended from the Israelites?

**DNA expert:** Not according to what they have told me. At the level of culture and language there is evidence indicating that people from the Near East were involved in Mesoamerica, but that wouldn't help the particular problem I'd face. A 1971 paper showed that there is a large, detailed body of parallels between the civilizations of the Near East and Mesoamerica in sacred architecture and practices, astronomy, calendar, writing, beliefs, symbolism, and other aspects of culture.[51] A Jewish scholar, Cyrus H. Gordon, and other notable researchers have compiled interesting data on that point.[52] A man named Alexander von Wuthenau published images of ceramic figures from Mesoamerica that definitely show Jewish faces.[53] And linguists have some evidence for possible connections between Semitic languages and Mesoamerican Zapotec and related tongues on one hand and Uto-Aztecan on another.[54] A University of California linguist, Mary L. Foster, has argued for a connection between "Afro-Asiatic" languages, especially Egyptian, and old Mesoamerican languages such as Mixe-Zoquean.[55]

Those studies lead me to think that there is a distant chance that someday we might know enough to identify one group in Central America where I might go with some prospect to locate genes descended from Lehi, but today I have no informed notion. Simply to go take DNA samples at random from this or that group of Mexican Indians would be like a geologist with no geological maps in his hands looking for uranium ore by simply wandering across the landscape hoping his Geiger counter will start to click.

**Donor:** You're not very encouraging, are you?

**DNA expert:** I must be pessimistic from the point of view of responsible scientific methods and ethics. I would like to accommodate your interest, and I wouldn't mind having half a million dollars from you to play with, but the honest fact is, I wouldn't know what to do with it.

However, there is one little project that might be fun to try out. Remember the Lembas of South Africa? They have dark skins and speak a language that has no relation to Hebrew, but they do have a tradition of Jewish ancestry. In other parts of the Old World there are other little enclaves—people of yellow, brown, or white skin—that claim to have a Jewish or Israelite connection. In a number of cases there seems to be some basis for their claims.[56]

Well, it happens that there is, or was, a small group of Mexican Indians who claim a Jewish origin. Raphael Patai, who became one of the greatest scholars on Judaism, went to Mexico as a young man in the 1930s to see what he could learn about those people. After several months he discovered that they indeed had some customs that looked Jewish, and they claimed to have a Torah. Patai ended up saying that he did not know what to make of them, unless they were Jews who came from Spain in colonial days and found it convenient to "fade into the Indian woodwork," so to speak.[57] Now, if they really were of Jewish descent and they had priests along who carried the distinctive Cohen Y chromosome, like the Lemba, that would be a leverage point. Maybe careful study by a modern scholar would shed more light than Patai could get on who they really were. If they came from Spain 300 years ago, that would be interesting, but not in reference to the Book of Mormon. Yet the tiniest possibility might exist that they actually descended from a pre-Spanish group of Indians. One would then like to know much more. Interestingly, Dr. Tudor Parfitt, director of the Center for Jewish Studies at the School of Oriental and African Studies in London, an expert on the Lemba who was instrumental in seeing that study made, has expressed interest in having a study made of the Mexican group—if they can still be found.[58]

Frankly, working with that little Indian enclave looks like the only show in town along the lines you want to see. My hunch is that there would only be one chance in thousands that it would pay off. But if you want to risk the money, maybe I could find the time.

**Donor:** I didn't expect you to discourage me as much as you have, but I guess we ought to stick to what is scientifically sound. Okay, plan it out and send me a budget.

By the way, do you happen to know any explorer-type guys who'd like to look for a tribe of white Indians I've heard about and then write a book about it?

## Notes

1. See Morris Swadesh, "Linguistics as an Instrument of Prehistory," *Southwestern Journal of Anthropology* 15 (1959): 20–35.

2. See Morris Swadesh, "Lexicostatistic Classification," in *Linguistics*, ed. N. A. McQuown, vol. 5 of *Handbook of Middle American Indians* (Austin: University of Texas Press, 1967), 79–116; and Dell H. Hymes, "Lexicostatistics So Far," *Current Anthropology* 1 (1960): 3–44.

3. See R. E. Longacre, "Swadesh's Macro-Mixtecan Hypothesis," *International Journal of American Linguistics* 21/1 (1961): 9–29; K. Bergsland and H. Vogt, "On the Validity of Glottochronology," *Current Anthropology* 3 (1962): 115–53; and D. L. Olmsted, "Lexicostatistics as 'Proof' of Genetic Relationship: the Case of 'Macro-Manguean,'" *VI Congrès International des Sciences Anthropologiques et Ethnologiques, Paris, 1960* (Paris: 1964), 2/2: 69–73.

4. See C. A. Callaghan and W. R. Miller, "Swadesh's Macro-Mixtecan Hypothesis and English," *Southwestern Journal of Anthropology* 18 (1962): 278–85; and K. V. Teeter, "Lexico Statistics and Genetic Relationship," *Language* 39 (1964): 638–48.

5. J. J. Graydon, "Blood Groups and the Polynesians," *Mankind* 4 (1952): 329–39.

6. A. E. Mourant, *The Distribution of Human Blood Groups* (Springfield, IL: C. C. Thomas, 1954), 144–47.

7. See R. T. Simmons et al., "A Blood Group Genetical Survey of Cook Islanders, Polynesia, and Comparisons with American Indians," *American Journal of Physical Anthropology* 13 (1955): 667–90.

8. See A. E. Mourant, "Blood Groups in the Pacific Area," *Eighth Congress of the International Society of Blood Transfusion (Tokyo 1960), Proceedings* (Tokyo: 1962), 149–53.

9. See Rupert I. Murrill, *Cranial and Postcranial Skeletal Remains from Easter Island* (Minneapolis: University of Minnesota Press, 1968), 77–79.

10. See Frank B. Livingstone, "An Analysis of the ABO Blood Group Clines in Europe," *American Journal of Physical Anthropology* 31 (1969): 1–10; M. Allison et al.,

"ABO Blood Groups in Chilean and Peruvian Mummies, II: Results of Agglutination-Inhibition Technique," *American Journal of Physical Anthropology* 49 (1978): 139–42; and T. E. Reed, "The Evidence for Natural Selection Due to Blood Groups," *World Population Conference (Belgrade, 1965), Proceedings* 2 (New York: United Nations, 1967), 498–502.

11.  This is still assumed in a current anthropology textbook. See Colin Renfrew and Paul Bahn, *Archaeology: Theories, Methods, and Practice*, 2nd ed. (London and New York: Thames and Hudson, 1996), 436: "The language spoken by a human community is the best predictor of what genetic characteristics . . . that community will have."

12.  See, for example, Juan Comas, "Características físicas de la familia lingüística Maya," *Universidad Nacional Autónoma de México, Serie Antropológica* 20 (México: UNAM, 1966). Comas compared the results of more than half a century of study of Maya-speaking groups to find marked biological differences among distinct groups within the language community, apparently due to intermarriage with non-Mayan groups, genetic drift, endogamy, and adaptive selection. See also M. Layrisse, Z. Layrisse, and J. Wilbert, "Blood Group Antigen Studies of Four Chibchan[-speaking] Tribes," *American Anthropologist* 65 (1963): 36–55; the tribes do not form a homogeneous genetic group.

13.  See R. T. Simmons, "The Biological Origin of Australian Aborigines: An Examination of Blood Group Genes and Gene Frequencies for Possible Evidence in Populations from Australia to Eurasia," in *The Origin of the Australians*, ed. R. L. Kirk and A. G. Thorne (Canberra: Australian Institute of Aboriginal Studies and Atlantic Highlands; New Jersey: Humanities Press International, 1976), 307–28.

14.  See, for example, S. M. Borgognini Torli and G. Paoli, "Survey of Paleoserological Studies," *Homo* 33/2 (1982): 69–89; and J. Comas, *Antropología de los puebloos iberoamericanos* (Barcelona: Editorial Labor, 1972), 35: "It seems that the beginning of the second half of the twentieth century coincides with the end of the myth of the (single) 'American homotype.'"

15.  See "The Human Biology of the Western Pacific Basin," *Yearbook of Physical Anthropology* 18 (1976): 202–45.

16.  See Rubén Lisker, "El origen de los grupos humanos en América: serología y hematología en general de los Ameríndios y sus posibles relaciones trans-pacíficas," *Thirty-Sixth International Congress of Americanists (Barcelona and Seville, 1964), Proceedings* 1 (Barcelona and Seville: 1966), 43–51.

17.  See L. Cavalli-Sforza et al., *The History and Geography of Human Genes* (Princeton: Princeton University Press, 1994).

18.  See Rebecca L. Cann, M. Stoneking, and A. C. Wilson, "Mitochondrial DNA and Human Evolution," *Nature* 325 (1987): 31–36.

19.  See A. R. Templeton, "Human Origins and Analysis of Mitochondrial DNA Sequences," *Science* 255 (1992): 737.

20.  See J. H. Greenberg, Christy G. Turner II, and S. Zegura, "Convergence of Evidence for the Peopling of the Americas," *Collegium Antropologicum* 9/1 (1985): 33–42. An expanded version by the same three authors appeared in 1986 as "The Settlement of the Americas: A Comparison of the Linguistic, Dental, and Genetic Evidence," *Current Anthropology* 27 (1986): 477–97.

21.  R. C. Williams et al., "GM Allotypes in Native Americans: Evidence for Three

Distinct Migrations across the Bering Land Bridge," *American Journal of Physical Anthropology* 66 (1895): 1–19.

22. Renfrew and Bahn, *Archaeology*, 437; see n. 11.

23. See Greenberg, Turner, and Zegura, "The Settlement of the Americas," 488–92. Commenting on this article, Lyle Campbell urged that "the whole speculative venture should be abandoned," and Emöke J. E. Szathmary charged that Turner "interprets his analytic results in the light of a preexisting hypothesis that he simply assumes to be true" (ibid., 488–91).

24. See Michael H. Crawford, *The Origins of Native Americans: Evidence from Anthropological Genetics*, rev. English version (Cambridge: Cambridge University Press, 1998), 21–24.

25. See M. S. Schanfield, "Immunoglobulin Allotypes (GM and KM) Indicate Multiple Founding Populations of Native Americans: Evidence of at Least Four Migrations to the New World," *Human Biology* 64 (1992): 381–402; and Joseph G. Lorenz and David G. Smith, "Distribution of Four Founding mtDNA Haplogroups among Native North Americans," *American Journal of Physical Anthropology* 101 (1996): 307–23.

26. See S. Pääbo et al., "Mitochondrial Evolution and the Peopling of the Americas," *American Journal of Physical Anthropology* 81/1 (1990): 277.

27. See Ann Gibbons, "The Peopling of the Americas," *Science* 274 (4 Oct. 1996): 32–33.

28. Roger Highfield, "Europeans Colonised America in 28,000 BC," Electronic Telegraph, issue 1730 (19 Feb. 2000): 1 (www.telegraph.co.uk).

29. See Theodore G. Schurr, "Mitochondrial DNA and the Peopling of the New World," *American Scientist* 88/3 (2000): 246–53; and Virginia Morell, "Genes May Link Ancient Eurasians, Native Americans," *Science* 280 (24 April 1998): 520.

30. Gibbons, "The Peopling of the Americas," 33.

31. See Dennis H. O'Rourke, S. W. Carlyle, and R. L. Par, "Ancient DNA: Methods, Progress, and Perspectives," *American Journal of Human Biology* 8 (1996): 557–71.

32. See Nicholas Wade, "DNA Backs a Tribe's Tradition of Early Descent from the Jews," *New York Times,* 9 May 1999, 1, 10; Karl Skorecki et al., "Y Chromosomes of Jewish Priests," *Nature* 385 (2 Jan. 1997): 32; A. B. Spurdle and T. Jenkins, "The Origins of the Lemba 'Black Jews' of Southern Africa: Evidence from p12F2 and Other Y-Chromosome Markers," *American Journal of Human Genetics* 59 (1996): 1126–33.

33. See M. J. Allison et al., "ABO Blood groups in Chilean and Peruvian Mummies," 139–42; see n. 10.

34. See C. W. Griggs et al., "Evidences of a Christian Population in the Egyptian Fayum and Genetic and Textile Studies of the Akhmim Noble Mummies," *BYU Studies* 33/2 (1993): 215–44.

35. Bryan Sykes et al., "The Origins of the Polynesians: An Interpretation from Mitochondrial Lineage Analysis," *American Journal of Human Genetics* 57 (1995): 1463–75, 1470–72.

36. See Jim Borg, "The History Within," *Hawaii Magazine,* February 1997, 36–41, based on an interview with Rebecca Cann at University of Hawaii.

37. Sykes et al., "The Origins of the Polynesians," 1472.

38. See ibid., 1463.

39. See J. K. Lum et al., "Polynesian Mitochondrial DNAs Reveal Three Deep Maternal Lineage Clusters," *Human Biology* 66/4 (1994): 567–90, 573.

40. Sykes et al., "The Origins of the Polynesians," 1474.

41. Borg, "The History Within"; compare Sykes et al., "The Origins of the Polynesians," 1472.

42. See, for example, R. H. Ward et al., "Extensive Mitochondrial Diversity within a Single Amerindian Tribe," *National Academy of Science USA, Proceedings* 88 (1991): 8720–24.

43. See L. Cavalli-Sforza et al., *History and Geography.*

44. See James L. Guthrie, "Human Lymphocyte Antigens: Apparent Afro-Asiatic, South Asian, and European HLAS in Indigenous American Populations," MS in possession of John L. Sorenson.

45. See Kelly Owens and Mary-Claire King, "Genomic Views of Human History," *Science* 286 (15 Oct. 1999): 451–53.

46. A. E. Mourant et al., *The Genetics of the Jews* (Oxford: Clarendon Press, 1978), 39.

47. See Mourant et al., *The Genetics of the Jews* , 39.

48. See Mourant et al., *The Genetics of the Jews* , 25.

49. Some work on genetic aspects of blood groups has been done, but it is not systematic and comes to no clear conclusion about what the ancestral Jewish genes might have been. See Mourant et al., *The Genetics of the Jews;* and Raphael Patai and Jennifer Patai, *The Myth of the Jewish Race,* rev. ed. (Detroit: Wayne State University Press, 1989).

50. See John L. Sorenson, "When Lehi's Party Arrived in the Land, Did They Find Others There?" *Journal of Book of Mormon Studies* 1 (1992): 1–34; republished in *Nephite Culture and Society: Collected Papers,* ed. Matthew Sorenson (Salt Lake City: New Sage Books, 1997), 65–104.

51. John L. Sorenson, "The Significance of an Apparent Relationship between the Ancient Near East and Mesoamerica," in *Man across the Sea: Problems of Pre-Columbian Contacts,* ed. C. L. Riley, J. C. Kelley, C. W. Pennington, and R. L. Rands (Austin: University of Texas Press, 1971), 219–41.

52. See Cyrus H. Gordon et al., *Before Columbus: Links between the Old World and Ancient America* (New York: Crown, 1971); *Riddles in History* (New York: Crown, 1974); and J. H. McCulloch, "The Bat Creek Inscription: Cherokee or Hebrew?" *Tennessee Anthropologist* 13/2 (1988): 79–123.

53. See Alexander von Wuthenau, *Altamerikanische Tonplastik: Das Menschenbild der Neuen Welt* (Baden-Baden: Holle, 1965); and *Unexpected Faces in Ancient America, 1500 BC–AD 1500* (New York: Crown, 1975).

54. See Pierre Agrinier, "Linguistic Evidence for the Presence of Israelites in Mexico," *Society for Early Historic Archaeology, Newsletter and Proceedings* 112 (1969): 4–5, which reports on glottochronological comparisons begun under M. Swadesh's guidance. Brian Stubbs's "Elements of Hebrew in Uto-Aztecan: A Summary of the Data" (FARMS, 1988), and subsequent reports have found at least 1,000 roots with phonological and other linguistic patterns consistent with creolization involving a Semitic language and Uto-Aztecan.

55. See Mary LeCron Foster, "The Transoceanic Trail: The Proto-Pelagian Language

Phylum," *Pre-Columbiana* 1 (1998): 88–113; "Old World Languages in the Americas," unpublished paper presented at the eighth annual meeting of the Language Origins Society, Selwyn College, Cambridge University, 7–10 Sept. 1992 (copy in the possession of John Sorenson).

56. *The Lost Tribes,* video documentary produced by Nova, copy in Maxwell Institute library.

57. See "The Jewish Indians in Mexico," *Jewish Folklore and Ethnology Review* 18 (1950): 1–12.

58. In an e-mail to John Sorenson dated 13 October 2000, he wondered if any LDS DNA specialists would be interested in collaborating.

# A Few Thoughts from a Believing DNA Scientist

*John M. Butler*

Recent claims concerning the supposed absence of DNA evidence in support of the Book of Mormon have caused me to investigate more closely what the record itself has to say on the topic. The mitochondrial DNA (mtDNA) lineage of Nephi's children (and of Laman's offspring) would come through Ishmael's wife since the four oldest sons of Lehi as well as Zoram married the five daughters of Ishmael (see 1 Nephi 16:7). Unfortunately, Ishmael's wife is of unknown background and heritage. In fact, she is mentioned only twice in the Book of Mormon (see 1 Nephi 7:6, 19) and may have died before Ishmael since she is not mentioned as a mourner when Ishmael dies at Nahom (see 1 Nephi 16:34–35). Perhaps the historical information in the large plates of Nephi, or even the 116 pages translated in 1828 and lost by Martin Harris, could shed some light on Ishmael's wife's background if only we had access to them.

The wives of Ishmael's two sons (see 1 Nephi 7:6) would also potentially introduce additional mtDNA lineages into the Nephite and Lamanite descendants, as would Nephi's sisters (see 2 Nephi 5:6). But, again, the Book of Mormon record is silent regarding their backgrounds. Thus, we are left without enough information from the Book of Mormon record itself to identify definitively an appropriate genetic source population that could be used to calibrate the claims of the Book of Mormon. Likewise, we do not have sufficient information to declare the Book of Mormon not true.

While Lehi's direct male offspring would possess a copy of his Y chromosome, it is unclear whether or not these offspring would also have Manasseh, Joseph, Jacob, Isaac, and Abraham in their patri-lineage, because Lehi is listed only as "a descendant of Manasseh" in Alma 10:3. Lehi could meet the definition of a descendant of Manasseh from a large number of genealogical lineages without being in the direct patrilineal line and possessing an Abrahamic Y chromosome. In addition, the fact that Mormon uses the phrase *pure descendant of Lehi* to describe himself in 3 Nephi 5:20 would seem to indicate that Lehi's lineage was a rare one in Mormon's day.

Interestingly absent from the critics' contentions is mention of the Jaredites. The Jaredite nation existed for more than 1,500 years before the Lehites arrived in the promised land. This group spanned at least 29 generations (see Ether 1:6–33) with combinations of marriages between people whose background we know virtually nothing about. The Jaredites most likely traveled from central Asia to northeast Asia and then via barges to the New World.[1] Genetically, their path of travel would have seemed much like land passage across the Bering Strait if others along that route joined them and Asian bloodlines entered their group as they traveled. After arriving in the New World, the Jaredite people had hundreds of years to grow and spread across parts of the continent, perhaps encountering and intermarrying with other groups of unknown origin.

We usually think of the Jaredite nation as being completely annihilated in the final battle between the armies of Coriantumr and Shiz (see Ether 15). However, the prophecy of Ether states that all of *Coriantumr's household* would be destroyed if he did not repent (see Ether 13:20–21), which does not necessarily mean all of the descendants of the original Jaredite colonization party. It is entirely conceivable that one or more groups had broken away from the main Jaredite colony and survived outside of the record describing the downfall of the Coriantumr and Shiz camps. In fact, Hugh Nibley has argued for some kind of interaction and influence between the Jaredite and Lehite groups because of the continuance of such Jaredite names as Korihor (see Alma 30; Ether 7:3) and Coriantumr (see Helaman 1:15) in Nephite times.[2] While it is possible to speculate endlessly about scenarios that would make Book of Mormon story lines compatible with current DNA evidence, the record itself is simply not descriptive enough to provide definitive calibration points with which to make confident scientific conclusions.

Thus, we are left where we started (and where I believe the Lord intended us to be)—in the realm of faith. A spiritual witness is the only way to know the truthfulness of the Book of Mormon. Although DNA studies have made links between Native Americans and Asians, these studies in no way invalidate the Book of Mormon despite the loud voices of detractors.

## Notes

1.  See Hugh Nibley, *Lehi in the Desert; The World of the Jaredites; There Were Jaredites* [1988], 181–82.

2.  See Nibley, *Lehi in the Desert; The World of the Jaredites; There Were Jaredites*, 245.

# Before DNA

*John L. Sorenson and Matthew Roper*

In recent years critics who question that the Book of Mormon is an ancient document have made noisy claims that "facts" from the science of molecular biology contradict what the Nephite record says about the peoples it describes.

This article provides a framework within which the quality and aptness of questions about DNA studies on Native Americans and their implications for Book of Mormon history should be approached. We raise a set of issues that anyone should confront when thinking clearly and honestly about this subject. Our answers are succinct because the space available is limited. For those who wish to know more, the endnotes point to additional sources of information.

Critics of the Book of Mormon frequently take the position that the New World events related in the Nephite record must be read as taking place on a stage consisting of the entire Western Hemisphere. This allows them to treat the scripture as though it purported to be a history of the American Indian. Their arguments about the supposed factual inaccuracy of the sacred record rest heavily on this claimed geography. But what the book actually says contradicts the idea that two entire continents were involved in the story. Although early Latter-day Saints assumed a hemispheric setting (and some church members today still hold that view), the record actually describes a setting where the people were limited in numbers and the lands they occupied were restricted in scale. Yet the issue touches more than geography alone; the entrained question is one of demography and descent. Were there other populations present in the Americas who were not exclusively descended from Lehi's party? We treat both issues below.

A responsible approach to the scripture requires getting clear about the actual geographic and demographic scale on which its events were played out, as Elder Dallin H. Oaks has pointed out. He recalled taking a class as a student at Brigham Young University in which

> I was introduced to the idea that the Book of Mormon is not a history of all of the people who have lived on the continents of North and South America in all ages of the earth. Up to that time I had assumed that it was. If that were the claim of the Book of Mormon, any piece of historical, archaeological, or linguistic evidence to the contrary would weigh in against the Book of Mormon, and those who rely exclusively on scholarship would have a promising position to argue.
>
> In contrast, if the Book of Mormon only purports to be an account of a few peoples who inhabited a portion of the Americas during a few millennia in the past, the burden of argument [about its historical accuracy] changes drastically. It is no longer a question of all versus none; it is a question of some versus none. In other words, in the circumstance I describe, the opponents of historicity must prove that the Book of Mormon has no historical validity for any peoples who lived in the Americas in a particular time frame, a notoriously difficult exercise. One does not prevail on that proposition by proving that a particular . . . culture represents migrations from [eastern] Asia. The opponents of historicity of the Book of Mormon must prove that the people whose religious life it records did not live *anywhere* in the Americas.[1]

Furthermore, DNA scientists have to answer the questions of location and scale if they are to know from where to draw data appropriate for historical analysis of the Book of Mormon. Our first questions assist in that task.

## 1. How does the Book of Mormon characterize the geographical scene in the American "promised land" where the events the book relates took place?

Numerous books and articles have addressed bits and pieces of this question.[2] The problem is very complex, for hundreds of passages in the Book of Mormon either tell us directly about or imply spatial relationships and other geographical parameters that characterized the setting.

As the primary author and editor of the Book of Mormon, the prophet Mormon evidently had his own mental map of Nephite lands, which made it possible for the total body of geographical information that he employed to be remarkably consistent. This is not surprising, because from his own account we know that he had personally traveled over a great deal of Nephite territory (see Mormon 1:6, 10–6:6). The geographical data in the book lead to the following salient points:[3]

1.    When mapped, the outline of lands familiar to the Nephites appears to have been more or less in the shape of an hourglass but with the nature of the northward and southward extremities being left unclear.

2.    What the Nephites considered their "east sea" in all likelihood was the Atlantic Ocean.[4]

3.    The Nephites' "west sea" was part of the Pacific Ocean. Lehi's party landed on the west sea coast at the extreme south of the territory they knew as "the promised land."[5]

4.    The two crucial landmasses were called the land southward and the land northward. They were connected by an isthmus described as "narrow." The Nephites thought of their land as "nearly surrounded by water" and, at least in their early days, as an "isle of the sea" (Alma 22:32; 2 Nephi 10:20). (Isle anciently did not neces-

sarily mean an area entirely isolated by water, but rather that the area so labeled could be reached via boat. See the dictionary in the Latter-day Saint edition of the King James Version of the Bible, s.v. "Isles.")

5.    The southern portion of the land southward, called the land of Nephi, was mostly elevated and mountainous (it included the headwaters of the principal river); the territory closer to the isthmus, called the land of Zarahemla, lay at an intermediate elevation.

6.    From the south highlands (the land of Nephi), the river Sidon, the only river identified in the record, flowed northward through a drainage basin that constituted much of the land of Zarahemla.

7.    The west sea coastal zone of the land southward was considered a "narrow strip," apparently with such a small population that it played no significant historical role in Book of Mormon history, but the flatlands adjacent to the east sea coast of the land southward were more extensive.

8.    Based chiefly on the travel times required to go between various points, we can confidently infer that the land southward was on the order of only a few hundred miles in length (northward–southward). At one point the land southward was plausibly about 200 miles wide. The distance across the narrowest part of the narrow neck, or isthmus, is left vague but might have been on the order of 100 miles.

9.    The dimensions of the land northward are also unclear, but the implication is that the size of that area was of the same order of magnitude as the land southward.

10.  Topographically the land northward consisted of lowlands (and drainage) toward the east sea, while westward the land was more elevated.

11.  Near the east sea a relatively small area of hills was located no great distance northward from the narrow pass. The final battle-ground of the Jaredites (at "the hill Ramah") and of the Nephites (at the same hill, called by them "the hill Cumorah") was in this area.

12. The climate throughout the entire territory was relatively warm, at least as far as the text indicates. While we read of extreme heat, there is no hint of cold weather or snow.

13. The groups occupying most of this territory at times reached a civilized level of development and at one point constituted a population of more than two million. At their greatest the inhabitants occupied numerous cities with extensive public buildings, kept many written records, fought in large-scale wars, and carried on extensive trade. In short, they were in a civilized condition.

*All* of these features (and many more) must characterize that part of the Americas where the events recorded in the Book of Mormon took place. It is not enough that just arbitrarily selected features from Mormon's record be made to match up with today's map.

## 2. Do all of the geographical facts sketched in the Nephite account agree with any actual location in the Americas? With more than one?

That the inhabitants of Book of Mormon lands knew and used formal writing systems and compiled numerous books (see Helaman 3:15) restricts the possible real-world location to Mesoamerica[6] (central and southern Mexico and northern Central America). In Mesoamerica there were thousands of books in use at the time of the Spanish Conquest, but nowhere else in the Western Hemisphere is there convincing evidence for genuine writing being used on a consistent basis. In addition to writing, other social and cultural conditions required by the scriptural text to be present in the Nephite homeland area confirm Mesoamerica as the only plausible location of Book of Mormon lands.

In addition to the cultural criteria, only in that area can all of the geographical requirements be met. For example, only in Mesoamerica are there lands of appropriate scale (that is, several hundreds, but not thousands, of miles in extent) that can appropriately be said to be "nearly surrounded by water" (Alma 22:32), as well as an isthmus bounded by Pacific and Atlantic waters.

Ingenious and impassioned arguments have been mustered in support of other theorized areas (from the Great Lakes to Peru or encompassing the entire hemisphere) as the scene for Nephite history. But every proposed geographical setting other than Mesoamerica fails to meet the criteria established by the text of Mormon's account.[7] So while it is theoretically possible that another area of the New World could meet the criteria to be the historical Nephite and Lamanite lands, it has proved impossible to identify any such territory. All proposed locations other than Mesoamerica suffer from fatal flaws.

DNA scientists can be confident that all or part of Mesoamerica was where the Nephite and Lamanite peoples took on their historical identities and where their history recorded in the Book of Mormon was played out, although their descendants might have spread into other New World zones and additional peoples might have migrated to Mesoamerica from other regions.

**3. What evidence is there that the original Book of Mormon peoples from the Mesoamerican area where the events related in the scripture took place spread to other parts of the Americas?**

Archaeologists cannot precisely identify at this time any of their study materials as those of "Book of Mormon peoples." But it is clear from their research that Mesoamerica was a center from which influence spread throughout certain portions of the Western Hemisphere. Latter-day Saints plausibly suppose that at least some Mesoamerican groups included "Nephites" or "Lamanites" and that Israelite genes could have spread out from the Mesoamerican core. For example, Amerindian groups in the southwestern United States area were heavily influenced by peoples in Mexico. Expert opinions differ on how persuasive the evidence is for the movement of actual gene bearers from the one area to the other. One scholar says, "Mesoamerican symbolism, ceremonialism, and ceremonial art swept through the Pueblo IV Anasazi [people of about AD 1300] like an early Ghost Dance religion."[8]

Archaeologist Charles Di Peso pointed out that in the late pre-Spanish period at Casas Grandes, near the Arizona border, no fewer than four Mesoamerican religious complexes "—involving the worship of [the Central Mexican gods] Quetzalcóatl, Xiuhtecutli, Xipe, and Tláloc—were present." It seems likely that the very specific cultural information that was at the heart of those cults arrived with small Mesoamerican immigrant groups rather than by vague cultural seepage northward. In fact, "it appears that Hohokam and Mogollon cultural groups of the southern Southwest were influenced by Mesoamerican culture over several millennia, perhaps from 2000–3000 BC until 1300–1400 AD."[9] A minor trickle of actual Mexican people moved northward bearing some of that cultural freight.

Is it possible that what archaeologists refer to as cultural "influences" spread by some indirect means, like pollen in the wind? The answer seems clear to us that in some circumstances human agents were necessary to convey such influences between distant points. Because the cultural items shared were so detailed and elaborate, it is most reasonable to suppose that actual persons carried specific knowledge from Mexico to Arizona or New Mexico.[10] It is quite certain that those persons who acted as transfer agents frequently also passed their genes into the local pool at the destination.[11] In any case, DNA scientists ought not to exclude the possibility that genetic carriers from Mesoamerica reached other areas.

Mesoamerican peoples and cultures were also generally influential on the Mississippi River valley and the southeastern United States. Maize spread there from Mesoamerica, and substantial knowledge of various cultural features also slowly spread into the area.[12] Mesoamerican influence is seen especially in the Mississippian period, from around AD 900 to perhaps after AD 1500. From

Georgia to Oklahoma and from Louisiana to Wisconsin, large temple mounds were erected, and ideas about rulership seem also to have been shared. Again, the tendency is for one wing of the archaeological community to consider that the similarities to Mexico do not demonstrate that any human biological connection was involved. Yet some of the concepts, implied or obvious, that connect the two areas strike others as sufficiently pointed to suggest specific imports, and probably people, going beyond vague "influence." While it cannot be shown for sure that actual persons arrived in the Mississippian area from Mexico, DNA scientists may do well to consider that there possibly was limited Mesoamerican gene intermixture.

There is also evidence for long-lasting relationships between Mesoamerica and South America. Maize moved southward from its origin in western Mexico more than 6,000 years ago. Many cultural characteristics as well as traits of human biology quite certainly accompanied it. Some of the linkage was facilitated by travelers on raft or ship who moved back and forth along the Pacific Coast of the Americas for thousands of years.[13] In a few cases, whole populations and their cultures seem to have made the move, such as the Kogi people.[14] Later indications are that South America was the source of south-to-north influence (a few actual Incan buildings have been found in western Mexico).[15] Dr. Marshall Newman has also presented morphological data from physical anthropology to argue that groups of people migrated to South America from Mesoamerica.[16]

Details on many of the indicated movements remain too vague or conjectural for complete clarity, but a significant number of specialists believe that both Mesoamerican concepts and people spread into some areas of South America, as into North America, long before the European conquest of the New World.[17]

## 4. How does this geographical picture square with traditions held among the Latter-day Saints about the scenes and peoples involved in Book of Mormon events?

We face a lack of detail in our historical sources as to what the earliest Latter-day Saints thought about Book of Mormon geography. Even so, there is little question that generally an obvious interpretation was in many readers' minds. The "land southward" they considered to be South America, the Isthmus of Panama was "the narrow neck," and North America was thought to be the "land northward."[18] However, there is no evidence that in the early years any detailed thought was given to geography. Actually, the Book of Mormon was little referred to or used among church members in the first decades except as a confirming witness of the Bible. The writings or preaching of some of the best-informed church leaders of that day show that they did not read the text carefully on matters other than doctrine.[19] For instance, no statement shows that anyone read the scripture closely enough to grasp the fact that the plates Mormon gave to Moroni were never buried in the hill of the final Nephite battle.

In 1842 a best-selling book by explorer John Lloyd Stephens[20] was read by Joseph Smith and associates in Nauvoo. Their reading prompted an extensive review of the book in the Nauvoo newspaper, the *Times and Seasons*. (No author is listed, but Joseph Smith was editor in chief with John Taylor as managing editor.) Stephens's was the first book in English reporting great ruins in Central America. It strongly impressed the newspaper writer (whoever he was), for on 15 September the paper reported, "We have to state about the Nephites that . . . they lived about the narrow neck of land, which now embraces Central America, with all the cities that can be found."[21] Stephens's new information obviously was causing the leadership in Nauvoo to think of Nephite geography in a new way. Two weeks later they continued to exult in their study of what was for them "the latest research": "We have [just] found another important fact relating to the truth of the Book of Mormon. . . . The city of Zarahemla . . .

stood upon this land," that is, Central America or Guatemala, which "once embraced several hundred miles of territory from north to south."[22] Since Zarahemla was located in the land southward, their new insight put the land southward to the *north* of Panama. The new thinking inferred that South America was of little or no significance for Book of Mormon geography.[23] The further inference is that the new thinking was that an area much smaller than the entire hemisphere could satisfactorily serve as the scene of the chief events in the Nephite record.

In the long run, nevertheless, the Stephens-stimulated view of Central America as the Book or Mormon heartland did not prevail among the Saints generally. The new implications were apparently overwhelmed by the inertia of the old belief in a whole-hemisphere geography. Orson Pratt, who was separated from the church during 1842 when the new thought on this topic was stirring, seems to have continued to believe in the original geographical theory.[24] His views along those lines are reflected in the geographical footnotes that he added to the 1879 edition of the Book of Mormon. His opinions led several generations of readers of the scripture to assume with him that only the Nephites and Lamanites of Mormon's account occupied the Americas, from the Arctic to the Antarctic, at least during Book of Mormon times. By the beginning of the 20th century, likely not more than a handful of readers of Mormon's book questioned the interpretation that Lehi landed in Chile, that Panama was the narrow neck, and that the final battle of the Nephites took place in New York.[25]

Anecdotal evidence (there are no systematic data) suggests that even now, after church members have been reading the Book of Mormon for a century and three-quarters, a large number of readers continue to assume the whole-hemisphere view of Book of Mormon geography. Moreover, some unbelievers insist in their anti-Book of Mormon propaganda that this view was and is completely orthodox (which makes their criticisms more damaging).[26] But the proportion of Saints who still accept that antiquated geography is irrelevant in light of the decisive information in the Book of Mormon. The text itself gives an unmistakable picture of a very restricted territory. And as President Joseph Fielding Smith said, "My words, and the teachings of any other member of the Church, high or low, if they do not square with the revelations, we need not accept them."[27]

## 5. What does the Nephite scripture tell us about the meanings of the terms *Nephite* and *Lamanite*?

At many points Mormon's record states or clearly implies that the terms *Nephite* and *Lamanite* bore multiple meanings during the Book of Mormon period. At least six senses of the term *Nephite* can be identified: The term sometimes referred to (1) those belonging to the relatively small lineage consisting of direct descendants from Lehi's son Nephi$_1$ (compare Mormon 1:5; 3 Nephi 5:20); (2) a larger "noble" group consisting of the descendants of the kings who succeeded Nephi$_1$, each of whom bore *Nephi* as a royal title (see Jacob 1:11);[28] (3) those descended from, as well as all those who were ruled by, any of the monarchs bearing the title *Nephi*; (4) believers in a particular set of religious practices and ideas (compare Jacob 4: 4–6; 4 Nephi 1:36–38); (5) participants in a particular cultural tradition (see 2 Nephi 5: 6, 9–18); and (6) an ethnic or "racial" group (see Jacob 3:5, 8–9). Most of the same principles of naming applied to the Lamanites. One could be called by that term on several bases, such as direct descent (e.g., Alma 55:4, 8), political choice (e.g., Alma 54:24; Moroni 9:24), or a combination of political, religious, and other factors (e.g., 3 Nephi 2:12, 14–16; D&C 10:48). Note that people could choose to change their affiliation by adoption or formal transfer of allegiance (see, e.g., Mosiah 25:13; Alma 43:4; Alma 45:13–14).[29]

The broadest societal category in the Book of Mormon is *Lamanite*, treated in the prophecies as including the "remnant" seed of Laman, Lemuel, and Ishmael, to whom particular promises had been made. Yet those same promises were extended also to others besides direct descendants. The words of Lehi's promise in 2 Nephi 1:5 refer not only to his elder sons' literal biological descendants but also to "all those who should be led out of other countries by the hand of the Lord." No one, Lehi added in pronouncing his blessings, would come into his promised land unless they were "brought by the hand of the Lord" (v. 6), so "this land [would be] consecrated unto him [everybody] whom he shall bring" (v. 7). This last expression refers not only to the eventual Gentile (European) settlers of the 16th through 21st centuries but also to those ancient peoples whom the Lord brought as well (see vv. 10–11).[30] By the time Lehi pronounced his blessings, the vessel that brought Mulek from Jerusalem either had already landed or at least was en route to the promised land (see Omni 1:15–16), and some of that party's descendants, called "the people of Zarahemla," eventually became Nephites (Omni 1:19; Mosiah 25:13). Jaredite survivors also must have been around,[31] and they too could have been blessed under the heading of "Lamanites" according to the prophetic ethnology.

Lehi saw from the beginning that *Nephites* and *Lamanites* were labels that would include a variety of groups that could have differing biological origins, cultures, and ethnic heritages. According to the title page of the Book of Mormon, the generic term *Lamanite* was applied by Moroni to all the amalgamated groups whose descendants would survive right down to Restoration times as "the [American] remnant of the house of Israel." There is no indication anywhere in the Book of Mormon that "the Lamanites" were to be a genetically exclusive line descending only from the two oldest sons in Lehi's family.

### 6. Have leaders of the Church of Jesus Christ of Latter-day Saints provided definitive answers to questions about the origin, composition, and geography of the Nephites and Lamanites and about the possibility that other peoples were present in the land?

Latter-day Saint ecclesiastical authorities have never claimed that revelation has settled where the lands of the Book of Mormon were located. Even the comments in the *Times and Seasons* in 1842 were put forward as tentative. Those challenging ideas ended with the convoluted caution, "We are not agoing [*sic*] to declare positively that the ruins of Quirigua [in Guatemala] are those of Zarahemla, but when the land and the stones, and the books tell the story so plain, we are of [the] opinion, that it would require more proof than the Jews could bring to prove the disciples stole the body of Jesus from the tomb, to prove that the ruins of the city in question, are not one of those referred to in the Book of Mormon. . . . It will not be a bad plan to compare Mr. Stephens' ruined cities with those of the Book of Mormon."[32]

Later statements have made clear that no definitive answer to issues of geography in the Book of Mormon has been pronounced or implied. George Q. Cannon, longtime counselor in the First Presidency, once stated: "The First Presidency have often been asked to prepare some suggestive map illustrative of Nephite geography, but have never consented to do so. . . . The reason is, that without further information they are not prepared even to suggest [a map]."[33] Church president Joseph F. Smith affirmed President Cannon's reticence. Regarding a proposed map of Book of Mormon sites, he "declined to officially approve of the map, saying that the Lord had not yet revealed it."[34] John A. Widtsoe, not only an apostle but a Harvard-educated former president of two universities, observed in 1950, "As far as can be learned, the Prophet Joseph Smith, translator of the book, did not say where, on the American continent, Book of Mormon activities occurred. Perhaps he did not know."[35]

In regard to the origins and ethnic composition of the ancient inhabitants of America in relation to the Book of Mormon, opinions among the leaders have varied. Again no definitive or "orthodox" viewpoint has claimed to provide "the" answer.

Joseph Smith himself laid the foundation for the variances in interpretation. While he served as the responsible editor of the *Times and Seasons* in Nauvoo, the paper printed another excerpt from

Stephens's book that quoted "a goodly traditionary account" from Guatemala. Descendants of the former native rulers there ("Toltec kings of the Quiche and Cakchiquel Indians") claimed that they had "descended from the house of Israel," their line having split off from Moses' party of Israelites after the escape from Egypt. When those Toltec ancestors made their way to Mexico, they "found it already inhabited by people of different nations."[36] Hugh Nibley observed, "Whether such a migration ever took place or not, it is significant that the Prophet was not reluctant to recognize the possibility of other migrations than those mentioned in the Book of Mormon." He continued, "There is not a word in the Book of Mormon to prevent the coming to this hemisphere of any number of people from any part of the world at any time, provided only that they come with the direction of the Lord; and even this requirement must not be too strictly interpreted."[37]

Have church leaders made clear whether or not people other than those directly noticed in the Book of Mormon were included among the "native" population of the Americas? Some have assumed that only people from the three immigrant parties mentioned in the book (Jaredites, Lehites, and Mulekites) were ancestors of today's Native Americans.[38] (The introduction to the 1981 edition of the Book of Mormon calls these groups "the principal ancestors of the American Indians." However, that phrasing (1) is not found in scripture, (2) was never used by Joseph Smith, and (3) did not appear in any previous edition of the Book of Mormon.) Other church leaders have specifically felt that different peoples also settled in the New World.

Apostle Orson Pratt, one of the most vocal 19th-century interpreters of the Book of Mormon, believed that since Book of Mormon times "there [have been] *many nations* who have come here [before Columbus]. And *lastly* Europeans have come from what is termed the old world across the Atlantic."[39] In 1909 Elder B. H. Roberts observed, "It is possible that Phoenician vessels might have visited some parts of" America, as well as, perhaps, other settlers "by way of the Pacific Islands" or via the "Behring straits."[40] In the 5 April 1929 general conference of the church, Anthony W. Ivins, first counselor in the First Presidency, urged: "We must be careful in the conclusions that we reach. The Book of Mormon teaches the history of three distinct peoples . . . who came from the old world to this continent. It does not tell us that there was no one here before them. It does not tell us that people did not come after. . . . We do believe that other people came to this continent."[41] Elder Widtsoe added in 1937, "There may also have been others [in ancient America] not recorded in the Book or not known to the ancient authors."[42] Elder Richard L. Evans characterized the Book of Mormon as "part of a record . . . of prophets and peoples who (with supplementary groups) were *among* the ancestors of the American Indians."[43] In short, some of the leading brethren have long believed that peoples not mentioned in the Book of Mormon lived or might have lived in ancient America, and they have assumed that the idea need not trouble believers in the Book of Mormon. Obviously there is no accepted or orthodox church position that only Book of Mormon peoples were present in the land. That being so, there is no reason why DNA analysts need to be constrained by the idea that all American Indians are Lamanites in a strict genetic sense.

### 7. Is it unrealistic to think ancient people could have sailed across the ocean to or from America?

This classic question used to be answered by scholars with the a priori response, "Of course it is unrealistic!" Nearly all who gave that answer were landlubbers. Their response has reflected their own psychology rather than real-world experience. One scholar has referred to this attitude as "intellectual *mal de mer* when archaeologists look seaward."[44] Others have called this isolationist opinion "thalassophobia," or fear of the sea.[45] Old hands at small-boat sailing have never voiced such qualms. Experience has shown that while some voyagers may indeed be lost at sea, there is still a reasonable chance for a successful passage along certain routes. For instance, Hannes Linde-mann, who made three solo voyages from West Africa to the West Indies, said that he and fellow sailors scoff at nonsailors' view of the "dangers" at sea. He felt that it takes "a damn fool to sink a boat on the high seas."[46] Charles A. Borden recounts stories of all sorts of unlikely craft that have crossed the ocean. He concluded that "sea-worthiness has little to do with size; little ships are often safest."[47]

Two phenomena have changed attitudes in this regard over the past 50 years. First, many hundreds of persons have crossed the oceans in or on all sorts of craft—log rafts, rubber boats, replicas of Polynesian canoes, rowboats, and, more recently, personal water-craft and sailboards, not to mention numerous kinds of small boats. A second reason for the change in atmosphere, especially among scholars, has been recent recognition that ancient (or, as critics were wont to say, "primitive") sailors ages ago were already making remarkable voyages. We now know that the first settlers of Australia crossed open sea from the north as early as 60,000 years ago,[48] while others reached islands east and north of New Guinea nearly 30,000 years ago.[49] These observations have tended to pull the teeth out of old objections about ancient nautical technology being too crude to allow sailing out of sight of land.[50]

Nowadays it is acceptable for an established archaeologist like E. James Dixon to assume that navigators would have been able to come from Asia to America around the North Pacific by "perhaps 13,000 years ago."[51] These changing opinions do not imply that the Jared-ite or Lehite voyages would have been easy, but at least those trips as described in the Book of Mormon now look quite feasible.

### 8. Does the Nephite record allow or indicate the presence of other peoples in America who are not specifically named?

Several lines of evidence in the Book of Mormon point directly to the presence of other peoples in the land from the very beginning of Nephite colonization. One of the most telling passages in the record of Nephi relates the confrontation of Sherem and Jacob. By the time Sherem showed up in the first Nephite settlement, the maximum population that could have resulted from the most rapid conceivable natural descent from Nephi₁ and his fellow settlers would not have exceeded a few dozen adults. Yet Sherem had never met Jacob, the chief Nephite priest (see Jacob 7:1–26), and he had come from some other settlement. Questions about population actually arise still earlier in the story. We find Nephi setting out to build a temple when his adult male relatives in the little colony in the land of Nephi apparently would have numbered only three: Nephi, Sam, and Zoram (plus Jacob and Joseph if they were old enough). So few men could not have put up much of a temple. Furthermore, what kind of wars could the group have fought against the Lamanites with the minuscule "army" that the handful of immigrants could have mustered at the end of 25 years in the land? (see 2 Nephi 5:34). Without increases in the early population of the two factions that can only be explained by the accretion of people from a resident population, reference to "wars" could not be a significant reality. We who are confident of the historicity of the Book of Mormon are assured from these incidents and other textual references that substantial numbers of local "native" residents had joined the immigrant parties. If we had the plates of Nephi that reported the more historical part of their story, perhaps we would find on them explicit information about such contacts with resident populations.

Other statements in the Book of Mormon also indicate that the writers were familiar with, rather than surprised by, the idea of non-Israelites living among the Nephites. The only example we will cite is when Alma visited the city of Ammonihah and Amulek introduced himself with the words, "I am a Nephite" (Alma 8:20). Since the city was nominally under Nephite rule (see Alma 8:11–12, 24) and was a part of the land of Zarahemla at the time, Amulek's statement seems nonsensical, unless many, perhaps most, of the people in the land of

Ammonihah did not consider themselves to be Nephites, by what-ever criteria.[52]

The familiarity of Lehi's people with the words of Old Testament prophets should have led them to expect to be placed in their new land in the midst of other people. The prophets in old Israel had often announced that the tribes of Israel would be "scattered among all people" (Deuteronomy 28:64), would be "removed into all the king-doms of the earth" (Jeremiah 29:18), and would become "wander-ers among the nations" (Hosea 9:17). Further, "the Lord shall scatter you among the nations, and ye shall be left few in number among the heathen, whither the Lord shall lead you" (Deuteronomy 4:27). These prophecies made plain that the whole house of Israel was subject to being scattered among non-Israelite peoples who would be more numerous than they. The people of Lehi were explicitly told that they would suffer this scattering:

> Yea, even my father spake much concerning the Gentiles, and also concerning the house of Israel, that they should be compared like unto an olive tree, whose branches should be broken off and should be scattered upon all the face of the earth. Wherefore, he said it must needs be that we should be led with one accord into the land of promise, unto the ful-filling of the word of the Lord, that we should be scattered. (1 Nephi 10:12–13)

The allegory of the olive tree spelled their fate out even more plainly. Branches broken off the tame tree, which represented his-torical Israel (see Jacob 5:3), were to be grafted onto the roots of "wild" olive trees, meaning non-Israelite groups. That is, there was to be a demographic union between two groups, "young and ten-der branches" from the original tree, Israel, represented as being grafted onto wild rootstock in various parts of the vineyard or earth (see Jacob 5:8–9). Jacob 5:25 and 43 clearly speak of Lehi's people being represented by such a broken-off branch. That branch was to be planted in "the choicest spot" of the vineyard. In that prime location, the Lord had already cut down "that which cumbered this spot of ground," clearly a reference to the elimination of the Jaredites. In addition, the statement that one part of the new hybrid tree brought forth good fruit while the other portion "brought forth wild fruit" is an obvious reference to the Nephites and the Lamanites respectively (v. 45).

So the Lehite "tree" of the allegory was constituted of a geographically transplanted population from the original Israelite promised land "grafted" onto a wild root—joined with a non-Israelite people. (Note that the Lord considered the new root to be "good" despite its being "wild," v. 48). This allegorical description requires that a non-Israelite "root"—"other peoples" in terms of this paper—already be present on the scene where the "young and tender branch," Lehi's group, would be amalgamated with them.

DNA analysts should expect that the immigrants, Lehi's party and Mulek's group too, would immediately begin to incorporate and hybridize with New World "native" populations.

## 9. What do Mesoamerican native traditions suggest about immigrant groups arriving by sea?

Traditions are not, of course, to be believed as completely historical reports, but when the core of a tradition is reported numerous times and in disparate sources, it is likely that there was a factual basis behind it. Mesoamerican traditions that report ancient arrivals by sea are found recorded in early Spanish sources. Most of them were of pre-Columbian vintage, not simply words put in the mouths of natives by Spanish recorders. And many are supported by traditions from other areas. Their consistency and distribution make it plausible that there were at least two and possibly three or more "families" of such stories of an arrival of ancestors from across the ocean. We have space here only to sample this genre.

Fernando de Alva Ixtlilxóchitl was a descendant of the rulers of the city of Texcoco, nominal co-rulers with the Aztec kings of the powerful alliance that dominated northern Mesoamerica in the decades preceding AD 1521. Don Fernando was Spanish educated. His *Obras Históricas*[53] was compiled in the first quarter of the 17th century using extensive records to which his noble ancestry gave him access. At one point he reported, "It is the common and general opinion of all the natives of all this Chichimec land, which now is called New Spain . . . that their ancestors came from western parts . . . as appears in their history; their first king was called Chichimecatl, who was the one who brought them to this New World where they settled . . . and they were those of the division of Babylon."[54] His mention of "Babylon" may, of course, be his personal interpolation, but it seems apparent that he was interpreting the tradition to refer to a transpacific voyage.[55]

The chief ruler at the great Aztec center, Tenochtitlán, Moctezuma Xocoyotzin (popularly known as Montezuma), greeted Hernán Cortés with these words:

> For a long time and by means of writings, we have possessed a knowledge, transmitted from our ancestors, that neither I nor any of us who inhabit this land are of native origin. We are foreigners and came here from very remote parts.
>
> We possess information that our lineage was led to this land by a lord to whom we all owed [allegiance]. He afterward left this for his native country.
>
> . . . But we have ever believed that his descendants would surely come here to subjugate this land and us who are, by rights, their vassals.
>
> Because of what you say concerning the region whence you came, which is where the sun rises . . . we believe and hold as certain that he [the Spanish king] must be our rightful [natural] lord.[56]

Fray Bernardino de Sahagún gathered a huge collection of materials from the best native Mexican informants available to him in the
middle of the 16th century. One thing he reported being told was
this:

> Concerning the origin of this people, the account which
> the old people give is that they came by sea from toward
> the north [from the direction of Florida, he adds], and it is
> certain that they came in some vessels of wood, but it is not
> known how they were built; but it is conjectured by one re-
> port which there is among all these natives, that they came
> out of seven caves and that these seven caves are the seven
> ships or galleys in which the first settlers of this land came
> . . . they came along the coast and disembarked at the Port
> of Pánuco, which they call Panco [near Tampico, Veracruz],
> which means, place where those who crossed the water ar-
> rived. These people came looking for a terrestrial paradise.[57]

Still today, reported Lorenzo Ochoa in 1979, in certain places
near Tampico, traditions exist paralleling Sahagún's to the effect that
ancestors arrived by sea navigating in "turtle shells."[58]

A native document from 16th-century Guatemala, *Titulos de
los Señores de Totonicapán*, said that their ancestors "came from the
other part of the ocean, from where the sun rises, a place called *Pa
Tulán, Pa Civán*."[59] Those whose signatures attested this 16th-century
document further noted, "[W]e have written that which by tradition
our ancestors told us, who came from the other part of the sea, from
Civán-Tulán, bordering on Babylonia." At least that was their geographical interpretation of the tradition as of 1554.[60]

Other traditional accounts could be cited, but they are generally
parallel to those above.[61] The conventional interpretation of these
traditions by scholars has been that they either stem from remem-
brance of crossings over local waters or are notions picked up by
Amerindians from the Christian fathers and the Bible. That might be

so in some cases, yet because of the widespread occurrence of the traditions, we consider that two or more tales of the arrival of ancestors from across the ocean were definitely maintained in pre-Columbian times among Mesoamerican peoples. If so, then any attempt to interpret the physical ancestry of a people by DNA analysis will need to be open to reconciling the data from the conventional interpretations of Amerindian genetics with these traditions that point to transoceanic intruders.

### 10. What languages were spoken in the Western Hemisphere? Is it known that Hebrew was in use in ancient America? What do these facts mean for the Book of Mormon?

The number of Native American languages spoken at the time European conquerors or settlers arrived is not known for sure, but a current best estimate is around 1,000 from Alaska to Argentina.[62] Methods of classifying those into larger groupings are varied and inconsistent, but hemisphere-wide the number of major groupings (whether called "families," "stocks," etc.) is on the order of 80. In addition, there were about 80 "isolates," that is, single tongues that have not been convincingly connected to any other language or grouping.[63] Mesoamerican languages fit into perhaps 14 families, with upwards of 200 separate tongues having once existed in the area. (A family is a group of tongues believed to have descended from a common ancestral language.) Indications are strong that there was considerable linguistic differentiation in Mesoamerica as early as 1500 BC.[64] Latter-day Saint students of the Book of Mormon should understand that long prior to Lehi's day, Mesoamerica was already linguistically complex.[65] Moreover, many archaeological sites were occupied continuously, or so it appears, for thousands of years without clear evidence in the material remains of any replacement of the culture of the inhabitants. That continuity suggests, although it does not prove, that many of those people probably did not change their tongues.

All this means that the old supposition by some Latter-day Saints that the Hebrew tongue used by Lehi's and Mulek's immigrant parties became foundational for all ancient American languages is impossible.

When we examine the social and cultural implications of what the Book of Mormon record tells us, we discover that it cannot possibly be a "history of the American Indians." Mormon's book was never meant to serve as a history of an entire territory but is what has been termed a "lineage history."[66] It relates certain events and interpretations of those events that relate to a fairly small number of people, chiefly the descendants of Nephi. These serve the same purpose as most of the historical books of the Bible, like Genesis and Exodus. Those records focus on stories about Abraham and those of his descendants who became the founders of the house of Israel. For example, the Old Testament source only briefly mentions Ishmael and his clan, let alone more distant ethnic entities like the Canaanites, and then only as far as the events involving those outsiders impinged on the key descent line.

In short, a lineage history is a partial record of historical events, emphasizing what happened to one group of people, phrased in the recorders' ethnocentric terms. The lineage histories of other groups on the scene, if they were kept, would report different versions of what was going on. Knowing that the Nephite record is of this limited sort, we can appreciate why, for example, their story gives a total of only 100 words or so to the "people of Zarahemla," although that group was much more numerous than ethnic Nephites (see Mosiah 25:1). Such narrowly told accounts were a very common form of "history" in many parts of the ancient world, including, as we could expect, among native peoples of Mesoamerica.

The upshot is that we need to think of the Nephite record keepers as a minority—an elite minority at that—who, like most ruling minorities, tended to have their speech and customs eventually smothered by the speech and lifeways of the majority population (think of the Norman conquerors of England, whose French language did not last long on the island). So it makes sense when Moroni reports, after nearly 1,000 years of his people's history, that by then "no other people knoweth our language" (Moroni 9:34).

Still, we may find remnants of Hebrew in Mesoamerican languages when we look carefully, just as English vocabulary reveals traces of Norman French. Little looking has yet been done by qualified scholars, yet the slim efforts have turned up interesting results. The prominent Mexican linguist Maurice Swadesh had student P. Agrinier search Zapotec and related languages in south-central Mexico for Hebrew words. They identified a significant number of Hebrew parallels, which Robert F. Smith later more than doubled.[67] Swadesh said of that project, "I was surprised at the number and closeness of the parallels" between the languages compared.[68] More pointedly, linguist Brian Stubbs has identified more than one thousand Hebrew and/or Arabic forms in tongues of the Uto-Aztecan family, which stretches from Central Mexico to Utah.[69] Mary LeCron Foster, a mature linguist long at the University of California, independently concluded that "Uto-Aztecan proves to derive either from Proto-Indo-European . . . or even from pre-IE ancestors," while "Quechua [the language of the Incas of Peru] shows "extensive borrowing from a Semitic language, seemingly Arabic."[70] Much more work must be done to convince the majority of linguists of the reality of Semitic language remnants appearing in Mesoamerican (and perhaps other native American) languages, but the evidence so far is promising and new studies are under way.

Now, if Semitic languages penetrated Mesoamerican societies, might we not expect evidence that so did Hebrew or Arab genes?[71] After more than a cursory effort is devoted to studying the question, we may see more concrete confirmation. We note, as a methodological parallel, that the implications of another example of an Asian language intrusion into America has been equally ignored by most linguistic professionals, not to mention geneticists. Otto J. Von

Sadovszky has demonstrated from remarkably extensive evidence that a series of Amerindian languages in north-central California are directly related to the Ugrian family of tongues of western Siberia (of which Finnish is a relative).[72] He has compiled more than 10,000 word relationships between the two areas (probably as of around 500 BC) as well as a large number of parallel customs and beliefs. It is obvious that DNA testing of the tribes concerned ought to demonstrate genetic links, but nobody has yet bothered to carry out the study. Soon the Mesoamerican linguistic links may be compelling enough to demand DNA testing of the implied relationship.

## 11. Has research in hard science supported the claim that a variety of Old World peoples came to live in the Americas?

Most researchers in the life sciences, like their colleagues in archaeology and geography, typically claim that the two hemispheres, commonly called the Old World and the New World, effectively had distinct histories. One of the key arguments against the proposition that people anciently settled the Americas from Eurasia, Oceania, or Africa has been the assertion by biologists throughout the 20th century that no cultivated plants (of any consequence, at least) were shared on both sides of the Atlantic or Pacific Oceans before Columbus's day.[73]

This conservative view has been progressively weakening for years, although defended by prestigious natural scientists. However, in 2002 a paper was presented (and now is in press) that tackled the issue on an unprecedented scale. New evidence was used to demonstrate beyond question that extensive cross-ocean voyaging has been taking place for at least the last 8,000 years.[74] The study documents that more than 80 species of plants had crossed all or part of the ocean to or from the Americas before AD 1500.[75] The list includes amaranth grains, the cashew nut, pineapple, the peanut, hashish, tobacco, coca, two species of chili pepper, the kapok tree, various squashes and pumpkin, at least six species of cotton, bananas, the prickly pear, the guava, several grasses and (human-dependent) weeds, corn, and two kinds of marigolds. For another 29 species, significant evidence invites more research on their transoceanic status, and for 34 more there is enough evidence to recommend further study.

Decisive evidence consists, for example, of clear representations of a plant in ancient art. Carl L. Johannessen (and other investigators) had earlier found and photographed hundreds of images of maize ears (maize is, of course, an American native plant) held in the hands of sacred beings in scenes carved on the walls of temples of medieval age in southern India. More art now shows corn that dates to BC times, while archaeological excavation (another form of decisive documentation) on the island of Timor in Indonesia places the crop there before 2500 BC.[76] In other Indian art we see sunflowers, the annona fruit, cashew nuts, and other plants of American origin. In fact, at least two dozen American species were in India before Columbus, which means that a great deal of two-way sailing must have taken place.

Finding a name of a plant in ancient historical and literary texts also confirms the early presence of that plant. For India a unique linguistic situation contributes to the significance of some plant references. The classical religious texts of India were written in the Sanskrit language. Sanskrit was in use as an active language until no later than about AD 1000. After that date, the language served like Latin in Europe, as a sacred "dead" tongue that was no longer adding new words and that one learned only to study the ancient sacred texts. So when a Sanskrit dictionary of known texts uses a name such as *sandhya-rága* (for the American native flower plant that we today call the "four o'clock"), this can only mean that the word and the plant were present in India many centuries before the time in the 1500s when the first European sailors could have brought either the plant or a name from America. Also, since a name for another New World plant, the sweet potato, was written in Chinese characters in a classic historical document, this guarantees that the plant was being grown in Asia many centuries ago.

The evidence on plant sharing across the ocean has been buttressed by data regarding fauna. The opinion has prevailed generally among the experts that America anciently was a virtual diseaseless paradise. Nevertheless, John L. Sorenson and Carl L. Johannessen have shown that a surprising number of disease organisms were present in the New World, as much as they were in the Old World. The key point, however, is that since organisms do not arise independently in different parts of the earth, it is necessary to determine how the two hemispheres could have shared so many "bugs." The causes of 14 ailments have been conclusively found in both hemispheres—two species of hookworms, the roundworm, the tuberculosis bacteria, lice, ringworm, a leukemia virus, and others. Furthermore, several larger faunal species also crossed the ocean. For instance, the turkey, that thoroughly American fowl, appears in art in Europe by the 13th century AD, and its bones have turned up in Hungarian and Swiss ruins of that time.

In regard to all the species mentioned above, only voyages by humans provide a suitable explanation. Those trips—and floral and faunal data—point to the transoceanic passage of perhaps hundreds of boats between 6000 BC and AD 1500. Voyages were certainly not routine, but neither were they unknown.

These data strongly imply that humans from numerous Old World areas reached the New World. Until DNA analysis finds evidence of the Old World visitors and migrants who arrived in those boats, molecular biologists ought to consider their picture incomplete.

### 12. Does evidence from archaeology and cultural studies support the idea that there were intrusions by Old World groups?

This is a vast topic, impossible even to summarize here. Only a few illustrative references to relevant material can be examined in the space available here.

One kind of information concerns cultural complexes and the populations that brought them that certainly arrived from across the ocean. Some archaeologists finesse the issue by insisting that only "concrete archaeological evidence" for a cultural intrusion will satisfy them.[77] This spurious response is well illustrated by the case of the Ugrian-language enclave in central California mentioned above; the supporting linguistic material is vast and highly "concrete," though in a nonmaterial sense. No archaeologist has yet assessed this evident connection between California and western Siberia on the basis of material remains. Contradictorily, in the case of the settling of the island of Madagascar off the east coast of Africa, the dominant language is so obviously Austronesian (related to Malayo-Polynesian) that no scholar questions that the people came from Indonesia, despite the fact that no artifact from there has ever been found on Madagascar.[78]

Another example within the Americas illustrates the same point. Julian Granberry established that the Timucuan language of Florida, and the people speaking it, originated in the Amazon area. He infers that they reached Florida by boat from western Venezuela at approximately 2000–1500 BC without any stopovers en route, a trip on the order of 1,000 miles long.[79] These relationships are evidenced beyond question by linguistics but not by any archaeological or ethnological facts, let alone by DNA evidence.

A similar example from Ecuador is provided by the Bahia culture, dated around the beginning of the Christian era. Excavation provided the first evidence for patently East Asiatic features that characterize this complex (ceramic model houses, neck rests in lieu of pillows, rectanguloid pottery net weights, golf-tee-shaped earlobe decorations, symmetrically graduated panpipes, seated figurines that look very much like Buddha, and use of the coolie yoke for carrying burdens),[80] but those Asiatic links are now little mentioned. There is no question that Asians could have reached South America, since studies have shown that balsa rafts manufactured in Ecuador are essentially identical to log rafts of China and Vietnam (despite the label *rafts*, these conveyances were virtual ships).[81] They were used in the seas off China from at least the fifth century BC.[82] Bahia pottery has been found in the Galápagos

Islands, 700 miles off the coast of Ecuador.[83] Despite these facts, many archaeologists ignore the Bahia intrusion, or at least its significance as a mechanism for the arrival of Asians.

Moreover, it is entirely possible that some transoceanic migrant groups adapted successfully to their new American homes for a while but in the long run failed to survive. James Dixon notes the case of the Norse settlers in Greenland and their North American Vinland, "a clearly documented case of a major and long-lived transoceanic colonization of the Americas that ultimately failed." According to Dixon, events since the Norse went extinct have obscured the scientific record so that not only is the archaeological evidence for their presence very limited but there are no recognized survivors in North America. He concludes that "the original Norse colonization [there] cannot be demonstrated ever to have happened."[84] As in the case of the Nephites, only in surviving historical accounts can one "prove" that Norse people lived in America.[85]

The idea of some influential connections between cultures in Asia and in America is increasingly being accepted by some scholars who once were adamantly opposed to the idea. Sir Joseph Needham, one of the 20th century's greatest scholars, with colleagues Wang Ling and Lu Gwei-Djen, first published extensive data on the contacts question in their masterful series entitled *Science and Civilisation in China*.[86] In 1985 Needham and Lu put out a concise but elegantly argued statement of the case for a voyaging connection.[87] Since then it has been more difficult for thoughtful scientists to ignore the issue. Even conservative scholars have begun to accept a limited version of the view that accepts transoceanic voyaging. For instance, Michael D. Coe, once an adamant opponent of voyaging from Asia, was quoted in 1996 as being impressed with the many resemblances between "mental systems known from Bali in Indonesia and Mesoamerica." He now thinks that some of the parallels were "almost identical on both sides of the Pacific." Coe acknowledges, however, that his thinking on the point is not orthodox: "Most anthropologists are so fuddy-duddy. They're not willing to let their minds roam ahead, speculate."[88] If the "fuddy-duddy," no-voyaging paradigm does break down, it will mean even more questions to be faced by DNA analysis because exotic populations can be expected to be involved in the hitherto monolithic study of "Amerindian" genetics.

A remarkable confirmation that such a shipborne link once existed that tied the central Old World civilizations to ancient America across the Atlantic (as the story of Mulek implies) comes from a Greek merchant ship that sank at Kyrenia, Cyprus, in the fourth century BC. When examined by underwater archaeologists, it was found to have utilized leaves of the agave plant as caulking.[89] That plant is considered by biologists to be exclusively Mexican, so there are no explanations for its presence and use in the Kyrenia vessel except that the ship had itself reached the New World, where it was recaulked before returning to the Mediterranean, or else that living agave plants had been transported to some Old World area where the harvested leaves could be used in routine caulking of ships there.

On the basis of research summarized above, there is no longer any real question that cultural, and presumably human biological, connections existed between Eurasia and Mesoamerica many centuries ago. What remains to be done to round out the picture is to carry out specific research aimed at determining the details of those connections. Future DNA study is going to have to consider these facts in generating and testing hypotheses. If molecular biology fails to find a place in its models to handle the historical contacts attested by such cultural data, that failure will cast doubt on the adequacy of the biological studies.

### 13. Have races or ethnically distinct populations that exhibit non-Amerindian characteristics been revealed in ancient Mesoamerican art?

For us the answer to this question is unequivocally "Yes!" Of course, there is no demonstrated direct connection between most features of human beings' external appearance and specific DNA; nevertheless, if we see striking differences in appearance (phenotype) of a population, we can plausibly expect differences in genetic makeup (genotype).

The concept that all American Indians formed a monolithic "race" whose ancestors came from northern Asia was made a part of early 20th-century physical anthropology by one of the field's first leaders, Ales Hrdlicka. He claimed that if "some members of the Asiatic groups and the average [*sic*] American Indians were to be transplanted and body and hair dressed like those of the other tribe, they could not possibly be distinguished physically by an observer."[90] That extreme view is no longer held, yet intellectual inertia seems to prevent many anthropologists from acknowledging that substantial variation exists among so-called Native Americans.

Nowhere is this variability shown more clearly than in the modeled clay figurines and other representations of humans in art. They show up in considerable numbers in Mesoamerica and in lesser numbers among human effigies in Peru. Heads and skin shades that would be at home on all of the different continents are seen.[91] Specific ethnicities are obvious in some of the representations: African blacks, Southeast Asians, Chinese, perhaps Koreans, possibly Japanese, and Mediterranean people are commonly encountered. Of special interest is a whole class of "Semitic" or "Jewish" or "Uncle Sam" faces, so called by some archaeologists or art historians because of the large aquiline noses and beards. This type of face also occurs not only in clay but also on stone sculptures.[92] At the very least, the presence of out-of-place images challenge Hrdlicka's old oversimplification. Some scholars have claimed that these "racially" distinctive heads are "stylized" versions of "normal" or majority Mesoamerican figurines, but anyone can see that most of the representations are not stylized in the least but are individualized portraits.[93] If even a part of the anomalous figures are authentically ancient and accurate portrayals of living people, we have to infer that DNA research has some major discoveries yet to make to account for them.

Another physiological anomaly confirms what we have just discussed. Students of ancient voyaging have commented on the presence of beards on male figures in Mesoamerican art. A preliminary study of the topic done a few years ago by Kirk Magleby yielded provocative results.[94] Inasmuch as nearly all Amerindians seem predisposed to producing only meager beards, it is reasonable to take that condition as the genetic norm. So when fulsome whiskers and mustaches are found on ancient figures, a genetic explanation is called for. In Magleby's research on hundreds of bearded representations, the frequency of beards proved highest in objects of Pre-Classic age (before AD 300), when the proportion of abundant beards was also highest. Beardedness was also found to decrease as one moved outward from central Mesoamerica. Some critics claim that there is no reason to think that such bearded people represented descendants of Old World immigrants. Nevertheless, the world center of the growth of heavy beards is the Near East. Furthermore, critics also point out that some of the beards seen in Mesoamerican art appear to be artificial. We agree that is possible (for example, artificial beards were donned by Egyptian pharaohs in an investiture rite). But then we wonder where the preference for a full beard would have come from. Obviously, the notion came from persons with beards. Or why would sparsely bearded native Amerindians have adopted artificial beards to be worn by their societies' leaders? Overall, the scenario that makes most sense is that Old World immigrants to Mesoamerica from the Eurasiatic homeland where heavy beards appear in art set a standard of elite appearance that was watered down as the responsible genes were submerged in a pool of Mongoloid DNA. At the least, beardedness seems to be a topic that deserves consideration in DNA studies of Amerindians.

## 14. What are some limits of DNA research in clarifying historical and genealogical relationships among the "native" inhabitants of the Americas?

It is in the nature of all scientific research that one cannot predict the course of its development nor the value of its results. Still there is reason to think that some scientists and also consumers of information from DNA studies have unrealistic interpretations of what such studies have accomplished and what they may yet do. A recent article by Peter N. Jones rings a loud alarm bell for everyone concerned with American Indian DNA studies by pointing out some of the flaws in methods and logic imposed on the field to date.[95]

The basis of this type of research so far has been specimens taken from very small samples of a total population.[96] Typically the published DNA characteristics for many American Indian tribes have been calculated on specimens taken from only a few dozen, or at most a couple of hundred, individuals. (Jones points out that most DNA investigators do not even know for sure whether the specimens of blood used in their research actually came from Indians or not.)[97] And quite aside from the quality of the specimens, the analytical models used are only a tiny sample of the methods that ultimately would be significant. We have, as it were, a net of very coarse weave that lets most of the fish escape. Recent cautionary writings teach us the highly tentative nature of the results so far from DNA research on the history of American Indians.

One set of concerns stems from the fact that, as a person's genealogical lines go back in time, the number of his or her ancestors obviously multiplies. Within a few centuries all of us have thousands of forebears. Ultimately or theoretically our foreparents could number in the millions. Yet there is a paradox here. Beyond a certain point in time the theoretical number of one's ancestors exceeds the number of persons who were actually alive then! The truth is that our genealogical lines eventually converge on a restricted set of people. Joseph Chang, a statistician at Yale, in a 1999 article[98] showed that there is a high probability that *every* European alive today shares at least one common ancestor who lived only about 600 years ago. Science writer Steve Olson, who has explained this principle in greater detail in his superlative book, *Mapping Human History*, observes:

> The forces of genetic mixing are so powerful that everyone in the world has [for example] Jewish ancestors, though the amount of DNA from those ancestors in a given individual may be small. In fact, everyone on earth is by now a descendant of Abraham, Moses, and Aaron—if indeed they existed.[99]

In parallel, if one assumes that Lehi was a real figure, Chang's or Olson's model would argue that all Amerindians today are likely to be his descendants. But would present-day DNA research indicate anything of the kind? Actually, it would be virtually impossible via today's DNA procedures to document such slender genealogical links as Chang and Olson are talking about.

Other scientists have noted that

> mtDNA represents a small, though essential, piece of our whole genome. . . . However, our genetic ancestry is much broader, because we know that a large fraction of any population many generations ago is included in our genealogical tree. . . . Mitochondrial genes contain information largely about energy production. But most of the information that characterizes us as human beings resides in our so-called nuclear genes, which constitute more than 99.99 per cent of the human genome. . . . If we could follow all the branches through which we have inherited our genes, we would probably find that all those people included in our genealogical tree have contributed—maybe in an extremely diluted way— to our genetic inheritance.[100]

While contemporary studies of human DNA and human populations primarily utilize mitochondrial DNA and Y chromosome
DNA, the genetic information from these tests represents less than
.01 percent of the genetic information passed down from our numerous ancestors. It is possible that, in the future, scientific methods may
conceivably expand in order to tap into some of that 99.99 percent of
the genetic information denied to us by today's limited tools, but such
studies may never be able to reveal the full diversity of our ancestry.

The next time you hear someone boasting of being descended
from royalty, take heart: There is a very good probability that
you have noble ancestors too. The rapid mixing of genealogical branches, within only a few tens of generations, almost
guarantees it. The real doubt is how much "royal blood" your
friend (or you) still carry in your genes. Genealogy does not
mean genes. And how similar we are genetically remains an
issue of current research.[101]

Neither can DNA scientists reliably tell whether Native Americans have links to Israelites. We may never know.

# Notes

1.   Dallin H. Oaks, "The Historicity of the Book of Mormon," in *Historicity and the
Latter-day Saint Scriptures*, ed. Paul Y. Hoskisson (Provo, UT: BYU Religious Studies
Center, 2001), 238–39; emphases added.

2.   Many are listed and summarized in John L. Sorenson, "Summary of Models," pt. 2 of
*The Geography of Book of Mormon Events: A Source Book* (Provo, UT: FARMS, 1992), 38–206.

3.   For details see John L. Sorenson, *Mormon's Map* (Provo, UT: FARMS, 2000).

4.   To all appearances, it was the Atlantic that Mulek's party crossed on their way
from Palestine to the New World. The east coastal "city of Mulek" was very probably the
first settlement spot of Mulek's party (see Alma 8:7) in the promised land, as first mentioned in Alma 51:26 (compare Alma 22:31).

5.   Lehi's party left from southern Arabia. In most cases, pre-Portuguese voyages
from that spot into the Indian Ocean went east and followed the predominant winds to
reach the southwestern part of the Indian peninsula. Since they landed in the New World
on the coast of the "west sea," we can only conclude that Nephi's ship had proceeded via
the Malacca Straits (Singapore) into and then across the Pacific Ocean, so that their "west
sea" in the promised land would have been on the Pacific side of America.

6. See John L. Sorenson, "The Book of Mormon as a Mesoamerican Record," in *Book of Mormon Authorship Revisited: The Evidence for Ancient Origins*, ed. Noel B. Reynolds (Provo, UT: FARMS, 1997), 391–521.

7. For more details on the map reflected in the Book of Mormon text, see, in addition to *Mormon's Map*, John L. Sorenson, *An Ancient American Setting for the Book of Mormon* (Salt Lake City: Deseret Book and FARMS, 1985, 1996), especially chap. 1. Also see John Clark, "A Key for Evaluating Nephite Geographies," *Review of Books on the Book of Mormon* 1 (1989): 20–70.

8. J. Charles Kelley, "Mesoamerica and the Southwestern United States," in *Archaeological Frontiers and External Connections*, vol. 4 of *Handbook of Middle American Indians*, ed. G. F. Ekholm and G. R. Willey (Austin: Univ. of Texas Press, 1966), 109; compare Charles C. Di Peso, *Casas Grandes: A Fallen Trading Center of the Gran Chichimeca*, vol. 1, ed. Gloria J. Fenner (Flagstaff, AZ: Northland Press, 1974); and several articles in Frances Joan Mathien and Randall H. McGuire, eds., *Ripples in the Chichimec Sea: New Considerations of Southwestern–Mesoamerican Interactions* (Carbondale: Southern Illinois Univ. Press, 1986).

9. Michael B. Stanislawski, "Mesoamerican Influence in Northeastern Arizona," in *International Congress of Americanists, XXXVI Congreso Internacional de Americanistas, España, 1964: Actas y memorias*, ed. Alfredo Jimenez Núñez (Seville, Spain: ECESA, 1966), 1:309.

10. Clarence H. Webb ("The Extent and Content of Poverty Point Culture," *American Antiquity: A Quarterly Review of American Archaeology* 33/3 [July 1968]: 297–321) long ago pointed out significant similarities between early Mesoamerica and the unique Poverty Point, Louisiana, site. There is no trace of those shared features at any site in the intervening 1,200–mile stretch. To all appearances, people from the former area traveled directly to the other.

11. See Robert N. Zeitlin (review of *Ripples in the Chichimec Sea: New Considerations of Southwestern-Mesoamerican Interactions*, by F. J. Mathien and R. H. McGuire, eds. [Carbondale: Southern Illinois Univ. Press, 1986], 59–65), who comments on the "parochialism" of American "isolationist" archaeologists who resist any idea that some area other than their own bit of turf was responsible for developments there. On the other hand, he accuses some of considering "the Southwest as little more than an outpost of Mesoamerica." His review of these preferences demonstrates, we believe, that the personal opinions of individual archaeologists, not the quality of the evidence they muster, often determine their viewpoints on this matter.

12. See James B. Griffin, "Mesoamerica and the Eastern United States in Prehistoric Times," in *Handbook of Middle American Indians*, 4:119.

13. See Jorge G. Marcos, "Breve prehistoria del Ecuador," in *Arqueología de la costa ecuatoriana: Nuevos enfoques*, ed. J. G. Marcos (Guayaquil, Ecuador: ESPOL y Corporación Editora Nacional, 1986), 25–50.

14. See Gerardo Reichel-Dolmatoff, "The Loom of Life: A Kogi Principle of Integration," *Journal of Latin American Lore* 4/1 (1978): 5–27. See also Jaime Errázuriz, *Tumaco-La Tolita: Una cultura precolombina desconocida* (Bogotá, Colombia: C. Valencia Editores, 1980); Reichel-Dolmatoff, *Colombia*, vol. 44 of *Ancient Peoples and Places* (New

York: Praeger, 1965), 111–15. For substantial discussion of evidence (shaft tombs, the chi-maera motif, knowledge of metallurgy, and the motif of a male figurine seated on a bench or stool) for direct movements between the west coast of Mexico and Ecuador/Peru, see articles by Clinton R. Edwards, Clement W. Meighan, and Joseph B. Mountjoy in *Precolumbian Contact within Nuclear America, Mesoamerican Studies*, vol. 4, ed. J. Charles Kelley and Carroll L. Riley (Carbondale: Southern Illinois Univ., University Museum, 1969). See also Presley Norton, "El señorio de Salangone y la liga de mercaderes: El cartel spondylus-balsa," in *Archaeología y etnohistoria del sur de Colombia y norte del Ecuador*, comp. José Alcina Franch and Segundo Moreno Yánez (Cayambe, Ecuador: Ediciones Abya-Yala, 1987); see also Robert C. West, "Aboriginal Sea Navigation between Middle and South America," *American Anthropologist* 63/1 (Feb. 1961): 133–35.

15. See Robert Chadwick, "Archaeological Synthesis of Michoacán and Adjacent Regions," in *Archaeology of Northern Mesoamerica*, pt. 2, vol. 11 of *Handbook of Middle American Indians*, ed. R. Wauchope, G. F. Ekholm, and I. Bernal (Austin: Univ. of Texas Press, 1971), 677.

16. Marshall Newman, "A Trial Formulation Presenting Evidence from Physical Anthropology for Migrations from Mexico to South America," in *Migrations in New World Culture History*, University of Arizona Social Science Bulletin no. 27 (Tucson: Univ. of Arizona Press, 1958). Since he published that item, most physical anthropologists have chosen not to be persuaded by the kind of data he used, yet it is not without significance.

17. A concise summary of information on this topic is found in "Mesoamericans in Pre-Spanish South America," in *Reexploring the Book of Mormon*, ed. John W. Welch (Salt Lake City: Deseret Book and FARMS, 1992), 215–17.

18. See *Times and Seasons*, 15 Sept. 1842, 922, which says that the Jaredites "covered the whole continent from sea to sea, with towns and cities." See also Sorenson, *Geography of Book of Mormon Events*, 9–15, 75–76.

19. See Grant Underwood, "Book of Mormon Usage in Early LDS Theology," *Dialogue: A Journal of Mormon Thought* 17/3 (autumn 1984): 35–74; see also Sorenson, *Geography of Book of Mormon Events*, 11–15.

20. *Incidents of Travel in Central America, Chiapas, and Yucatan* (New York: Harper & Brothers, 1841).

21. "Extract," *Times and Seasons*, 15 Sept. 1842, 914.

22. "Zarahemla," *Times and Seasons*, 1 Oct. 1842, 927.

23. The 15 Sept. 1842 *Times and Seasons* article also suggested that the "wonderful ruins of Palenque" in Chiapas, Mexico, "are among the mighty works of the Nephites," and that they compared favorably with the temple of Nephi. Since the Book of Mormon places the land of Nephi and its temple in the land southward, this early model would seem to exclude South America.

24. See, for example, *Journal of Discourses*, 12:340–42; 14:324–30, 333.

25. In 1856 George Q. Cannon, who in Nauvoo had worked in the *Times and Seasons* office with his uncle John Taylor and was familiar with the works of Catherwood and Stephens, put forward an exception to the usual whole-hemisphere view of Book of Mormon geography. He questioned the argument that the Indians were too primitive to build cities and temples, since these discoveries were made "in the country declared by

the Book of Mormon to be the principal residence of one of the colonies that were led to this land" (George Q. Cannon, "Buried Cities of the West," *Western Standard*, 15 Oct. 1856; reprinted in *Millennial Star*, 10 Jan. 1857, 18; emphasis added). In 1876 another writer, after learning of parallels between native Mesoamerican traditions and the Book of Mormon, shifted his earlier support for Orson Pratt's model. "Is it not possible," he asked in light of this new information, "that the Rio Usumasinta, 'flowing north into the sea', may be the ancient river Sidon? Those remarkable and world-famous ruins known under the name Palenque may yet be proven to be the remains of that 'great city and religious center' of the aboriginals, called Zarahemla" (G. M. Ottinger, "Votan, the Culture Hero of the Mayas," *Juvenile Instructor* 14/5 [1 Mar. 1879]: 58). The implications of placing Zarahemla at either Quirigua in Guatemala or at Palenque in southern Mexico would obviously shift the land Bountiful to a more northerly location, leaving the Isthmus of Tehuantepec as the only viable candidate for the narrow neck of land. In contrast, Pratt's popular model puts the Sidon River, Zarahemla, and Bountiful in the northern regions of South America between Colombia and Panama (see *Journal of Discourses*, 14:324–33). We clearly have at least two drastically different models of Book of Mormon geography being bandied about, suggesting that such things were not considered to have been settled by revelation.

26. See, for example, B. H. Roberts, *Studies in the Book of Mormon*, ed. Brigham Madsen (Urbana: Univ. of Illinois Press, 1985); Dan Vogel, *Indian Origins and the Book of Mormon: Religious Solutions from Columbus to Joseph Smith* (Salt Lake City: Signature Books, 1986); Brent Lee Metcalfe, "Apologetic and Critical Assumptions about Book of Mormon Historicity," *Dialogue* 26/3 (fall 1993): 154–84; "Editor's Introduction," in *American Apocrypha: Essays on the Book of Mormon*, ed. Dan Vogel and Brent Lee Metcalfe (Salt Lake City: Signature Books, 2002), vii–xvii; and Thomas W. Murphy, "Lamanite Genesis, Genealogy, and Genetics," in *American Apocrypha*, 47–77. For one response, see William J. Hamblin, "An Apologist for the Critics: Brent Lee Metcalfe's Assumptions and Methodologies," *Review of Books on the Book of Mormon* 6/1 (1994): 434–523.

27. *Doctrines of Salvation: Sermons and Writings of Joseph Fielding Smith*, comp. Bruce R. McConkie (Salt Lake City: Bookcraft, 1956), 3:203–4; emphasis removed.

28. That is, the title Nephi was used in the same manner as Czar (a shortened form of Caesar) was used in historical Russia.

29. For further scriptural references, see Sorenson, *Ancient American Setting*, 54.

30. See John L. Sorenson, "When Lehi's Party Arrived in the Land, Did They Find Others There?" *Journal of Book of Mormon Studies* 1/1 (fall 1992): 19–24; Hugh Nibley, *Lehi in the Desert; The World of the Jaredites; There Were Jaredites*, ed. John W. Welch, Darrell L. Matthews, and Stephen R. Callister (Salt Lake City: Deseret Book and FARMS, 1988), 237, 240–48.

31. See Anthony W. Ivins, "Are the Jaredites an Extinct People?" *Improvement Era* 6/1 (Nov. 1902): 43–44; Janne M. Sjodahl, "Have the Lamanites Jaredite Blood in Their Veins?" *Improvement Era* 31/1 (Nov. 1927): 56– 57; and Nibley, *Lehi in the Desert; The World of the Jaredites; There Were Jaredites*, 240–46.

32. *Times and Seasons*, 1 Oct. 1842, 927; emphasis added.

33.  Editorial, "The Book of Mormon Geography," *Juvenile Instructor*, 1 Jan. 1890, 18.

34.  The statement was made about 1918; see *Juvenile Instructor*, April 1938, 160, which also reprints Cannon's statement.

35.  "Is Book of Mormon Geography Known?" *Improvement Era*, July 1950, 547.

36.  *Times and Seasons*, 15 Sept. 1842, 921. The full tradition may be read in English in Don Domingo Juarros, *A Statistical and Commercial History of the Kingdom of Guatemala, in Spanish America . . .* , trans. J. Baily (London: John Hearne, 1823; reprint, New York: AMS Press, 1971).

37.  *Lehi in the Desert; The World of the Jaredites; There Were Jaredites*, 250–51.

38.  See, for example, Joseph Fielding Smith, "Book of Mormon Establishes Location of Historic Region," *Church News*, 27 Feb. 1954, 2–3. Such a view was often considered to be supported by a statement attributed by some sources to Joseph Smith concerning Lehi's supposed landing in Chile and by statements about the "Zelph" skeleton, as in Donald Q. Cannon, "Zelph Revisited," in *Regional Studies in Latter-day Saint Church History: Illinois*, ed. H. Dean Garrett (Provo, UT: BYU Dept. of Church History and Doctrine, 1995), 97–109. For critical treatments of the problematic value of those statements in regard to geography, see Kenneth W. Godfrey, "The Zelph Story," *BYU Studies* 29/2 (1989): 31–56; "What Is the Significance of Zelph in the Study of Book of Mormon Geography?" *Journal of Book of Mormon Studies* 8/2 (1999): 70–79; and Frederick G. Williams III, *Did Lehi Land in Chile? An Assessment of the Frederick G. Williams Statement* (Provo, UT: FARMS, 1988).

39.  *Journal of Discourses*, 12:343; emphasis added.

40.  B. H. Roberts, "Indirect External Evidences—American Antiquities, Preliminary Consideration.—Continued," ch. 25 of "Of the Probability of Intercourse between the Eastern and the Western Hemispheres during Jaredite and Nephite Times," pt. 3 of *New Witnesses for God* (Salt Lake City: Deseret News, 1909), 2:356.

41.  In *Conference Report*, April 1929, 15.

42.  John A. Widtsoe and Franklin S. Harris Jr., *Seven Claims of the Book of Mormon: A Collection of Evidences* (Independence, MO: Zion's Printing and Publishing, 1937), 87.

43.  Richard L. Evans, "What Is a Mormon?" in *Religions of America: Ferment and Faith in an Age of Crisis*, ed. Leo Rosten (London: Heinemann, 1957), 94; emphasis added. The 1975 edition of this book states that Evans's article had been slightly modified before being approved by the First Presidency for publication, during which this statement was left unchanged.

44.  N. A. Easton, "Mal de mer above terra incognita, or What Ails the Coastal Migration Theory?" *Arctic Anthropology* 29 (1992): 28–41.

45.  A. P. Elkin and N. W. G. MacIntosh, eds., *Grafton Elliot Smith: The Man and His Work* (Sydney, Australia: Sydney Univ. Press, 1974), 181.

46.  Hannes Lindemann, *Alone at Sea* (New York: Random House, 1957); compare Alan Villiers, *Wild Ocean: The Story of the North Atlantic and the Men Who Sailed It* (New York: McGraw-Hill, 1957).

47.  Charles A. Borden, *Sea Quest: Global Blue-Water Adventuring in Small Craft* (Philadelphia: Macrae Smith, 1967). In 1991, 11 Frenchmen even rowed across the Atlantic in 36 days, and none of them had had sailing experience. Still more recently,

another Frenchman succeeded in swimming across the middle Atlantic. "On arriving in Barbados less than sixty days after his start, he admitted that it was quite easy to drift along in the current" (Patrick Ferryn, "A European View of Diffusion and Transoceanic Contacts before 1492," in *Across before Columbus? Evidence for Transoceanic Contact with the Americas prior to 1492*, ed. Donald Y. Gilmore and Linda S. McElroy (Edgecomb, ME: NEARA, 1998), 261–66.

48. See A. Thorne et al., "Australia's Oldest Human Remains: Age of the Lake Mungo 3 Skeleton," *Journal of Human Evolution* 36/6 (June 1999): 591–612.

49. R. G. Bednarik (in "Replicating the First Known Sea Travel by Humans: The Lower Pleistocene Crossing of Lombok Strait," *Human Evolution* 16/3–4 [2001]: 229–42) cites the literature on early voyaging in and from Southeast Asia and deep-water islands in the Mediterranean, the latter on the order of 300,000 years ago.

50. For a summary of historical and current thinking, see Clive Gamble, *Timewalkers: The Prehistory of Global Colonization* (Cambridge: Harvard Univ. Press, 1993). For a fuller treatment, consult the index to John L. Sorenson and Martin H. Raish, *Pre-Columbian Contact with the Americas across the Oceans: An Annotated Bibliography*, 2nd rev. ed., 2 vols. (Provo, UT: Research Press, 1996).

51. E. James Dixon, *Quest for the Origins of the First Americans* (Albuquerque: Univ. of New Mexico Press, 1993), 119; and E. James Dixon, *Bones, Boats, and Bison: Archeology and the First Colonization of Western North America* (Albuquerque: Univ. of New Mexico Press, 1999), 31–34.

52. For further citations in the Book of Mormon, see John L. Sorenson, "When Lehi's Party Arrived in the Land," 1–34.

53. See Fernando de Alva Ixtlilxóchitl, *Obras Históricas*, ed. Eduardo Chavero, 2 vols. (México: Editora Nacional, 1950).

54. Ixtlilxóchitl, *Obras Históricas*, 1:15–16.

55. The late Thomas S. Barthel, in a number of publications, argued eruditely that Hindu cultural and linguistic elements were introduced at different times to central Mexico and Palenque by intruders from "Greater India." See especially "Hindu-Maya Syncretism: The Palenque Focus," *Ibero-Amerikanisches Archiv* 11 (1985): 51–63; and also his "Planetary Series in Ancient India and Prehispanic Mexico: An Analysis of Their Relations with Each Other," *Tribus* 30 (1981): 203–30. Maurice Swadesh believed that the Nahuatl (Aztec) language showed relationships to Indo-European; see his "On Interhemisphere Linguistic Connections," in *Culture and History: Essays in Honor of Paul Radin*, ed. Stanley Diamond (New York: Columbia Univ. Press, 1960), 894–924. Swadesh's views were independently confirmed in linguistic analyses by the late Mary LeCron Foster of the University of California, Berkeley, in "Old World Language in the Americas: 1," an unpublished paper read at the annual meeting of the Association of American Geographers, San Diego, 20 April 1992; and also in her "Old World Language in the Americas: 2," an unpublished paper given at the annual meeting of the Language Origins Society, Cambridge University, September 1992; copies are in the possession of Sorenson and Roper.

56. Quoted in Zelia Nuttall, "Some Unsolved Problems in Mexican Archaeology," *American Anthropologist* 8/1 (Jan.–Mar. 1906): 135.

57. Fray Bernardino de Sahagún, *Historia General de las Cosas de Nueva España* (México: Editorial Nueva España, 1946), 13–14.

58. *Historia prehispánica de la Huaxteca* (México: Instituto de Investigaciones Antropológicas, Serie Antropológica 26, Universidad Nacional Autónoma de México Ciudad Universitaria), 112.

59. *The Annals of the Cakchiquels*, trans. A. Recinos and D. Goetz; [and second part of the title] *Title of the Lords of Totonicapán*, trans. D. J. Chonay and D. Goetz (Norman: Univ. of Oklahoma Press, 1953), 169.

60. See *Annals of the Cakchiquels*, 194.

61. See John L. Sorenson, "Some Mesoamerican Traditions of Immigration by Sea," *El Mexico Antiguo* 8 (Dec. 1955): 425–38.

62. See Terrence Kaufman and Victor Golla, "Language Groupings in the New World: Their Reliability and Usability in Cross-disciplinary Studies," in *America Past, America Present: Genes and Languages in the Americas and Beyond*, ed. Colin Renfrew (Cambridge, England: McDonald Institute for Archaeological Research, 2000), 47–57, esp. 48. However, Merritt Ruhlen's article ("Some Unanswered Linguistic Questions," 163–75) in the same volume challenges their logic and conclusion.

63. See Kaufman and Golla, "Language Groupings in the New World," 47–49.

64. See Terrence Kaufman, "Areal Linguistics and Middle America," in *Native Languages of the Americas*, ed. T. A. Sebeok (New York: Plenum Press, 1977), 2:65.

65. Hints of linguistic complexity exist in the Book of Mormon; see, for example, Omni 1:17, 25; Mosiah 24:4; Alma 7:1 and 9:21; Moroni 10:15–16; and Ether 12:23–26.

66. See the discussion in Sorenson, *Ancient American Setting*, 50–56.

67. See P. Agrinier, "Linguistic Evidence for the Presence of Israelites in Mexico," *S.E.H.A. Newsletter* 112 (Feb. 1969): 4–5; the report is greatly amplified by Robert F. Smith in a manuscript in possession of Sorenson and Roper. Alma M. Reed, in *The Ancient Past of Mexico* (New York: Crown, 1966), reprises information about this study.

68. Quoted in Reed, Ancient Past, 10.

69. See "Was There Hebrew Language in Ancient America? An Interview with Brian Stubbs," *Journal of Book of Mormon Studies* 9/2 (2000): 54–63.

70. Mary LeCron Foster, "Old World Language in the Americas" (see note 55 herein), copy in Sorenson's possession and abstracted, including this quotation, in Sorenson and Raish, *Pre-Columbian Contact*, as item F-146B. See Foster, "Old World Language in the Americas: 2," unpublished paper presented at the annual meeting of the Language Origins Society, Cambridge University, Sept. 1992, copy in Sorenson's possession; see Sorenson and Raish, *Pre-Columbian Contact*, item F-146C. See also Foster's "The Transoceanic Trail: The Proto-Pelagian Language Phylum," *Pre-Colombiana* 1/1–2 (1998): 113.

71. See Ruhlen, "Some Unanswered Linguistic Questions," 171ff.

72. Otto J. Von Sadovszky, *The Discovery of California: A Cal-Ugrian Comparative Study* (Budapest: Akadémiai Kiadó; Los Angeles: International Society for Trans-Oceanic Research, 1996).

73. See, for example, E. D. Merrill, "The Phytogeography of Cultivated Plants in Relation to Assumed Pre-Columbian Eurasian-American Contacts," *American Anthropologist* 33/3 (July–Sept. 1931): 375–82, which was highly influential.

74.   See John L. Sorenson and Carl L. Johannessen, "Biological Evidence for Pre-Columbian Transoceanic Voyages," in *Contact and Exchange in the Ancient World*, ed. Victor H. Mair (Hawaii: Univ. of Hawaii Press, 2006), 238–97.

75.   Because of their length, full references are omitted from this paper; for details see the primary article when it appears.

76.   See Carl L. Johannessen and Wang Siming, "American Crop Plants in Asia before AD 1500," *Pre-Columbiana: A Journal of Long-Distance Contacts* 1/1–2 (1998): 9–36. For the corn, see Ian C. Glover, "The Late Stone Age in Eastern Indonesia," *World Archaeology* 9/1 (June 1977): 42–61.

77.   For example, see Gordon R. Willey, "Some Continuing Problems in New World Culture History," *American Antiquity* 50/2 (April 1985): 351–63.

78.   See Wolfgang Marschall, *Influencias Asiáticas en las Culturas de la América Antigua: Estudios de su Historia* (Mexico: Ediciones Euroamericanas Klaus Theile, 1972), 61.

79.   Julian Granberry, "Amazonian Origins and Affiliations of the Timucua Language," in *Language Change in South American Indian Languages*, ed. Mary Ritchie Key (Philadelphia: Univ. of Pennsylvania Press, 1991), 195–242.

80.   See Emilio Estrada and Betty J. Meggers, "A Complex of Traits of Probable Transpacific Origin on the Coast of Ecuador," *American Anthropologist* 63/5 (1961): 913–39.

81.   Clinton R. Edwards says, "From the practical seaman's point of view Pacific crossings in such craft were entirely feasible." See "Commentary: Section II," in *Man across the Sea: Problems of Pre-Columbian Contacts*, ed. C. L. Riley et al. (Austin: Univ. of Texas Press, 1971), 304.

82.   See Clinton R. Edwards, *Aboriginal Watercraft on the Pacific Coast of South America* (Berkeley: Univ. of California Press, 1965); and Edwin Doran Jr., "The Sailing Raft as a Great Tradition," in *Man across the Sea*, 115–38.

83.   See Norton, "El señorio de Salangone."

84.   Dixon, *Quest for the Origins of the First Americans*, 130–31; for the changing picture, now see Heather Pringle, "Hints of Frequent Pre-Columbian Contacts," *Science* 288/5467 (2000), 783, about "stunning new traces of the Norse . . . in the Canadian Arctic."

85.   Swadesh (in *Culture and History*, 896) observes, in parallel, that "new languages probably came into America in the late millennia just before Columbus, but their speakers must have been absorbed . . . without leaving any language that has continued to modern times."

86.   Joseph Needham, Wang Ling, and Lu Gwei-Djen, *Civil Engineering and Nautics*, pt. 3 of *Physics and Physical Technology*, vol. 4 of *Science and Civilisation in China* (Cambridge: Cambridge Univ. Press, 1971).

87.   Joseph Needham and Lu Gwei-Djen, *Trans-Pacific Echoes and Resonances; Listening Once Again* (Singapore and Philadelphia: World Scientific, 1985).

88.   Quoted in Caleb Bach, "Michael Coe: A Question for Every Answer," *Américas* 48/1 (1996): 14–21.

89.   See J. Richard Steffy, "The Kyrenia Ship: An Interim Report on Its Hull

Construction," *American Journal of Archaeology* 89/1 (Jan.): 71–101. This finding was confirmed by Steffy in an e-mail message to John L. Sorenson, 18 April 2001.

90.  Ales Hrdlicka, "The Genesis of the American Indian," *Proceedings, 19th International Congress of Americanists, Washington, 1915* (Washington), 559–68.

91.  See, for example, John L. Sorenson, *Images of Ancient America: Visualizing Book of Mormon Life* (Provo, UT: Research Press, 2001). A larger selection can be seen in O. L. Gonzalez Calderón, *The Jade Lords* (Coatzacoalcos, Veracruz, México: the author, 1991) and three published books by Alexander von Wuthenau: *Altamerikanische Tonplastik: Das Menschenbild der neuen Welt* (Baden-Baden, Germany: Holle, 1965); *Terres cuites précolumbiennes* (Paris: Albin Michel, 1969); and *Unexpected Faces in Ancient America, 1500 BC–AD 1500: The Historical Testimony of Pre-Columbian Artists* (New York: Crown, 1975). Some scholars believe the topic should not be discussed because Wuthenau and Calderón are not "accepted experts" among orthodox anthropologists. Whatever merit, if any, there might be in such an exclusivist posture, it does not eliminate the fact that the figurines actually exist and in many cases are unquestionably ancient.

92.  See, for example, Matthew W. Stirling, "Great Stone Faces of the Mexican Jungle . . . ," *National Geographic Magazine*, Sept. 1940, 327; John F. Scott, "Post-Olmec Mesoamerica as Recalled in its Art," *Actas, XLI Congreso Internacional de Americanistas, 2–7 Sept. 1973* (México, 1975), 2:380–86; and the discussion in Wuthenau, *Unexpected Faces*, 69–70.

93.  This point is confirmed with regard to Maya Late Classic ("Jaina style") portrait figurines by two prominent scholars. Román Piña Chan said, "They are extraordinary because of their faithfulness to their human models" (quoted in Linda Schele and Jorge Pérez de Lara, *Hidden Faces of the Maya* [Poway, Calif.: ALTI, 1997], 11). Schele and de Lara observed that "the Maya figurines represented individual people who had readable expressions on their faces" (p. 13).

94.  See Kirk Magleby, *A Survey of Mesoamerican Bearded Figures* (Provo, UT: FARMS, 1979).

95.  See Peter N. Jones, "American Indian Demographic History and Cultural Affiliation: A Discussion of Certain Limitations on the Use of mtDNA and Y Chromosome Testing," *AnthroGlobe Journal*, Sept. 2002.

96.  Note this observation: "However, with the exceedingly spotty sampling of Native America populations, it may be a long time until we have sampled enough populations truly to tell how localized or widespread any polymorphism really is." See D. A. Merriwether et al., "Gene Flow and Genetic Variation in the Yanomama as Revealed by Mitochondrial DNA," in *America Past, America Present: Genes and Languages in the Americas and Beyond*, ed. Colin Renfrew (Cambridge: McDonald Institute for Archaeological Research, Univ. of Cambridge, 2000), 89–124, esp. 117.

97.  Jones, in his study "American Indian Demographic History," gives a devastating critique of the typical inadequate sampling. For example: "It is evident that the population groups current studies are using to infer American Indian cultural affiliation and demographic history are not acceptable. One cannot use contemporary allele frequencies from a few individuals of a contemporary American Indian reservation to arrive at an unequivocal haplotype for that group, either presently or prehistorically."

98.    Joseph T. Chang, "Recent Common Ancestors of All Present-Day Individuals," *Advances in Applied Probability* 31 (1999): 1002–26.

99.    Steve Olson, *Mapping Human History: Genes, Race, and Our Common Origins* (New York: HoughtonMifflin, 2002), 114.

100.    Susanna C. Manrubia, Bernard Derrida, and Damián H. Zanette, "Genealogy in the Era of Genomics," *American Scientist* 91 (March–April 2003): 165.

101.    Manrubia, Derrida, and Zanette, "Genealogy in the Era of Genomics," 165.

# Addressing Questions surrounding the Book of Mormon and DNA Research

*John M. Butler*

## What is DNA?

Our cells contain a genetic code known as deoxyribonucleic acid, or DNA. It provides a blueprint for life, determining to a great extent our physical attributes and appearance. We inherit half of our genetic code from our mother and half from our father. The diversity we see among people results from unique combinations of nucleotides, the building blocks of DNA that exist in every living organism. Because of the many different ways these nucleotides can combine, all humans, with the exception of identical twins, differ from each other on a genetic level.

## How are DNA ancestry studies performed?

Examining the DNA of an individual and comparing it with the DNA of close relatives can reveal the source of different genetic patterns contributed by parents, grandparents, or other shared ancestors. Genetic markers on the Y chromosome that are transferred exclusively from father to son are used to examine paternal lineages, while maternal lines are traced by analyzing genetic material called mitochondrial DNA, which is only transferred from mother to offspring.

## How do DNA ancestry studies compare to forensic DNA testing used in court cases?

The information derived from any DNA analysis does not work in a vacuum. Test results always compare genetic information from a source in question with the same type of information from a known source. In the case of forensic DNA testing that is widely accepted in courts of law, DNA from a suspected criminal is compared with DNA collected from the scene of a crime.[1] When the DNA matches at the regions examined, then it is likely that the suspect was indeed the person who was involved in the crime. In forensic DNA testing there is a one-to-one correlation of DNA results—the individual's DNA either matches or does not match the evidence.

In ancestry studies, DNA information from multiple modern population groups is projected over many generations between populations tested. Even though the same genetic markers may be used as in forensic DNA testing, in ancestry testing, there is usually not a one-to-one unique match being made. Instead, scientists are often guessing at what genetic signatures existed in the past based on various assumptions—with a bit of educated "storytelling" to fill in gaps.[2] These stories of human migration patterns are constantly being refined with new genetic research. As noted by John Relethford in his book *Genetics and the Search for Modern Human Origins,* "Although working in such a young and developing field is exciting, it is also frightening because the knowledge base changes so rapidly."[3] Since the methods for examining DNA in this way are far from perfected, drawing final conclusions about the ancestry of a people from current data would not be prudent. In addition, it is important to keep in mind that *reference samples are always needed to provide relevant results* with any kind of DNA testing. If a reliable reference is not available, confident conclusions cannot be made.

### What current data exist on Native American DNA?

To date there have been more than one hundred scientific articles describing the examination of DNA from thousands of modern-day Native Americans. These studies have shown that almost all Native Americans tested thus far possess genetic signatures closely resembling modern-day Asians, and thus conclusions are usually drawn that these

populations are related to one another. Since no Israelite genetic connection has yet been made with Native Americans, critics of the Book
of Mormon are quick to point out that this information seems to contradict a statement made in the modern introduction to the book that
the Lamanites are "the principal ancestors of the American Indians."

### What do we know about the genetic background of Book of Mormon peoples?

The angel Moroni informed the Prophet Joseph Smith during
his first visit on the evening of 21 September 1823 that the Book of
Mormon record gave "an account of the former inhabitants of this
continent, and the source from whence they sprang" (Joseph Smith—
History 1:34). The Book of Mormon mentions three different groups
that journeyed to the New World: the Lehites (1 Nephi 18), the Jaredites (Ether 6:12), and the Mulekites (Helaman 6:10; 8:21), sometimes
referred to as the people of Zarahemla (Omni 1:14–16; Alma 22:30).

The title page of the Book of Mormon proclaims that the
Lamanites are a remnant of the house of Israel. Lehi found on the
plates of brass recovered from Laban a genealogy of his fathers in
which he learned that he was a descendant of Joseph (1 Nephi 5:14),
specifically from the tribe of Manasseh (Alma 10:3). Mulek is mentioned in Helaman 8:21 as a son of Zedekiah who was king of Judah
when Jerusalem fell to the Babylonians (2 Kings 25:7). The Jaredites
descended from multiple families who were led by the Lord from the
Tower of Babel to the promised land (Ether 1:33).

The prophets who contributed to the Book of Mormon record
focused on religious teachings rather than on geographical or genetic
details; they provided only a partial picture of the events of their days
and usually within the confines of their family lineage. Thus, the
Book of Mormon record does not supply sufficient information to
provide a reliable calibration point in the past that may serve as a reference for modern-day DNA comparisons. DNA information alone
therefore cannot disprove or prove the Book of Mormon.

## Could other people have lived in ancient America concurrently with Book of Mormon peoples?

Careful examination and demographic analysis of the Book of Mormon record in terms of population growth and the number of people described implies that other groups were likely present in the promised land when Lehi's family arrived, and these groups may have genetically mixed with the Nephites, Lamanites, and other groups.[4] Events related in the Book of Mormon likely took place in a limited region,[5] leaving plenty of room for other Native American peoples to have existed.

## Does DNA testing of modern individuals detect all previous genetic lineages?

Another way to state this question is "could a group of people vanish without a genetic trace as measured by Y-chromosome and mitochondrial DNA testing and yet be the ancestors of someone living today?" It is important to realize that examination of Y-chromosome and mitochondrial DNA genetic markers permits only a small fraction of an individual's ancestry to be tracked.

Most genetic analysis studies of human history involve comparing a group of samples of living individuals to another group of living individuals without any detailed knowledge of the genealogy of the individuals in the groups being tested. These types of DNA studies make assumptions about the average time for each generation in the past along with a fixed mutation rate whereby genetic variation may occur over time. Similarities in the modern populations examined are then used to claim a shared origin between the two populations with an estimated time for divergence between the populations.

An interesting study reported in the June 2003 issue of the *American Journal of Human Genetics* leads me to believe that it is possible for Book of Mormon peoples to be ancestors of modern Native Americans and yet not be easily detected using traditional

Y-chromosome and mitochondrial DNA tests. This study, conducted by a group of scientists from a company called deCODE
Genetics, used the extensive genealogies of people from Iceland
combined with probably the most massive population study ever
performed. They traced the matrilineal and patrilineal ancestry of
all 131,060 Icelanders born after 1972 back to two cohorts of ancestors, one born between 1848 and 1892 and the other between 1742
and 1798.[6]

Examining the same Y-chromosome and mitochondrial DNA
markers used in other genetic studies, these 131,060 Icelanders "revealed highly positively skewed distributions of descendants to
ancestors, *with the vast majority of potential ancestors contributing one
or no descendants and a minority of ancestors contributing large numbers of descendants.*"[7] In other words, the majority of people living today in Iceland had ancestors living only 150 years ago that could not
be detected based on the Y-chromosome and mitochondrial DNA
tests being performed and yet the genealogical records exist showing
that these people lived and were real ancestors. To the point at hand,
if many documented ancestors of 150 years ago cannot be linked to
their descendants through Y-chromosome and mitochondrial DNA
tests from modern Iceland, then it certainly seems possible that the
people who are reported in the Book of Mormon to have migrated to
the Americas over 2,600 years ago might not have left genetic signatures that are detectable today.

### Shouldn't we be able to detect Israelite DNA if the Lamanites are descended from Lehi and are the principal ancestors of modern-day Native Americans?

First, as discussed above, we do not have enough information
from the Book of Mormon to confidently determine a source population for the Lehites or Mulekites, and so we cannot compare this
population with modern-day Native American results. Another point
to consider is that present-day Native Americans represent only a

fraction of previous genetic lineages in the Americas because of large-scale death by diseases brought to the New World by European conquerors. As researcher Michael Crawford concludes in his book *The Origins of Native Americans: Evidence from Anthropological Genetics*, "This population reduction has forever altered the genetics of the surviving groups, thus complicating any attempts at reconstructing the pre-Columbian genetic structure of most New World groups."[8] Again, without reliable reference samples from the past, we cannot proclaim the Book of Mormon true or false based on DNA data.

In forensic science, a documented "chain of custody" is crucial to verifying a link between the DNA profile produced in the lab with the original crime scene evidence. No such "chain of custody" exists with DNA or genealogical records connecting people from Book of Mormon times to people living today.

Part of the problem in this whole contrived controversy is the oversimplification of results from DNA studies that are being conducted by scientists in an effort to examine potential patterns of human migration throughout ancient history. The impact of this oversimplification is in many ways similar to the impact that the popular TV show *CSI: Crime Scene Investigation* has had over the past few years on forensic laboratories. In the name of entertainment, the *CSI* television shows have created a perception in which the general public now thinks that forensic scientists go to crime scenes, work in fancy and well-equipped laboratories, question suspects in a case, and obtain conclusive results on every complex case in a matter of a few minutes. The truth is that scientists work in poorly supplied labs, are underpaid, and in many situations have large backlogs of samples that prevent rapid responses to new individual cases. In addition, forensic scientists never interrogate the suspects of a crime, and many cases are never solved. The public perception of *CSI* has now created an expectation in many juries that DNA evidence should be present in every case.

Even with this oversimplification of its portrayal of forensic laboratories, there is some truth within the set of the *CSI* shows. For example, the instruments on the TV show are real. However, they do not collect data and generate results as rapidly as portrayed nor are complex cases solved so succinctly. Likewise, oversimplification of DNA results and what they are capable of revealing in examining the authenticity of the Book of Mormon has been greatly exaggerated by critics of the Church of Jesus Christ of Latter-day Saints. For the many reasons stated above, DNA testing results from modern Native Americans do not negate the possibility of Book of Mormon peoples having existed anciently on the American continent.

### Can science ever provide a final answer to a religious question?

Today's society is impatient and wants quick and easy answers to everything. In science we make measurements and conduct studies hoping to advance knowledge. As an active DNA researcher for the past thirteen years, I can affirm that we are uncovering new information with each passing year that gives us a better picture of the past and the present. But we must remember that that picture is in no way complete or comprehensive. Science can demonstrate that certain assumptions are unlikely, but it cannot prove that testimonies are false. I believe that science and religion can coexist as long as we remember that each measures different things (see Isaiah 55:8–9 and 1 Corinthians 2). The definitive proof of the Book of Mormon's authenticity comes in the Lord's laboratory of spiritual revelation by following the formula laid out in Moroni 10:3–5.[9]

## Notes

On 16 February 2006 the *Los Angeles Times* ran a front-page article questioning the authenticity of the Book of Mormon based on studies of human DNA. Citing DNA "evidence" that suggests an Asian ancestry for people native to the Americas, critics of the Church of Jesus Christ of Latter-day Saints have for the past several years claimed that these DNA studies demonstrate that the Book of Mormon account of a group of colonists coming from the Middle East in 600 BC cannot be authentic. The following article briefly addresses questions surrounding the applicability of DNA studies to the peoples whose story is told in the Book of Mormon. Points of view expressed here are mine and in no way reflect the official opinion of the Church of Jesus Christ of Latter-day Saints or the U.S. Department of Commerce or National Institute of Standards and Technology. This was originally posted in February 2006 on the FARMS Web site at farms.byu.edu/publications/dna/ButlerBofMandDNA_Feb2006 .php (accessed 24 April 2006).

1.  See John M. Butler, *Forensic DNA Typing: Biology, Technology, and Genetics of STR Markers*, 2nd ed. (New York: Elsevier, 2005).

2.  David B. Goldstein and Lounès Chikhi, "Human Migrations and Population Structure: What We Know and Why It Matters," *Annual Review of Genomics and Human Genetics* 3 (2002): 129–52, at 143.

3.  John H. Relethford, *Genetics and the Search for Modern Human Origins* (New York: Wiley-Liss, 2001), 205.

4.  See John L. Sorenson, "When Lehi's Party Arrived in the Land, Did They Find Others There?" *Journal of Book of Mormon Studies* 1/1 (1992): 1–34.

5.  See John L. Sorenson, *An Ancient American Setting for the Book of Mormon* (Salt Lake City: Deseret Book and FARMS, 1985).

6.  Agnar Helgason, et al., "A Populationwide Coalescent Analysis of Icelandic Matrilineal and Patrilineal Genealogies: Evidence for a Faster Evolutionary Rate of mtDNA Lineages than Y Chromosomes," *American Journal of Human Genetics* 72/6 (2003): 1370–88.

7.  Helgason et al., "Populationwide Coalescent Analysis," 1370, emphasis added.

8.  Michael H. Crawford, *The Origins of Native Americans: Evidence from Anthropological Genetics* (New York: Cambridge University Press, 1998), 261.

9.  See John M. Butler, "A Few Thoughts from a Believing DNA Scientist," *Journal of Book of Mormon Studies* 12/1 (2003): 36–37.

# DNA and the Book of Mormon:
# A Phylogenetic Perspective

*Michael F. Whiting*

The past decade has seen a revolution in the way in which biologists collect data and proceed with their research. This revolution has come about by technological innovations that allow scientists to efficiently sequence DNA for a wide range of organisms, resulting in vast quantities of genetic data from a diverse array of creatures. From estimating the genealogical relationships among fleas to understanding the population genetics of crayfish, DNA sequence information can provide clues to the past and allow scientists to test very specific hypotheses in a way that was unapproachable even a few years ago. The announced completion of the Human Genome Project is not really a completion of DNA work at all, but simply one step on the road toward a better understanding of ourselves as biological organisms, our shared genetic history as humans, and the genetic history we share with all living organisms. Work is under way in many fields to generate DNA sequences from a wide variety of organisms for a spectrum of genes to address an almost dizzying array of scientific and medical questions. As it stands, there is possibly no other data source that holds more potential for biological inquiry than DNA sequence data, and this information is currently one of the most powerful tools in the arsenal of scientists.

However, as with all scientific tools, there are bounds and limits to how this tool is applied and what questions it can adequately address. This is because DNA sequence information is useful for only certain classes of scientific questions that need to be properly formulated and carefully evaluated before the validity of the results can be accepted.

There are many interesting questions for which DNA sequence data is the most appropriate data source at hand, as current scientific investigations attest. But there are some classes of problems for which DNA may provide only tangential insight, and some very interesting biological questions for which DNA is altogether an inappropriate source of information. Moreover, there are certain biological problems that scientists would love to answer but that are complicated and resist solution, even given DNA information. Within the scientific community, DNA-based research is carefully scrutinized to be certain that underlying assumptions have been tested, that data have been correctly collected and analyzed, and that the interpretation of the results are kept within the framework of the current theory or methodology. DNA research is only as good as the hypotheses formulated, data collected, and analyses employed, and the pronouncement that a certain conclusion was based on DNA evidence does not ipso facto mean that the research is based on solid science or that the conclusion is correct. The National Science Foundation rejects literally hundreds of DNA-based research proposals every year because they are lacking in some way in scientific design. The inclusion of a DNA component does not necessarily guarantee that the study was properly designed or executed.

Recently, some persons have announced that modern DNA research has conclusively proved that the Book of Mormon is false and that Joseph Smith was a fraud.[1] This conclusion is based on the argument that the Book of Mormon makes specific predictions about the genetic structure of the descendants of the Lamanites and that these descendants should be readily identifiable today. These critics argue that when the DNA is put to the test, these descendants lack the distinctive genetic signature that the critics claim the Book of Mormon predicts. They bolster their arguments by appealing to DNA research, claim that their conclusions are thoroughly scientific, and pronounce that the Church of Jesus Christ of Latter-day Saints must now go through a Galileo event, in reference to the 17th-century astronomer who discovered that the sun, not the earth, was the center of the solar system, much to the consternation of the prevailing religious view. They have trumpeted this conclusion to the media and have gained a modicum of press coverage by playing on the stereotype of modern science being suppressed by old religion. Moreover, they argue that the silence at Brigham Young University over this topic is evidence that their arguments and conclusions are above reproach. However, these claims err scientifically in that they are based on the naive notion that DNA provides infallible evidence for ancestry and descent in sexually reproducing populations and that the results from such analyses are straightforward, objective, and not laden with assumptions. Moreover, proponents of this naive view blindly ignore decades of theory associated with DNA sequence evolution and data analysis and rarely speak to the extremely tentative nature of their conclusions.

The purpose of this paper is to debunk the myth that the Book of Mormon has been proved false by modern DNA evidence. What I put forth here is a series of scientific arguments highlighting the difficulty of testing the lineage history given some of the known complicating events. This paper should not be regarded as a summary of current research on human population genetics nor as an extensive analysis of all possible complicating factors; rather, it focuses on the current attempts to apply DNA information to the Book of Mormon.

## What Is the State of DNA Research on the Book of Mormon?

The first point that should be clarified is that those persons who state that DNA evidence falsifies the authenticity of the Book of Mormon are not themselves performing genetic research to test this claim. This conclusion is not coming from the scientists studying human population genetics. It is not the result of a formal scientific investigation specifically designed to test the authenticity of the Book of Mormon by means of genetic evidence, nor has it been published in any reputable scientific journal open to scientific peer review. Rather, it has come from outside persons who have interpreted the conclusions of an array of population genetic studies and forced the applicability of these results onto the Book of Mormon. The studies cited by these critics were never formulated by their original authors as a specific test of the veracity of the Book of Mormon. To my knowledge there is no reputable researcher who is specifically attempting to test the authenticity of the Book of Mormon with DNA evidence.

### Is DNA Research on the Book of Mormon Fundable?

As I am writing this article, I am sitting in an airplane on my way to Washington, D.C., to serve as a member of a scientific review panel for the Systematic Biology program of the National Science Foundation. The NSF is a major source of basic research funding available to scientists in the United States, and every six months the NSF brings in a panel of researchers to review grant applications and provide recommendations for funding. Each research proposal is a 15-page explanation of what research is to be performed, how the research project is designed, the specific hypotheses to be tested through the proposed work, preliminary data

indicating the feasibility of the particular scientific approach, careful analyses of these data, preliminary conclusions based on those analyses, and a justification for why the proposed research is scientifically interesting, intellectually significant, and worthy of funding. As someone who has received a half-dozen NSF grants and has written even more research proposals, I recognize how much time and effort go into writing a successful research proposal and how carefully thought out that research must be before funding will ever be made available. While anyone can claim to do scientific research, it is widely accepted within the scientific community that the touchstone of quality in a research program is the ability to obtain external funding from a nationally peer-reviewed granting agency and to publish the results in a reputable scientific journal. To be funded at the national level means that a research proposal has undergone the highest degree of scrutiny and been approved by those best able to judge its merits.

Given that no research program thus far has been designed to specifically test the authenticity of the Book of Mormon, I would like to center my discussion on the following question: *If one were to design a research program with the stated goal of testing the validity of the Book of Mormon based on DNA information, what specific hypotheses would one test, what experimental design is best suited to test each of these hypotheses, what sort of assumptions must be satisfied before these tests are valid, and what are the limitations of the conclusions that can be drawn from these data?* In other words, would a proposal to test the validity of the Book of Mormon by means of DNA sequence information have a sufficiently solid base in science to ever be competitive in receiving funding from a nationally peer-reviewed scientific funding agency such as the NSF?

## Is the Authenticity of the Book of Mormon Testable by Means of DNA Information?

One could of course argue that it is impossible to directly test the authenticity of the Book of Mormon with the tools of science, since the Book of Mormon lies within the realm of religion and outside the realm of science. It would be like asking a scientist to design an experiment that tests for the existence of God. There are no data that one could collect to refute the hypothesis that God exists, just as there are no data that one could collect to refute the hypothesis that he does not exist: science simply cannot address the question, and one might argue that the same is true for the Book of Mormon. If one holds this view, and there may be some very good reasons why one might, then there is no need to read any further: DNA can tell us nothing about the authenticity of the Book of Mormon.

However, one might argue that it is possible to indirectly judge the validity of the text by testing the authenticity of the predictions made within the text. If one can demonstrate that some predictions are specifically violated, then perhaps one would have some basis for claiming that the text is false. This is the line of reasoning followed by those who pursue the genetic argument. They suggest that the Book of Mormon makes specific predictions about the genetic structure of the Nephite-Lamanite lineage, that this genetic structure should be identifiable in the descendants of the surviving Lamanites, and that if the Book of Mormon is "true," then these predictions should be verifiable through DNA evidence. The critics argue that the Book of Mormon predicts that the Lamanite lineage should carry the genetic signature of a Middle Eastern origin and that the genetic descendents of the Lamanites are Native Americans. They then scour the literature to show that current DNA research suggests that Native Americans had an Asian origin. These results are then trumpeted as invalidating the authenticity of the text.

However, by simply applying the results of population genetic studies, which again were never intended to test the Lamanite lineage history put forth in the Book of Mormon, these critics have ignored crucial issues that any reputable scientists designing a research program would have to consider. My thesis is that it is extraordinarily difficult, if not impossible, to use DNA sequence information to track the lineage of any group of organisms that has a historical population dynamic similar to that of the Nephites and Lamanites. This is not an argument that the Nephite-Lamanite lineage is somehow immune to investigation through DNA evidence because its record is a religious history, but simply that the Nephite-Lamanite lineage history is an example of a class of problems for which DNA evidence provides—at best—ambiguous solutions. It does not matter to me whether we are talking about humans or fruit flies; you could substitute the term *Lamanite* with *Drosophila* and the argument would be the same. The lineage history outlined in the Book of Mormon is a conundrum from a DNA perspective; the critics have grossly underplayed or are ignorant of the complications associated with testing this history. Further, because of the complicated nature of this lineage history, I would suggest that the Book of Mormon can neither be corroborated nor refuted by DNA evidence and that attempts to do so miss the mark entirely. *I would be just as critical of someone who claimed that current DNA testing proves the Book of Mormon is true as I would of those who claim that DNA evidence proves it is not true.* The Lamanite lineage history is difficult to test through DNA information, DNA provides at best only tangential information about the text, and anyone who argues that it can somehow speak to the authenticity of the text should consider the following complicating factors.

### What Hypotheses Emerge from the Book of Mormon?

Good science does not consist of someone dreaming up a pet theory and then quilting together pieces of evidence to support it from as many disparate sources as possible while conveniently ignoring pieces of evidence that may undercut the theory. Good science consists of formulating specific hypotheses that can be directly tested from a particular data source. The problem is that, unlike a good NSF research proposal, the Book of Mormon does not explicitly provide a list of null and alternative hypotheses for scientific testing. For instance, the spiritual promise offered in Moroni 10:4 is not open to scientific investigation because it does not put forth a hypothesis that can be tested with any sort of scientific rigor. Likewise, the entire text of the Book of Mormon was meant for specific spiritual purposes and was not intended to be a research proposal listing an explicit hypothesis that is open to scientific investigation. Hence, any hypothesis that emerges from the Book of Mormon is entirely a matter of interpretation, and any specific, testable hypothesis is based very much on how one reads the Lamanite history and considers the degree to which external forces may have influenced the composition of the Lamanite lineage. A person cannot test the authenticity of the Book of Mormon by means of genetics without making some statement about the specific hypotheses that are being tested, why these hypotheses are an accurate interpretation of the text, and how these hypotheses somehow speak to the authenticity of the text. At the very best, one might demonstrate that the predictions have been violated, but the question remains as to whether the supposed predictions were correct to begin with.

From my perspective, there are two possible basic lineage histories—differing in scope, magnitude, and expectation—that one might derive from the Book of Mormon. These histories make predictions that could possibly form the basis of hypotheses that may be tested to varying degrees by means of DNA evidence. I have set these up in a dichotomy of extremes, and certainly one could come up with any combination of these two scenarios, but the extremes are useful for illustrating difficulties associated with applying DNA sequence information to the Book of Mormon. For lack of better terms, I will refer to these as the global colonization hypothesis and the local colonization hypothesis.

## The Global Colonization Hypothesis

The global colonization hypothesis is the simplest view of the Lamanite history and the one most readily testable through DNA evidence. This is the view that when the three colonizing groups (Jaredites, Mulekites, and Nephites + Lamanites) came to the New World, the land they occupied was entirely void of humans. It presumes that these colonizers were able to form a pure and isolated genetic unit of Middle Eastern origin living on the American continent and that this genetic heritage was never "contaminated" by the genetic input from any other non-Middle Eastern sources or peoples during the time recorded in the Book of Mormon. It also assumes that the colonizers accurately carried the genetic signature of the Middle Eastern source population and that such a signature indeed existed both within the source population and the migrants. It further requires that genetic input from the time when the Book of Mormon record ends to the present day was negligible or absent and that the direct genetic descendants of these colonizers exist today and can be identified prior to any genetic analysis. This hypothesis also incorporates the notions that these groups expanded to fill all of North and South America, that there was a tremendous population explosion from these single colonization events, and that any subsequent genetic input, if it occurred, would be swamped out by the strength of the Middle Eastern genetic signal present in the majority of the population. This hypothesis requires that introgression (i.e., gene flow from an external population to the one under study) of genetic signal from other sources be negligible or absent and that the genetics of the individuals compared in an analysis have remained largely pure since the time of colonization. This interpretation of the lineage history of the Book of Mormon is the most easily tested hypothesis by way of DNA analysis.

If we grant that the global colonization hypothesis is the correct lineage history emerging from the Book of Mormon, this hypothesis predicts that the modern-day descendants of the Lamanite lineage should contain the Middle Eastern genetic signature. Since current population genetics suggests that Native Americans (presumed by some to be the direct genetic descendants of the Lamanites) have an Asian genetic signature,[2] the above hypothesis is indeed incorrect. To this point all we have shown is that the global colonization hypothesis appears falsified by current genetic evidence. But is the global colonization hypothesis the only hypothesis emerging from the Book of Mormon? This is the crux of the matter. Critics who argue that DNA analysis disproves the authenticity of the Book of Mormon need to demonstrate that the global colonization hypothesis is the only way to interpret the Lamanite lineage history and the only hypothesis under question. *The authenticity of the Book of Mormon is in question only if this is an accurate interpretation of the historical population dynamics inferred as existing before, during, and after the Book of Mormon record takes place.* However, if the above description of the lineage history in the Book of Mormon is oversimplified, then these genetic results demonstrate only that this oversimplified view does not appear correct. But Book of Mormon scholars have been writing about certain complicating factors for decades, so this conclusion about oversimplification really comes as no surprise.[3]

## The Local Colonization Hypothesis

The local colonization hypothesis is more limited in scope, includes many more complicating factors from a genetic perspective, is much more difficult to investigate by way of DNA evidence, and, in my view and that of Book of Mormon scholars, is a more accurate interpretation of the Lamanite lineage history. This hypothesis suggests that when the three colonizing parties came to the New World, the land was already occupied in whole or in part by people of an unknown genetic heritage. Thus the colonizers were not entirely isolated from genetic input from other individuals who were living there or who would arrive during or after the colonization period. The hypothesis presumes that there was gene flow between the colonizers and the prior inhabitants of the land, mixing the genetic signal that may have been originally present in the colonizers. It recognizes that by the time the Book of Mormon account ends, there had been such a mixing of genetic information that there was likely no clear genetic distinction between Nephites, Lamanites, and other inhabitants of the continent. This distinction was further blurred by the time period from when the Book of Mormon ends until now, during which there was an influx of genes from multiple genetic sources. Moreover, the hypothesis suggests that the Nephite-Lamanite lineage occupied a limited geographic range. This would make the unique Middle Eastern genetic signature, if it existed in the colonizers at all, more susceptible to being swamped out with genetic information from other sources.

The problem with the local colonization hypothesis (from a scientific standpoint) is that it is unclear what specific observations would refute it. This is because it makes no specific predictions that can be refuted or corroborated. For instance, there is no expectation that the descendants of the Lamanites should have any specific type of genetic signal, since their genetic signal was easily mixed and swamped out by other inhabitants of unknown genetic origin. Hence, this hypothesis can be neither easily corroborated nor easily refuted by DNA evidence, since any observation could be attributed to genetic introgression, drift, founder effect, or any of the other complicating factors described below.

## Local Colonization Hypothesis: Complicating Factors

Suppose you threw caution to the wind and believed that the local colonization hypothesis was the correct one emerging from the Book of Mormon, you really think it is testable, and you are specifically seeking funding to test it. Further, suppose that someone with knowledge of modern population genetics, phylogenetic systematics, molecular evolution, and the Book of Mormon was sitting on the NSF panel reviewing your proposal. Below is a short description of some of the complicating factors that you would have to address in your proposal before the research could be funded. This is not meant to be complete or exhaustive, but just an example of some complicating factors. More detailed descriptions of these basic concepts can be found in standard population genetic, molecular systematics, and molecular evolution textbooks.[4]

1. *Was there a unique, Middle Eastern genetic signature in the source population?* In order for the colonizers to carry a Middle Eastern genetic signature with them, that signature needed to first exist in the source population. It is possible that the Middle Eastern population may not have had a single genetic signature that would allow one to unambiguously identify an individual as being from the Middle East and from no other human population. This is an important consideration because there are many cultural and racial groups today for which there are no discrete markers unambiguously identifying an individual as a member of that group. Moreover, typically the larger the population and the greater that population tends to migrate, the smaller the probability that a unique, discrete genetic marker exists for that group.

*2. Were genetic variants present in the colonizers?* In order to perform your study, you would need to present evidence that each of the colonizing groups possessed the unique and defining Middle Eastern traits and did not possess any genetic variants that were atypical of this Middle Eastern genetic heritage.

*3. How do you know that small founder size does not confound your results?* The Book of Mormon makes clear that each colonization event involved a very small number of founders. Such small population sizes would have had profound effects on how the genetic markers changed over time. In fact, moving a few individuals of any species from one population to a new locality can have such a profound effect on the underlying genetic profile that it is considered to be a major mechanism in the formation of new species. This is called founder effect, which is caused by undersampling genes from a much larger population of genes and is closely tied to the concept of genetic drift (described below). In other words, founder effect describes the evolutionary process that results in the colonizing population having a gene pool that is not likely to reflect the gene pool of the original source population.

*4. What are the effects of genetic drift?* Genetic drift is the well-established evolutionary principle that in small populations random sampling biases will cause certain genetic markers to disappear and other markers to become widespread in the population just by chance. As an example, suppose you go to the grocery store to purchase a container of 1,000 jelly beans in 10 flavors. When you bring the jelly beans home, you determine that each of the 10 flavors is present in equal frequency; that is, you have as many tangerine-flavored jelly beans as you have lime-flavored jelly beans. Now from that container of 1,000 jelly beans, randomly sample 100 jelly beans and place them in a new container. If you count the jelly beans in the new container, you will realize that the frequency has changed; some flavors happened to be selected 11 or 12 times, some were sampled only 3 or 4 times, and some might not be sampled at all. Now instead of sampling 100 jelly beans, this time sample 30 from your original container. You would find that the frequency of flavors is more greatly skewed with the smaller sample size and that you have lost more flavors. As you reduce your sample size, you increase the probability that the frequency of jelly beans in the new sample will be all the more different from the original population. If each flavor represents a unique genetic heritage, this means that he sampling of genes from one generation to the next can cause certain genetic markers to go extinct and others to be present in higher frequency due entirely to random sampling. When the colonizers left the Middle East, they brought with them only a sample of the genetic heritage of that population that may not have accurately represented the markers present in the whole population; and when they arrived in the New World, the frequency of those genetic markers was likely to continue to change as the population was established.

5. *What were the effects of the colonizers' arriving to a locality that was not a complete genetic island (i.e., other humans were present and could contribute to the gene pool)?* If there were other inhabitants already present on the American continent when the colonizers arrived, then it becomes extremely difficult to distinguish whether the genetic signature a descendant carries is due to its being carried by the original colonizers or due to gene flow from the other, original inhabitants. This is especially problematic if the colonizing population is small and the native population is large once gene flow commences, since it will speed up the swamping-out effect of the colonizers' genetic markers with those of the native inhabitants. John L. Sorenson, among others, has presented evidence suggesting that the colonizers were not alone when they reached the Americas; and as I read the Book of Mormon, I can find no barriers to gene flow between the native population and those who formed the Lamanite lineage. Note that this could have occurred early in the colonization process or later as the Nephite and Lamanite nations flourished, but the swamping-out effect would be very similar in either case.

6. *What were the effects of gene flow after the Book of Mormon ends?* Certainly there was gene flow from the time when the Book of Mormon record closes to when DNA samples are obtained in the present day. It is preposterous to suppose that there has been complete genetic isolation in the Lamanite lineage during this time period. As the designer of the scientific experiment, you would need to account for the effects of gene flow in this undocumented time period and provide a justification for why it did not contaminate the genetic signature of the Lamanite lineage. Simply speaking, that genetic signature, if one existed, could be obliterated by gene flow from outside groups.

7. *How do you account for the difficulties associated with a small population range?* The local colonization hypothesis suggests that the geography of the Book of Mormon was quite limited in scope and that the Lamanite lineage did not populate the whole North and South American continent.[5] This implies that you cannot just sample anywhere in North or South America, but that you need to have some basis for deciding where you are going to sample and why it is likely that you will find pure genetic descendants of the Lamanite lineage in that specific location.

8. *Who are the extant genetic descendants of the Lamanite lineage?* If you are treating your research as a scientific test of the local colonization hypothesis, you need to identify who these Lamanite descendants are before you put them to the genetic test. When we go out to sample "Lamanite DNA," whom do we sample to get that DNA? There is no statement within the text of the Book of Mormon identifying who these descendants might be, though later commentators and church leaders have associated them with the Native Americans and/or inhabitants of South and Central America. The introduction to the Book of Mormon states that the Lamanites were the "principal ancestors of the American Indians," but this, again, is commentary not present in the original text and was based on the best knowledge of the time.

9. *How do you identify unambiguously the Middle Eastern population that contains the ancestral genetic signature that you will use for comparison?* Just as the genetic signature of the colonizers may have changed over time, the genetic signature of the Middle Eastern source population may have changed as well, making it unclear just whom we should sample to find that ancestral Middle Eastern genetic marker. We know that the Middle East has been the crossroads of civilization for many millennia and that many events affecting entire populations have occurred there since 600 BC, such as the large-scale captivity of groups and the influence of other people moving within and through the area. All of these factors complicate the identification of a discrete genetic profile characterizing the original Middle Eastern source population.

10. *Has natural selection changed the genetic signature?* One assumption in performing molecular phylogenetic analyses is that the genetic markers under study are not subject to the effects of natural selection. For instance, if a particular genetic marker is closely linked to a genetic disease that reduced fitness (the number of offspring that survive to reproduce) in a population, then, over time, selection would tend to eliminate that genetic marker from the population and the phylogenetic information associated with that marker may be misleading. Likewise, a genetic marker linked to a favorable trait may become the dominant marker in the population through the results of natural selection, and the marker would then be of limited phylogenetic utility.

The above tally is not intended to be an exhaustive list of scientific concerns, and many other more complicated ones abound. For instance, how has mutation obfuscated the identification of the original genetic signature (a process called multiple hits)? How does the shuffling of genetic markers affect your results (a process called recombination)? How do you account for the effects of groups of genes being inherited in a pattern that is not concordant with lineage history (a process called lineage sorting)? How do you deal with the well-established observation that genetic markers almost never give a single, unambiguous signal about an organism's ancestry, but are rather a deluge of signals of varying strengths (a concept called homoplasy)? How do you know that your gene genealogy reflects organismal genealogies (a concept called gene tree versus species tree)? Researchers who use DNA to infer ancestry continually worry whether the genetic markers selected are tracking the individual's history or the gene's history, since one does not necessarily follow from the other.

### Driving the Point Home

Let's look at the problem another way. Suppose you were a scientist going to the NSF to get funding to study an ancient fruit fly colonization event and you want to test the hypothesis that a few thousand years ago a single female fruit fly from a Utah population was picked up in a storm and blown all the way to Hawaii to lay its eggs. You know that the offspring of this fruit fly can freely mate with the Hawaiian population and produce viable offspring, but so can all the other fruit flies blowing in from all over the world during this time period. Now suppose you use all the genetic tools in your arsenal to try to detect that Utah colonization event. Could you detect it? Perhaps, if the population dynamics were just right. But your inability to detect this event does not mean that it did not happen; it just means that given the particular population dynamics, it was extremely difficult to test because there was not a genetic signal remaining for the colonization event. Would you get funded for this study? Probably not. There are many better-designed experiments that are more worthy of funding than this shot in the dark.

### Conclusion

Critics of the Book of Mormon have argued that DNA evidence has demonstrated once and for all that the book was contrived by

Joseph Smith and is hence a fraud. They appeal to the precision of DNA evidence and tout their conclusions as being objective, verifiable, assumption free, and decisive. However, these critics have not given us anything that would pass the muster of peer review by scientists in this field, because they have ignored the real complexity of the issues involved. Further, they have overlooked the entire concept of hypothesis testing in science and believe that just because they label their results as "based on DNA," they have somehow proved that the results are accurate or that they have designed the experiment correctly. At best, they have demonstrated that the global colonization hypothesis is an oversimplified interpretation of the Book of Mormon. At worst, they have misrepresented themselves and the evidence in the pursuit of other agendas.

I return to my original question: Is testing the Book of Mormon by means of genetic information a fundable research project? I do not think so. Given the complications enumerated above, it is very unclear what would constitute sufficient evidence to reject the hypothesis that the Lamanite lineages were derived from Middle Eastern lineages, since there are so many assumptions that must be met and so many complications that we are not yet capable of sifting through.

I have not made the argument that DNA is not useful for inferring historical events nor that population genetics is inherently wrong. Current research in population genetics is providing marvelous insights into our past and, when properly wielded, is a powerful tool. Nor am I disputing the inference that Native Americans have a preponderance of genes that carry a genetic signature for Asian origination. But what I am saying is that given the complexities of genetic drift, founder effect, and introgression, the observation that Native Americans have a preponderance of Asian genes does not conclusively demonstrate that they are therefore not descendants of the Lamanite lineage, *because we do not know what genetic signature that Lamanite lineage possessed at the conclusion of the Book of Mormon record.*

If you were to go back in time to when the Book of Mormon is closing and began sampling the DNA of individuals who clearly identified themselves as Lamanites, you might indeed find a strong Asian signature and no trace of a Middle Eastern signature because of the effects, as we have noted, of genetic drift, founder effect, and especially introgression, particularly if the surrounding population was derived from an Asian origin. The point is that the current DNA evidence does not distinguish between this and other possibilities because a study has never been designed to do precisely that.

But in all this discussion of the limitations of DNA analysis, it is important to remember that science is only as good as the hypotheses it sets forth to test. If you test the veracity of the Book of Mormon based on a prediction that you define, then of course you will "prove" it false if it does not meet your prediction. But if the prediction was inappropriate from the beginning, you have not really tested anything.

In sum, the Book of Mormon was never intended to be a record of genetic heritage, but a record of religious and cultural heritage that was passed from generation to generation, regardless of the genetic attributes of the individuals who received that heritage. The Book of Mormon was written more as an "us versus them" record, with the "us" being primarily Nephites and the "them" being a mixture of the genetic descendants of Lamanites plus anyone else who happened to occupy the land at the time. This interpretation accepts as a strong possibility that there was substantial introgression of genes from other human populations into the genetic heritage of the Nephites and Lamanites, such that a unique genetic marker to identify someone unambiguously as a Lamanite, if it ever existed, was quickly lost. It would be the pinnacle of foolishness to base one's testimony on the results of a DNA analysis. As someone who has spent a decade using DNA information to decipher the past, I recognize the tentative nature of all my conclusions, regardless of whether or not they have been based on DNA. There are some very good scientific reasons for why the Book of Mormon is neither easily corroborated nor refuted by DNA evidence, and current attempts to do so are based on dubious science.

# Notes

1. The most noted is that of Thomas W. Murphy, "Lamanite Genesis, Genealogy, and Genetics," in *American Apocrypha,* ed. Dan Vogel and Brent Lee Metcalfe (Salt Lake City: Signature Books, 2002), 47–77; see the "Editors' Introduction" therein, vii–xvii.

2. See Peter Forster et al., "Origin and Evolution of Native American mtDNA Variation: A Reappraisal," *American Journal of Human Genetics* 59/4 (1996): 935–45; and Santos et al., "The Central Siberian Origin for Native American Y Chromosomes," *American Journal of Human Genetics* 64 (1999): 619–28, for reviews of the evidence.

3. For a review of studies, including some from the early 19th century, see John L. Sorenson, *The Geography of Book of Mormon Events: A Source Book* (Provo, UT: FARMS, 1992), 7–35. Consult also Sorenson's study *An Ancient American Setting for the Book of Mormon* (Salt Lake City: Deseret Book, 1985), 91–95, 138–89; and "When Lehi's Party Arrived in the Land, Did They Find Others There?" *Journal of Book of Mormon Studies* 1/1 (fall 1992): 1–34.

4. The distinction in tracking historical relationships among sexually reproducing populations (phylogeny) versus within sexually reproducing populations (tokogeny) was best elucidated by Willi Hennig in his *Phylogenetic Systematics* (Urbana: Univ. of Illinois Press, 1979). For a standard textbook on molecular systematics, see David M. Hillis, Craig Moritz, and Barbara K. Mable, *Molecular Systematics* (Sunderland, MA: Sinauer Associates, 1996). For a textbook on molecular evolution, see Wen-Hsiung Li, *Molecular Evolution* (Sunderland, MA: Sinauer Associates, 1997). For a textbook on population genetics, see Daniel L. Hartl and Andrew G. Clark, *Principles of Population Genetics* (Sunderland, MA: Sinauer Associates, 1997).

5. See John E. Clark, "A Key for Evaluating Nephite Geographies," in *Review of Books on the Book of Mormon,* 1 (1989): 20–70; and "Book of Mormon Geography," in *Encyclopedia of Mormonism,* ed. Daniel H. Ludlow (New York: Macmillan, 1992), 176–79.

# Detecting Lehi's Genetic Signature: Possible, Probable, or Not?

*David A. McClellan*

The influence genetics and genetic information have had on the overall body of scientific knowledge cannot be overestimated. Genetic research has substantively enhanced our ability to treat medical conditions ranging from inherited genetic disorders to worldwide viral epidemics. It has revolutionized the way we think about and study the natural world, from cells to organisms, from species to ecosystems. It factors into pharmaceutical discovery and vaccine design, plant and animal domestication, and wildlife conservation. Needless to say, we now know much more about genetic concepts and applications than in even the recent past. In fact, our body of knowledge has grown so vast that mastery of all aspects of genetic research by a single researcher is now virtually impossible. For this very reason, minor misunderstandings abound, both among the lay public and within the scientific community.

One such misunderstanding is the current controversy over DNA evidence and its bearing on the veracity of the Book of Mormon. On the one hand, statements by the Prophet Joseph Smith indicate that Native Americans are descended from the Lamanites. On the other, recent scientific studies have evaluated the current genetic compositions of selected worldwide human populations, and several of these have concluded that the principal genetic origin of the sampled Native American peoples has been Asiatic, likely due to the constant documented flow of humans back and forth across the Bering Strait.[1] The real issue, however, is not necessarily if Native Americans are the inheritors of Asian genetic material; it is whether or not this evidence refutes the story line of the Book of Mormon and the claims of Joseph Smith relative to Native Americans.

The question of whether the Americas were populated prior to the arrival of the Lehites and Mulekites is addressed elsewhere, as well as the implications of the messages of the Book of Mormon and the statements of Joseph Smith.[2] Both are important components of this complex challenge. The remaining challenge left to be addressed relative to this issue is whether or not we are to infer from recent scientific evidence that the Book of Mormon and associated Latter-day Saint doctrine are false.

First, however, I feel compelled by my faith to state that the only reliable way to test the veracity of the Book of Mormon or statements by modern prophets such as Joseph Smith is to put Moroni's promise to the test on a personal level:

> Behold, I would exhort you that when ye shall read these things, if it be wisdom in God that ye should read them, that ye would remember how merciful the Lord hath been unto the children of men, from the creation of Adam even down until the time that ye shall receive these things, and ponder it in your hearts.
>
> And when ye shall receive these things, I would exhort you that ye would ask God, the Eternal Father, in the name of Christ, if these things are not true; and if ye shall ask with a sincere heart, with real intent, having faith in Christ, he will manifest the truth of it unto you, by the power of the Holy Ghost.
>
> And by the power of the Holy Ghost ye may know the truth of all things. (Moroni 10:3–5)

Attempting to settle the matter solely upon the merits of empirical data will always leave one wanting.

That stated, the purpose of this essay constrains me to deal exclusively with those aspects, concepts, and principles of science that may contribute to a complete—or as complete as possible—understanding of the essential question at hand. Within this essay, therefore, I intend to present the basic biological principles that are, in my opinion, relevant to whether it is possible to identify the genetic signature of Lehi or Mulek; address the question using the powerful tools of scientific method and population genetic theory; and briefly review the current status of human population genetics in the context of these principles and concepts, outlining some of the limits under which genetic data may be interpreted.

The background information presented herein is meant as a supplement for the nonscientist. Explanations about what a chromosome is or how genetic information is used in population studies may not be directly pertinent to the essential question of this essay, but they are meant to serve as a primer for the uninitiated. Some of these informational reviews may seem burdensome to those that may have substantial backgrounds in biology. To readers who fit into this category, I would suggest skipping directly to the conclusions section.

## Basic Biological Principles

As outlined above, the central question of this essay is whether acceptance of current genetic data necessitates the wholesale rejection of the Book of Mormon story line and the claim that Native Americans are descended from Lamanitish ancestors. On the surface, given certain characteristics of the data it appears that this may be possible. This may seem threatening to the Latter-day Saint layperson, who may therefore be tempted to discount the science surrounding the matter rather than sacrifice belief in the Book of Mormon. Before either of these alternatives becomes a "logical" conclusion for anyone, though, let us redefine the issue in terms of an essential question that may be scrutinized directly by scientific evaluation philosophically, theoretically, and empirically.

In my opinion, the most plausible essential question having to do with human genetic data may be something like: Is it possible to recover a genetic signature from a small migrating family from 2,600 years in the past? To answer this question in a coherent manner, let me first present a few basic concepts by which all genetic hypotheses are tested; these will empower nonbiologists to judge for themselves the accuracy of the conclusions presented herein. I am confident that the conclusions of this essay, emergent from the accepted principles of biology, will illustrate the complete harmony between scientific thought and the fundamentals of Latter-day Saint belief.

At the very heart of the question posed above are the basic principles of genetics and evolution as they have unfolded over the past 150 years and especially in the past 50 years. The discoveries over this period of time have been numerous—too numerous to describe in any detail. Our knowledge, however, remains far from complete—constant controversies arise within the scientific community over minute theoretical details, and much remains to be discovered. Nevertheless, there is little controversy over the basic principles of the science; these have been verified in many different ways and have survived the test of time and effort: 150 years of scientific method seeking to displace previously held ideas with more general explanations.

### Genome Organization

Most cells that constitute the human body contain a more or less complete copy of the human genetic complement. This genetic complement comes in two varieties, each with a unique function and a unique genetic language, or code. First, the *nuclear genome,* the genetic complement that resides in the nucleus of each cell, comprises by far the greatest portion of cellular genetic material. It is governed by the *universal genetic code,* the standard genetic language used to create the vast majority of cellular proteins produced naturally within the bodies of most currently living species of organisms. In human beings, it encodes proteins from insulin to hemoglobin. Second, we possess another genome that, in most cells, resides in tiny intracellular structures known as *mitochondria,* the powerhouses of the cell.

The few proteins produced by this mitochondrial genome work in conjunction with nuclear proteins to manufacture the energy needed for cells to function. Cells that need more energy, such as muscle cells, have more mitochondria, each of which contains a complete mitochondrial genome. The genetic code that governs man's mitochondrial genome—and is shared by the mitochondrial genomes of all vertebrate organisms, including fish, amphibians, reptiles, birds, and mammals—differs from the universal code in only a few ways, but those few differences can have significant effects on the long-term molecular evolution of intracellular metabolism.[3]

*Nuclear genomes.* The genetic material of every genome, human or otherwise, is composed of deoxyribonucleic acid, or DNA. In man and in all plants, animals, and fungi, DNA is organized into discrete packages called *chromosomes.* The basic unit of the chromosome is the *nucleosome,* a structure that is composed of several proteins around which is twice wrapped a strand of DNA that is held in place by another protein, much like you might place your finger on a ribbon when helping someone tie a bow on a gift box. Nucleosomes connected by DNA are coiled into a fiber called *chromatin,* which is looped and coiled to form the arms of a chromosome (see fig. 1). The human nuclear genome contains 46 chromosomes that come in 23 *homologous* pairs—that is, they correspond in structure and in the sequence of genes. Each chromosome in a pair was inherited from a parent, one being maternal in origin and the other paternal. The sex chromosomes (referred to as X and Y) are inherited this same way, but the Y chromosome is always paternally inherited; females inherit one X chromosome from each parent, while males always inherit an X chromosome from their mother and a Y chromosome from their father.

Along each chromosome lie several regions that encode either a protein or a ribonucleic acid (RNA) molecule. The precise number of human coding regions, or *genes,* remains to be determined but is currently in the process of being resolved. Estimates from the year 2000 placed the range of this number from around 35,000 to 120,000

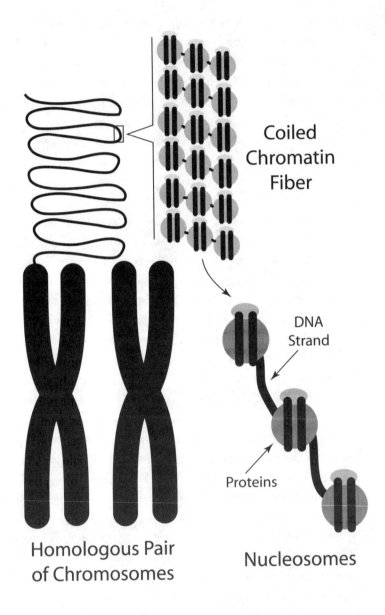

Coiled
Chromatin
Fiber

DNA
Strand

Proteins

Homologous Pair
of Chromosomes

Nucleosomes

Figure 1. The structure of chromosomes.

protein-coding genes,[4] while estimates from the year 2001 derived from the results of the Human Genome Project confirmed the lower portion of this range, around 23,000 to 39,000 genes (26,383 genes have now been confirmed by multiple lines of evidence).[5] There are also regions that do not encode genes but may have a distinct genetic history nonetheless. The diversity among noncoding regions is truly amazing, and many are even viral in origin and are thus parasitic to our genome. In several genetic studies, coding regions are used to estimate genetic diversity and identity, but many noncoding regions are also used as diagnostic genetic markers.

Just as the basic unit of the chromosome is the nucleosome, the basic unit of DNA itself is the *nucleotide.* The entire human nuclear genome is approximately 3.175 billion nucleotides in length,[6] 2.91 billion of which appear to contain active DNA.[7] Nucleotides come in four types, with their names and classifications being based on their chemical structure: there are two pyrimidines, referred to as cytosine and thymine, and two purines, adenine and guanine. These nucleotides bind together in triplet sets, or *codons,* which form the basic unit of the genetic code. Each possible combination of three nucleotides either directly encodes an amino acid, the basic unit of proteins (in the universal code, this accounts for 61 of the 64 possible codons), or encodes what is known as a termination signal that basically tells the cellular protein-construction mechanism, the *ribosome,* to stop making a particular protein.

*Mitochondrial genomes.* The mitochondrial genome is composed of a single, circular piece of DNA that is not very unlike the genomes of some bacteria. It is not packaged like the chromosomes of the nuclear genome, most probably because it is small enough that such complex organization is unnecessary. One unusual characteristic of the mitochondrial genome is that it is maternally inherited: every individual's mitochondrial genome is inherited from his or her mother. However, current evidence suggests that mitochondrial inheritance may not be exclusively maternal.[8] The mitochondrial genome of every man most likely hits an abrupt dead end; he cannot pass it on to his children. However, if a man has sisters with children, his mitochondrial genome will live on in his nephews and nieces and in his nieces' children.

The human mitochondrial genome bears 13 protein-coding genes, 2 ribosomal RNA genes (to build the mechanism that interprets the genetic code), and 22 transfer RNA genes (that act as vehicles by which amino acids are guided into place in a growing protein). There is very little nonfunctional DNA within the mitochondrial genome, but a noncoding control or regulatory region called the D-loop figures prominently among DNA sequences used to reconstruct species relationships.[9]

Since the mitochondrial genome is inherited as a single unit, all the genes contained in it are linked. But unlike the nuclear genome, in which genetic information is routinely exchanged between homologous pairs—a process termed *recombination,* which will be discussed in more detail below—mitochondrial genomes have no opportunity to exchange information. This is a primary reason why they are often used to track lineages; a particular mitochondrial genetic variant (including all 37 coding regions and the D-loop) represents a single lineage and must be completely replaced in order to be unrecoverable or to become so obscure that it is very unlikely to be found by a scientist looking for it. This, initially, is one reason why the lack of a Middle Eastern genetic signature was so "troubling" to those anticipating it.[10]

*DNAs encode, but proteins adapt.* DNA is relatively protected from the demands and influences of the environment surrounding the cell because it is the task of proteins to interact with their surroundings and carry out functions; the primary responsibility of genes is to encode, whereas proteins must function properly to ensure the survival and reproduction of the organism. Thus, DNA is always at least one step removed from any influence that the environment may have on the organism. A change in DNA, referred to as a *mutation,* may or may not result in a change in the primary structure of the associated protein that interacts directly with the demands of the environment. If a given mutation in the DNA results in an amino acid change, however, the whole organism may pay the price by contracting a life-threatening disease. Examples include those rare cases of mutation in which people spontaneously develop cystic fibrosis[11] or spinal muscular atrophy[12] without having inherited the disease from either of their parents. The environment directly affects these unlucky recipients of a disease-causing mutation by making them less likely to survive to bear children and thus contribute to the gene pool. The unforgiving truth of the matter is that the great majority of possible mutations that occur in those regions of the genome responsible for the adaptation of the organism are deleterious in some way and are often fatal. More will be said below about the role of mutations in molecular evolution.

## Mendelian Genetics

As mentioned above, nuclear chromosomes occur naturally in pairs, one inherited from each parent. The rules that govern inheritance of chromosomes were first discovered by Gregor Mendel (1822–1884), an Austrian monk who published his findings on the genetics of pea plants in 1865.[13] The genetic principles enunciated by Mendel can be boiled down to two fundamental principles: segregation and independent assortment. These principles of inheritance, which will be described in more detail below, have since been confirmed as the processes that chromosomes go through prior to the creation of the specialized reproductive cells known as *gametes* (sperm and eggs). The processes of segregation and independent assortment of chromosomes can now be seen under a microscope just prior to the cell divisions that create gametes, but Mendel discovered these principles without knowledge of chromosomes. He was able to infer these truths by observing the frequency with which pea plants expressed different trait variants, such as height, coloration, and texture.

*Mitosis and meiosis in nuclear genomes.* Since the time of Mendel, biologists have determined that there are two different types of cell division in the human body. The most common, which takes place at one time or another in all *somatic* (or nongerminal tissue) cells, involves a process called *mitosis,* in which each of the 46 chromosomes, unpaired at this point, laterally splits to form two *chromatids,* each of which is composed of two arms—one on top and one on bottom—instead of the four illustrated in figure 1. These chromatids then migrate to the forming nucleus of a different daughter cell. At this time, each daughter cell will generally start to produce proteins and then undergo a synthesis phase that restores each chromosome to the form it had prior to mitosis. Mitotic cell division thus results in two daughter cells that are complete and exact copies of the mother cell. Mitosis takes place most rapidly during gestation, while the embryo is quickly developing. After birth, the rate of cell division slows dramatically, with some cell lines, such as in muscle and nerve tissue, coming to a complete stop.

The second type of cell division produces gametes—called *gametogenesis*—and occurs exclusively in specific places in the male and female gonads. Gametogenesis implements a process called *meiosis,* in which two successive cell divisions break down the genome so that, instead of having 23 pairs of chromosomes, the four daughter cells have 23 single chromosomes. Meiosis separates the homologous pairs in the first cell division and then laterally splits each chromosome into two chromatids in the second cell division. The first meiotic division is the point at which segregation and independent assortment physically take place. The second division is quite similar to the process seen in mitosis except that there are half the number of chromosomes.

At the beginning of the first meiotic cell division is a stage referred to as the *pachytene stage,* in which homologous chromosomes come very close together to form a structure called a *tetrad,* because each structure looks like it has four arms—two on top and two on bottom (see fig. 1). Because of the close proximity of homologous pairs, regions of chromosomes that encode the same type of genes are naturally attracted to one another. Quite often, there is an exchange of information between homologous chromosomes when large chunks of genetic material are swapped. This process, called *recombination*, is a very important mechanism for creating the genetic diversity that makes each of us unique. Most of the time these chunks are of roughly equal size, but sometimes they are not, creating redundancy in the genetic sequence of some chromosomes but eliminating potentially vital genes in others. Recombination, also referred to as crossing-over, is error prone, but these errors actually enhance the long-term survival of a species at the expense of a few individuals who end up without their full genetic complement. Unequal crossing-over is the principal genetic mechanism that gives rise to gene families via gene duplication. It allows for evolutionary specialization relative to different demands, such as those required by distinct stages of embryological development or the production of dissimilar cellular tissues such as muscle and bone. The genetic redundancy generated by unequal crossing-over does not produce additional body structures or superhuman qualities, but it does allow babies to produce proteins that are uniquely suited for proper maturation; the adult versions of the same proteins may not be appropriate for the distinctive changes a baby's body must go through to develop properly. It also allows the body to produce trypsin, which helps us digest protein in the digestive track, and haptoglobin, which binds free hemoglobin in the bloodstream. Although these proteins now have very different functions, they have retained similar structures, suggesting that they originated from the same generalized ancestral gene by unequal crossing-over.[14] Truly novel protein structure is produced only rarely, so the creation of redundancy with the possibility of modification presents a wonderful opportunity for molecular adaptation to respond to constantly changing environmental conditions, changes both within the organism and from external surroundings.

Since *linked genes* (genes on the same chromosome) are inherited as a single unit more often than genes of different chromosomes, they will assort nonindependently—as discrete units—in the absence of recombination. Generally speaking, genes that are physically closer to one another on a chromosome assort nonindependently more often than genes that are farther apart. Inferring information about how frequently linked genes assort nonindependently is the basis upon which gene mapping is founded.

*Segregation and independent assortment.* As mentioned, the first stage of meiosis is the time at which the processes of segregation and independent assortment are likely to occur. *Segregation,* in modern terms, means that an individual's chromosome pairs are not likely to end up in the same gamete; instead, each gamete receives one chromosome from each pair. In accordance with this principle, human gametes do not have 46 chromosomes organized into 23 homologous pairs but have 23 single chromosomes, one from each homologous pair of the parent cell. Violations of this rule have serious genetic repercussions; they may result in spontaneous miscarriage of a poorly developed embryo or in developmental retardation of living offspring, as is the case with Down syndrome children.[15]

In terms of chromosomes, the concept of *independent assortment* is that as each chromosome pair segregates, either chromosome may go to either daughter cell without being influenced by what is happening in the segregation of the other pairs around it. As a result, a given gamete will generally carry an assortment of maternal and paternal chromosomes. This randomization of chromosomal assortment results in an enormous variety of possible genetic combinations that offspring may inherit from their parents. In humans, the number of possible combinations totals over 70 trillion ($2^{23}$ for each parent) for every set of parents, without considering mutation or recombination.

The processes of segregation and independent assortment apply to nuclear genetic material, which provides the greatest portion by far of an individual's genetic inheritance. Mitochondrial genes, on the other hand, do not follow the basic rules of segregation and independent assortment because mitochondrial genomes do not segregate at all. They are all inherited as a single unit, or *linkage group,* and always from one's mother. The reproduction of the mitochondrial genome is inherently asexual, each descendant genome being nearly an exact clone of its progenitor. Instead of millions of combinations that may be produced by segregation and independent assortment among nuclear chromosomes, the mitochondrial genome may only produce one kind of genetic offspring.

*Individuals are genetically unique.* With the exception of identical twins, segregation and independent assortment guarantee that every individual has a unique genetic complement. Coupling these genetic mechanisms with recombination and mutation, we can accurately conclude that every individual is genetically unique. This characteristic of genomic evolution, however, also leaves open the possibility that offspring may have genetic problems that their parents did not pass on to them. For example, one of the most studied genes in the human genome is the one responsible for cystic fibrosis, CFTR (cystic fibrosis transmembrane conductance regulator). A normal copy of this gene enables cells in the lining of the lungs to kill the bacterium *Pseudomonas aeruginosa.* It is estimated that 2 out of about 30,000 cystic fibrosis patients experience the onset of the disease because of new mutations.[16] As can be seen in this example, however, mutation as a genetic mechanism is generally considered a weak evolutionary force, although it is constant and unforgiving. Mutation generally plays a much bigger role when considering genetic change over much longer periods of time, in terms of thousands of generations, especially if any of those changes are significantly affected by selection acting on the functional constraints of gene products.

According to neutral theory, which will be discussed below, most persistent changes, including most crossing-over events, are selectively neutral[17] or nearly so.[18] Thus, most changes that become diagnostic (like those that result in a unique genetic signature) do not have a significant effect on the reproductive success of any given individual. There are some changes, although rare, that may be adaptive in nature, and these also have distinct opportunities of becoming perpetuated in a genetic signature. Adaptive and neutral changes, therefore, allow unique diagnostic genetic signatures to develop over long periods of time—again, in the order of thousands of generations.

## Molecular Evolution

Genetic mutations may occur in a variety of forms, including single nucleotide-level point mutations, insertions or deletions of various sizes, gene duplications, chromosomal inversions, complete genome duplications (*polyploidy*), and so on. Most of these are relatively infrequent and probably have not contributed significantly to the evolution of the human genome within recorded history.[19] The overall rate of mutation among humans, including all the types listed above, has been estimated to occur, on average, at a rate of 1.6 mutations per genome per generation,[20] or about $5 \times 10^{-10}$ mutations per nucleotide site per generation. Most of these mutations take the form of nucleotide-level point mutations, small insertions, or small deletions, especially within noncoding DNA regions that are largely free from functional and structural constraints. It is clear that noncoding DNA, such as that which appears within the numerous chromosomal microsatellite regions, may evolve several orders of magnitude faster, creating new *short-tandem repeats* (in which every repeat is only a few nucleotides in length but may exist as hundreds of copies, one right after the other) at a rate of one new repeat approximately every 833 generations.[21] Regardless of which estimate one accepts, the mitochondrial genome evolves much faster—about 10 times faster[22]—than the nuclear genome, probably because mitochondrial DNA is maternally inherited and does not recombine, although there is considerable heterogeneity in both genomes.[23] The exception is the Y chromosome, which is incredibly conservative in its rate of genetic change, probably due to what is known as a *selective sweep*, whereby a single, positively selected mutation pulls all other mutations with it to *fixation* (to a relative frequency within a population of 100 percent), resulting in very little genetic diversity within that particular linkage group.

*Molecular-clock hypothesis and neutral theory.* One implication of the relatively constant rate of genomic mutation is that mutation may be clocklike, or approximately constant, over extremely long periods of time.[24] This led naturally to the idea that if the accumulation of mutations is clocklike, then the vast majority of persistent mutations are probably neutral—neither advantageous nor detrimental—or nearly so.[25] This natural extension of the *molecular-clock hypothesis* has since become known as the *neutral theory*, or, more recently, as the *nearly neutral theory.*

These hypotheses form the conceptual backbone of subsequent studies that explore the mechanisms governing the accumulation of genetic variation in populations. They offer a convenient framework within which to implement scientific method for studying mutation rates and their implications. The conclusions resulting from such studies are equally informative whether the hypotheses are ultimately accepted or rejected. Additionally, the implications of acceptance or rejection of these hypotheses are extremely well explored in the theoretical literature. Thus, using them as a framework for research endows the researcher with the power to interpret experimental results easily. Despite the fact that they are often rejected, they have persisted as scientific tools that allow researchers the freedom to set up a predefined set of conditions, the rejection of which is often more interesting than acceptance would be.

*Genetic drift and the probability that a mutant allele will become fixed.* When a mutation takes place in a gene at a particular *locus* (the physical location of the gene on its respective chromosome), a new genetic variant, or *allele,* is born. Initially, a new allele exists at a very low frequency in a population; there is only one copy of it out of all of the chromosomes in all of the individuals in a population who possess it. If that new allele is to eventually be "successful" and become the standard version of the gene in the population, it must displace all alternative alleles and reach a frequency of 100 percent—it must become *fixed.* If, however, the allele is not "successful," it will eventually go completely extinct. This latter case is much more likely because of the low frequency at which the new allele starts out. It is possible, though, for the frequency of the allele in the population to remain constant under certain circumstances in a relatively isolated population that exists at a constantly large effective size.

Genetic drift is the idea that within a small *effective population*—that is, the number of individuals who are responsible for parenting children—random error causes successive generations to have slightly different allele frequencies due to the chance association of gametes, resulting in greater fluctuations in allele frequencies than if an effective population were very large. In large populations, new mutations have very little chance of becoming fixed or of even perpetuating for very long. If the effective population size is small, however, mutant alleles may become fixed much more easily because of the increased effect of genetic drift.

A real-world example governed by the same principle upon which genetic drift is based is a coin flip. Each possible result (heads or tails) may have a 50 percent chance of occurring, but in practice what actually happens depends on how many times the coin is flipped. Flip it 10 times and you may get, purely by chance, 4 heads and 6 tails—40 percent to 60 percent—which is not very close to the 50–50 split you predicted, even though the actual number of heads and tails tallied is only 1 off the prediction. Flip the coin 100 times and you may get 45 heads and 55 tails—45 percent to 55 percent—which is closer to your prediction, even though the actual number of heads and tails tallied is now 5 off the prediction. Now flip it 1,000 times, and you may get 490 heads and 510 tails—49 percent to 51 percent. Each time you increase the sample size an order of magnitude, you get closer to the predicted ratio of heads to tails. If you were to flip the coin an infinite number of times (which is not realistic, but for the sake of this example let's allow this extreme situation), you will most likely flip almost exactly 50 percent heads and 50 percent tails.

To make this example more similar to genetic drift, let's pretend that when you flip the coin the first 10 times, the results you tally actually determine the ratio of probabilities governing the next 10 flips. The first 10 times you flip the coin, you tally 4 heads and 6 tails. That result dictates that the probability of getting a head is now 40 percent and that of getting a tail 60 percent for the next set of 10 flips. With the probability of flipping a tail now increased, chances are good (50-50, to be precise) that the next set of 10 flips will weight the ratio even more in favor of tails. If this pattern continues, it will not take many sets of flips for the probability of flipping a tail to become 100 percent. If you were to increase the number of flips per set to 100, however, it would take longer for this to happen because each set of flips would most likely be closer to the predicted ratio. In fact, each time you increase the number of flips per set an order of magnitude, you would decrease the probability that random error would have a significant effect on the actual long-term results. This is exactly what makes allele frequencies drift in small populations. Each time there is a random error that makes the allele frequencies of a generation different from those of the one that precedes it, the probability of transmitting that allele to a subsequent generation changes in proportion. In this way, molecular evolution can take place even if no one allele has a distinct advantage or disadvantage.

*The effect of selection on mutations in populations.* Mutations must achieve a relative frequency of 100 percent in a population—that is, they must become fixed—to have a lasting evolutionary effect. However, most new alleles must travel a bumpy road to get to that point. According to neutral theory, most mutations are at least somewhat deleterious and are not perpetuated very long because the detrimental effects of deleterious mutations often result in decreased *fitness,* meaning that the organism possessing the mutation usually has fewer offspring than organisms of the same species that do not possess the mutation. The relative frequency of the mutant allele therefore decreases in the population from generation to generation.

This decrease in fitness is said to be the effect of *natural selection,* or the idea that nature will determine how advantageous or disadvantageous a genetic variant is, just like a farmer may determine which domesticated animals he or she will breed based on desirable physical characteristics. In both cases, desirable variants are perpetuated, one by a discerning farmer and the other by nature itself.

If the environment in which an organism lives changes, however, the fitness of the organism may also change. One example of the differential influence of environmental conditions on fitness might be that of a woman with diabetes. If she is not under the care of a physician, she may have serious problems and not be able to bear children without drastically reducing her probability of survival. If, however, she is introduced to an expert endocrinologist specializing in diabetic care and has access to synthetically produced human insulin, she can lead a very normal life. The first case would result in the woman having a reduced fitness, while the second would potentially result in her relatively normal fitness. Although this is probably an oversimplified example, it illustrates how a change in environmental conditions may bring about a change in fitness. Another example might be a person who has sickle-cell anemia. In most places in the world, sickle-cell anemia results in a dangerous condition, especially during pregnancy, which can exacerbate the sickle-cell condition. It has been found, however, that people who are carriers of the sickle-cell trait are somewhat resistant to malaria. This may not have a significant effect in the United States, where malaria has been eradicated; but in Africa, where malaria is common and causes 2.7 million deaths per year,[26] it may make a big difference. Not coincidentally, the highest incidence of sickle-cell anemia corresponds to those areas in which malaria is endemic and widespread.[27] This associated trait of increased resistance to malaria may be why sickle-cell anemia still persists in the world despite its extremely detrimental side effects.

Unlike the sickle-cell allele, which bestows a benefit in certain places of the world when it is possessed by a carrier, most detrimental alleles will not be maintained in a population. Generally speaking, if a mutation is deleterious, it most probably will not become fixed in a population because deleterious alleles are more likely to result in a decrease in the number of offspring than are advantageous and neutral alleles. Due to genetic drift, however, a slightly deleterious allele may have a much greater chance of becoming fixed in a small effective population because the influence of genetic drift becomes stronger as population size decreases. Because of this, alleles that may be deemed detrimental in large populations and gradually disappear due to natural selection are said to be "effectively neutral" in smaller populations[28] because they do not disappear, despite detrimental effects.

If a mutation is advantageous, almost the opposite is true. The recipient of an advantageous allele will, on average, bear more children, resulting in a faster increase in allele frequency than if it had not been advantageous. Advantageous alleles thus generally become fixed in a population relatively quickly. However, mutations resulting in new advantageous alleles are extremely rare according to neutral theory, so the accumulation of advantageous alleles is an inherently slow process, taking literally thousands of generations. Unlike detrimental alleles, advantageous alleles have less chance of becoming fixed in small populations. It may seem peculiar for genetic drift to have opposite effects on advantageous and deleterious alleles, but this serves a useful purpose in acting as a leveling influence in the evolutionary processes within small populations; increasing the probability of fixation among deleterious alleles while decreasing the probability of fixation among advantageous alleles results in both extremes behaving more nearly neutrally over time.

Genetic drift also acts on allelic variants originating in uniparental (or *haploid*) DNA—the maternally inherited mitochondrial genomes and paternally inherited Y chromosomes. Generally speaking, however, the random error associated with haploid alleles is roughly twice that associated with biparentally inherited (or *diploid*) alleles,[29] meaning that the effect of genetic drift is amplified among mitochondrial and Y-chromosome alleles because they are inherited from only one parent. There are exceptions to this rule of thumb owing to the variety of ways in which homologous alleles interact in biparentally inherited DNA (such as dominance, codominance, and recessiveness), but in each case haploid alleles should theoretically experience more random error than diploid counterparts, resulting in selection having even less of an overall effect.

These are some of the most basic of the scientific principles that influence the dynamics of genetic variation in populations or factor into the question of human genetic ancestry. Although I have not yet addressed the probability of recovering a genetic signature from a single family migrating 2,600 years ago, I have presented all the pertinent scientific concepts that will assist me in doing so. What follows is a scientific approach to estimating this probability, be it high, low, or somewhere in between.

## Theory behind Scientific Method and Population Genetics

One of the most basic claims made by critics of the Book of Mormon based on human population genetic data is that the Book of Mormon story line presents a testable hypothesis. The fundamental assumption of this claim is that it is possible to recover the genetic signature of a small migrating family 2,600 years in the past. They further claim that the fact that no Middle Eastern genetic signature has been recovered indicates that the Book of Mormon is fictitious. These claims and associated assumptions have not been critically evaluated in light of scientific method and population genetic theory, the most basic scientific principles connected with the analysis of human population genetic data. In this section of the essay I will carry out the thought exercises necessary to evaluate the claim that the Book of Mormon story line is a testable hypothesis and the assumption that it is possible to recover the genetic signature of Lehi or Mulek.

## Scientific Method

The foundational philosophical assumption of scientific method must first be emphasized and, indeed, cannot be overemphasized: Nothing in science can be proven; hypotheses can only be rejected. In fact, rejectability is the central criterion of a hypothesis. If an idea is not rejectable, it is not a hypothesis nor can it be tested. Therefore, in the context of the present discussion we must clearly define the central essential question, identify alternative testable hypotheses for this question, and characterize the implications of each.[30]

The essential question as identified at the beginning of this review is as follows: Is it possible to detect an ancient genetic signature of a small migrating family, such as the family of Lehi or Mulek? Competing hypotheses relative to this essential question include the *null hypothesis* (the hypothesis that, upon rejection, would leave only one other alternative possibility such that interpretation of results is unambiguous), which might be phrased as follows: Based on the currently understood principles of science, it *is* possible to recover such a genetic signature. If the null hypothesis is rejected upon the analysis of available data, however, we are forced to accept the alternative hypothesis: It *is not* possible to recover such a genetic signature. These hypotheses may be more formally written thus:

$H_0$: It is *possible to recover the ancient genetic signature of small migrating families.*

$H_a$: It is not *possible to recover the ancient genetic signature of small migrating families.*

If we *fail* to reject $H_0$, implications may include the following:

• Current human genetic data may not support the veracity of the Book of Mormon, but neither does it force us to reject it—if there were additional sampling, it might be possible to support the Book of Mormon story line but never to discredit it.

• Detractors of the Book of Mormon have no basis for their claims when relying solely on human genetic data because the Book of Mormon story line does not present a rejectable hypothesis based on the genetic signature question.

Alternatively, if we *do* reject $H_0$, we are forced to accept $H_a$, that it is *not* possible to recover the genetic signature. If that were the case, the following would be true:

- Current human genetic data cannot be used to support or reject the veracity of the Book of Mormon, and no amount of data will ever be sufficient to do so because it is not possible to find the genetic signature of Lehi or Mulek.

- Detractors of the Book of Mormon have no basis for their claims based on human genetic data since it is impossible to answer the essential question relative to these data.

Therefore, although on the surface it would appear that the lack of genetic evidence to support the Book of Mormon story line implies that it is false, the fact remains that, regardless of whether or not it is possible to recover the ancient genetic signature of a small migrating family, we cannot discount the truthfulness of the Book of Mormon based on the implications of its story line using the scientific method. The validity of the Book of Mormon story line is not testable because it does not present a rejectable hypothesis. Genetic data can never be used to invalidate these claims; its only possible use would be to support them.

This thought exercise has not yet approached the question of whether it is possible to recover the genetic signature of Lehi or Mulek, but it has presented logic suggesting that it really does not matter. Detractors have no basis for their claims that current human genetic data calls into question the story line of the Book of Mormon. Current genetic data cannot, nor will any future data ever, falsify the Book of Mormon story line. The claim that Lehi left Jerusalem and settled in the Americas cannot be rejected based on the philosophy of scientific method, the most powerful secular tool the people of the world have ever had for generating knowledge.

## Population Genetics Theory

The thought exercise presented above illustrates the need for and use of testable hypotheses. The fundamental principles of population genetics have been framed and mathematically explored such that truly testable hypotheses concerning the genetics of populations may be generated if an adequate sampling of global variation is available. Unlike some other branches of biology that may only be evaluated qualitatively, population genetics has historically been dominated by mathematicians and statisticians, resulting in its natural resemblance to "hard sciences" like physics and chemistry. The theory behind population genetics constitutes a convenient conceptual framework from which other quantitative fields of biology have emerged, entirely or in part, such as phylogenetic systematics (the science of reconstructing genetic relationships, or gene genealogies, based on genetic variation), molecular evolution (the science of inferring patterns of molecular change from extant data), and more recently, bioinformatics (the science of using computational methods to analyze complex data structures and reveal biologically relevant information). The null hypotheses generated from the basic concepts of population genetics represent a set of default predictions by which the characteristics of empirical data may be ascertained. By rejecting null hypotheses, researchers can easily establish what has not occurred and, by default, what most likely did occur. The use of null hypotheses therefore presents a powerful strategy by which important information may be revealed.

As discussed above, the segregation of chromosomes during meiosis results in any given *autosomal allele* (alleles found on chromosomes other than the X or Y chromosomes) having a random chance of being maternal or paternal in origin within gametes. This is not true for the inheritance of the mitochondrial genome, which is entirely maternal in origin, or for the Y chromosome, which is entirely paternal in origin. Thus, the human genome—and that of any other species with *sexually dimorphic* chromosomes (such as X and Y)—possesses both double-copy *biparental* genetic information (a diploid component) that has possibly undergone recombination prior to inheritance, and single-copy *uniparental* genetic information (a haploid component) that is basically composed of a clone of the parental copy. The Y chromosome, however, still has a random chance of being inherited by any given offspring (depending on the ratio of X- and Y-chromosomal sperm in the population of male gametes), whereas the mitochondrial genome is maternally inherited by *all* offspring.

Both uniparental and biparental alleles become fixed in a population in the same way: the chromosomal lineage of the individual from which an allele originated must grow in numbers until all other lineages are extinct and no other alleles exist at that locus in any member of the population. When new adaptive alleles arise through mutation, they can spread by means of natural selection throughout the population regardless of its size, given enough time and flow of genetic information.[31] New alleles, however, may also spread quickly by genetic drift when historical populations are extremely small, whether the allele is adaptive or not. Although the two homogenizing principles of natural selection and genetic drift have the same result, it is statistically possible to differentiate them from one another and from other historical phenomena using complex yet elegant statistical approaches.[32] This science of teasing apart genetic information to reveal complex dynamics has seen many recent advances[33] and has become a powerful diagnostic tool for reconstructing the historical events from which present-day genetic variation originated.

*The Hardy-Weinberg equilibrium principle.* When Mendel's research was rediscovered in the early 1900s, there was an initial sentiment that Mendelism was fundamentally at odds with Darwinism because Charles Darwin (1809–1882) had proposed a different mechanism of inheritance. However, a small portion of the scientific community sought to harmonize the discoveries of Darwin and Mendel. Due in part to the early work of Reginald Crundall Punnett (1875–1967) to explain and illustrate Mendelian concepts using what has since become known as a *Punnett square,* it became much easier for the scientific community to reconcile these two principles that now codominate biological thought. Punnett was convinced that under specific circumstances, multiple alleles at a single locus within a population could exist at equilibrium frequencies with no eventual fixation. Others had tried to describe this system but were unable to succeed with satisfactory results.[34] Punnett took his ideas to a prominent mathematician, Godfrey H. Hardy (1877–1947), who in 1908 published the first equations to accurately describe allelic frequency equilibria.[35] Wilhelm Weinberg (1862–1937) published similar findings that same year,[36] so the description became known as the Hardy-Weinberg equilibrium principle. An allele system that is able to remain in equilibrium, they predicted, would have a specific set of characteristics, now known as the Hardy-Weinberg assumptions. These assumptions include:

• Completely neutral variants. No allele at a given locus has a selective advantage over any alternative allele. Also, no allele at a given locus has a selective disadvantage relative to any alternative allele.

• No mutation. No new allele will be created by any mutation process. Also, no allelic variant will go extinct due to a mutational reversal.

• No migration. There will be no genetic flow of information by reason of the physical movement and subsequent mating of individuals from different populations.

• Constant, nearly infinite population size. The size of the breeding population within a given group of individuals will remain extremely large and completely constant through time as a result of constant and equal rates of birth and death in the population.

• Completely random mate choice. All potential mates have an equal probability of being chosen by any other potential mate of the opposite gender.

Although the Hardy-Weinberg assumptions appear ridiculously impractical and incapable of being met by a natural population, it is truly amazing how often alleles in ordinary populations are found to be in equilibrium. In reality, the requisite primary criterion is that there must not be *significant* violations of the assumptions. Obvious violations, however, will always result in deviations from expected allele frequencies.

*Violations of the Hardy-Weinberg assumptions.* The Hardy-Weinberg assumptions must hold if genetic signatures are to be maintained relative to autosomal alleles, sex-chromosome alleles, and mitochondrial alleles. Violations of the Hardy-Weinberg assumptions will result in changes in allele frequency, with the more blatant violations resulting in greater changes. However, all alleles are not created equal. Violations of these assumptions will have a greater effect on X-chromosome alleles than autosomal alleles and a greater effect on mitochondrial and Y-chromosome alleles than on X-chromosome alleles. This phenomenon is based on chromosomal population size. There are two copies of each autosomal locus, one on each homologous chromosome in a pair—in other words, they are *diallelic*. There are also two copies of each X-chromosome locus in women because women have two X chromosomes, but only one in males because they have only one X chromosome. Finally, there is always just one copy of each mitochondrial and Y-chromosome locus because these linkage groups do not possess homologs. These differences in relative population sizes mean that random error has different influences among these linkage groups. As discussed above, the smaller the population size is, the greater the influence of genetic drift will be. Genetic drift results from a violation of the population-size assumption. Violations of the other assumptions are also dependent on population size: the smaller the population size is, the greater the effect of the violation will be. Therefore, effects of violations of the Hardy-Weinberg assumptions will generally be amplified among mitochondrial and Y-chromosome loci. The lone exception to this is the violation of the assumption of random mate choice, because mitochondrial and Y-chromosome loci are not diallelic.

The violation of each Hardy-Weinberg assumption has been shown to have a specific dynamic effect in a population; these effects have been demonstrated over and over, both algebraically and empirically. The following are the predicted results of violations of these assumptions:

- Selection. According to neutral theory, neutral allele frequencies will fluctuate randomly until they become fixed (reach 100 percent) or go extinct (reach 0 percent). Thus, in the long term they will either replace all other alleles at that locus or disappear from the population altogether. The rate at which this is achieved is completely dependent on the size of the effective population.

If, however, there is differential reproductive success among individuals in the population, the assumption of neutrality is violated and natural selection has a significant influence. If possession of an allelic variant results in an increase in reproductive success—that is, if the allele is positively selected—the likelihood that the allele will eventually become fixed goes up and the path toward fixation becomes less stochastic and more direct. The greater the reproductive success, the faster the increase in relative frequency. Conversely, if possession of an allelic variant results in a decrease in reproductive success—if the allele is negatively selected—the likelihood that the allele will eventually become fixed decreases. The greater the decrease in reproductive success, the faster the allele will go extinct.

- Mutation. Mutation results in the introduction of new alleles into a population. New mutations may also result in *molecular reversals* (the creation of a new allele by mutation and the subsequent mutation back to the original state), *parallelisms* (occurrences of the same mutation independently in related lineages), and *convergences* (mutations that independently produce the same result in unrelated lineages), although the probability is small that they will do so. New mutations may also produce either more advantageous or deleterious alleles, which are also violations of the Hardy-Weinberg assumption of no selection. Regardless of the characteristics of the mutation, the creation of a new allele results in the new variant achieving a nonzero relative frequency, which thus also changes at least one other allele frequency, even if not by very much. This change in allele frequencies would result in the evolution of the population, albeit only slightly.

Mutation is by itself a very weak evolutionary force. However, when it is coupled with another of the violations of the Hardy-Weinberg equilibrium, like selection or a change in population size, the result is often a very potent combination of evolutionary forces that can change the genetic signature of a population in a relatively short period of time. There is also evidence to suggest that an increase in mutation rate is often favored upon colonization of a new environment where adaptation is required.[37]

• Migration. In terms of population genetics, migration is not merely the physical movement of individuals but the exchange of genetic information, or *gene flow*, between populations. Migration has the potential of introducing new alleles into a population in much the same way as mutation does but with the possibility of a greater frequency of occurrence. Migration also has the added effect of potentially increasing the effective population size beyond the actual size of a single population. Furthermore, it increases endemic *heterozygosity* (the frequency of individuals who possess more than one allelic variant at a particular locus—one on each homologous chromosome). Like selection, migration can be a potent evolutionary mechanism resulting in relatively speedy evolution of genes. If migration is coupled with another evolutionary force, it becomes even more potent, resulting in faster rates of molecular change.

• Change in population size. The relationship between population size and the probability of fixation connotes that if a population grows in size, it becomes harder for alleles to become fixed under neutral conditions. The converse is also true: if a population decreases in size, it becomes easier for alleles to become fixed. Population *bottlenecks*, such as when epidemic disease or warfare drastically contracts the size of the effective population, and colonization (or *founder events*), in which a new population with a small effective size is founded in isolation, may both result in a general lack

of diversity because the rate of fixation may exceed the rate of mutation. Thus, a researcher may infer that a bottleneck may have taken
place if there is an obvious lack of variation among the members of a
historical population.

- Nonrandom mating. The most common form of nonrandom
mating is *inbreeding*. Inbreeding takes place when individuals mate
with those to whom they are related. This results in the dispropor-
tional expression of rare recessive alleles, which can result in a decrease in reproductive success. The avoidance of inbreeding is the justification behind laws that prohibit the marriage of siblings and first
cousins in the United States. Even when deleterious alleles do not
increase in relative frequency, inbreeding can result in a decrease in
heterozygosity. *Outcrossing*, the avoidance of inbreeding, can restore
levels of heterozygosity relatively quickly; but if inbreeding results in
the prolonged isolation of a lineage, outcrossing may not be possible
because reproductive success may be too low for the production of
offspring.

Generally speaking, these violations of the Hardy-Weinberg assumptions all result in the genetic signature of the population in
question changing relative to what it had historically been. These evolutionary forces cause changes in allele frequencies that, given certain
conditions, may change the fundamental genetic characteristics of
the lineage. Nevertheless, some equilibrium violations are more likely
to result in substantive change than others.

When evolutionary forces are combined, greater change becomes
more likely and even expected. The primary caveat of the study of
population genetics is that there are always situations in which it is
impossible to reconstruct the characteristics of past evolutionary
events. Violations of the Hardy-Weinberg assumptions are generally
assumed not to have occurred unless there is extrinsic evidence available that indicates to the contrary. This is the primary reason why the
results of population studies must be loosely interpreted.

*Did the people of Lehi or Mulek violate Hardy-Weinberg assumptions?*
Generally speaking, the Book of Mormon peoples violated most of the
Hardy-Weinberg assumptions presented above. Clearly, they violated the
assumptions of no migration and constant, large population size. These
violations included: (1) Lehi (1 Nephi 18:8–23) and Mulek (Helaman
6:10; 8:21) migrating to the Americas in small groups; (2) multiple accounts of groups that left the central population to colonize other lands,
like the initial split of the Nephites and the Lamanites (2 Nephi 5:5–6)
or the story of Hagoth building a ship and launching into the west sea
(Alma 63:5–8); (3) constant wars that killed thousands of people and
may have resulted in population bottlenecks (for example, Omni 1:3,
10, 24 through Mormon 6:10–14); (4) the catastrophes prior to the coming of Christ to the Americas in which thousands of people lost their
lives (3 Nephi 8:5–18); (5) groups that dissented and separated themselves from the main body of Nephites (such as the Zoramites in Alma
31:8); (6) partitioning of major populations into cultural tribes and sub-
divisions (referred to as "-ites" as in 4 Nephi 1:17, 36–37); (7) secondary
contact between Nephite dissenters and Lamanites resulting in gene flow
(e.g., Alma 21:2–3; 25:4); and (8) secondary contact between the Anti-
Nephi-Lehies who converted and left the Lamanites to live among the
Nephites (Alma 23:17–18; 27:25–27).

The assumption of no selection may also have been violated
when the people journeyed through the wilderness in the Old
World (see 1 Nephi 16:20, 35; 17:1–2 [a direct reference to bearing
children amid hardship], 21) and the New World (see Omni 1:27–30)
and experienced hardships due to expansion (as in Alma 63:5–8;
Helaman 3:3–4, 7, 9). They inhabited a new land that may have been
very different from the habitat endemic to Jerusalem and the rest
of Israel. These new environmental factors may have meant that alleles that were neutral in the old environment became selectively advantageous, while formerly advantageous alleles may have become
neutral or even detrimental. Alleles that proved to be advantageous
would have enjoyed a newfound reproductive success and spread

throughout the population, accumulating over successive generations. Although selection is definitely a possible violation of Hardy-Weinberg assumptions, it remains largely unclear as to whether it had a significant influence or what that influence may have been, based on the Book of Mormon story line.

Another potential violation of a Hardy-Weinberg assumption may have been nonrandom mating. Although Lehi's family brought with them the family of Ishmael, all the mate choices from within the founding population's first generation following the initial colonization would have been exclusively first cousins, and most would have been double first cousins—that is, their fathers were brothers and their mothers were sisters. Possible exceptions to this pattern would have been the children of Zoram; their mother was a daughter of Ishmael (1 Nephi 16:7) and therefore a sibling of either the husband or wife of the other Lehite couples, but their father was probably genetically unrelated to the rest of the party. It is also possible that some of the children of Laman, Lemuel, and the sons of Ishmael, once their parents became separated from the other colonists (2 Nephi 5:5–6), may have produced offspring with partners originating from native populations, thus not allowing an Israelitish mitochondrial genome to be passed on among those lineages.[38]

There is, however, no reason to suspect the mutation rate to have changed, although fewer allelic variants are produced in a small population than in a large population as a result. Mutation, as explained above, is a very weak evolutionary force, so it probably would not have had a great effect by itself anyway. It is true that higher rates of mutation may be favored upon colonizing novel environments, but there is no direct Book of Mormon evidence that this was the case.

### Human Genetics and Genealogical Inference

If genetic change is constant, we should be able to accurately trace racial and lineal ancestry, right? As discussed above, there is a specific set of circumstances under which this would be true, but in reality these circumstances generally have not been met within the recorded history of humankind. Implicit assumptions that must be invoked in tracing ancestry using genetic information include the following: (1) the sample population has had a large and relatively constant effective size; (2) the population has been largely reproductively isolated from other populations; and (3) the majority of the genetic variations used to trace the population's ancestry and infer historical relationships have become fixed in the sample populations and, in effect, represent diagnostic markers. In most organisms, these are pretty fair assumptions; but humans have deviated considerably from this model. There has been recent exponential population growth among human beings in most areas of the world, and our capacity and propensity for movement have always been such that, even thousands of years ago, most populations were far from genetically isolated.[39] As a result, there has been a continuous historical flow of genetic information among most of the world's populations.[40] These violations of the most basic of assumptions have resulted in the human gene pool being "profoundly different" from that of other higher primates, such as chimpanzees,[41] within which genetic variation is more diverse in a single social group than in the entire human race![42] Researchers studying historical human genetic variation must therefore be very careful with their experimental design; they must try to sample only those populations that they have reason to believe have been relatively stable and isolated through the relevant period of history.

*Analytical concerns.* Alan Templeton, a world-famous researcher and expert on the analysis of population genetic information working out of Washington University in St. Louis, and others, including Keith Crandall, a professor of integrative biology, microbiology, and molecular biology at Brigham Young University, have outlined a research protocol that may help avoid these problems.[43] When Templeton applied this new technique to the analysis of human genetic population structure, one of his primary conclusions was that human populations have experienced ubiquitous genetic interchange throughout their history.[44] He underscored the idea that although a population may have a strong genetic signature originating from a particular geographic location, there is nearly always some genetic variation that cannot be explained by the predominant hypothesis. Rather than discounting this unexplained variation, he maintained that it is an indication that variation from other sources may have a significant influence, even though the source of the information may not be ascertainable.

Templeton also found that different types of DNA varied in their ability to resolve questions of range expansion, long-distance dispersal, and isolation by distance factors, largely owing to the ways in which the particular type of DNA recombines or does not recombine. Mitochondrial DNA does not recombine at all, and Y chromosomes may recombine with X chromosomes in some regions but not in others. X chromosomes and *autosomal* chromosomes (chromosome pairs 1–22), however, recombine among homologs relatively frequently. Implementation of a given type of DNA in population-based studies may require a unique experimental design because recombination blurs analytical results, making interpretation of the data ambiguous. For example, it has been demonstrated that the mitochondrial genome and the nonrecombining portion of the Y chromosome are subject to a large degree of stochastic error because they do not recombine, meaning that any calculations of timing of divergences resulting from analysis of these molecules should be seen as uncertain estimates.[45] One study based on a marker on the Y chromosome concluded that the common ancestor of all living males lived 270,000 years ago, but the 95 percent confidence interval placed on this value means effectively that this common ancestor may have lived at any time between yesterday and 800,000 years in the past.[46] When considering uniparental, nonrecombining DNA, uncertainty is the rule of thumb, and results must be considered gross estimates, the exact value of which is completely dependent on influential factors such as natural selection, effective population size, and the degree of gene flow.

Most surviving mutations in the mitochondrial genome have been shown to be selectively neutral, but this is not necessarily true in the nuclear genome. When the effective female population is small—that is, when only limited numbers of the females in the population do all of the childbearing—population genetics theory predicts that mutations may become fixed more quickly in mitochondrial genomes, resulting in overestimates of the timing of *coalescence* (the approximate date when an ancestor may have lived from which an extant variation originated).[47] Likewise, when gene flow between populations is prevalent, populations evolve much more slowly and as if they are much larger; but if gene flow is sparse, populations will evolve independently and much more quickly. It is clear that techniques used to resolve interspecies relationships (which are generally not at the population level but at higher taxonomic levels, where considering the effects of these phenomena is not as important) should not be applied carte blanche to studies of populations within species.[48] Even population-level genetic relationships should not be equated with lineal genealogies. Thus, careful experimental design, biologically appropriate methods, and conservative interpretation of results are a must.

*Conclusions from empirical studies.* A recent article addressing the subject of historical Amerind (Native American) population genetics underscores the perspective that conclusions resulting from the analysis of human genetic markers must be interpreted conservatively:

> Human geneticists might be well advised to only modestly suggest that their suggestions with regard to the identification of population waves for archaeological consideration are simply exercises in speculation that have little precision. Our research continues to document the unique composition of genomes in space and time, but interpretations of the exact process by which genetic diversity has accumulated should be stated with greater caution, if it is to have credibility among a broader range of disciplines. . . .

The difficulties that attend the appropriate incorporation of information from biparentally inherited loci into the effort to reconstruct population history—an effort that is the ultimate goal of most anthropological geneticists—can be only broadly imagined on the basis of this example [the case of the Amerinds presented in the article].[49]

Thus, recovering a specific genetic signature, even one that may have been of major historical importance, may not be possible. Furthermore, if a genetic novelty is recovered and it is suspected that it may correspond to a historical event, it may not be advisable to suggest the correlation unless there are multiple lines of evidence. It would be extremely inadvisable for any scientist to claim to have found Lehi's genetic signature, even if the claim was merely to have recovered the remnant of a limited Middle Eastern migration. If *my* research yielded such results, I would simply claim that other variants exist that are not easily explained but that there may be some historical relationship or similarity to Old World genetic lineages with possible descendants in present-day Middle Eastern communities. Any conclusions that go beyond the presentation of demonstrable data would invite the scrutiny and criticism of the scientific community, and rightly so. Conservatism in one's conclusions should always be the rule, never the exception.

*Ancient DNA.* The use of ancient DNA for studying human evolutionary relationships has experienced a moderate level of success. For example, DNA was extracted from a Neanderthal (*Homo neanderthalensis*) fossil that was collected nearly 150 years ago from western Germany. Results indicated that Neanderthals and modern humans are four times more distantly related than the most divergent of human lineages[50] and confirmed that no extant human is even partially descended from a Neanderthal lineage.[51] Ancient DNA obtained from museum specimens has also been useful when inferring species relationships among extinct organisms such as the quagga, a zebra relative.[52] Therefore, the use of DNA from preserved skeletal material and mummies may be very useful in studying human origins and diversity. However, studies incorporating ancient DNA must be interpreted with more than usual care due to the high probability of spontaneous DNA degradation and possible violations of the assumptions used to estimate genetic relationships (for instance, the possibility that the specimens do not originate from the same time frame or temporal context). Results must be interpreted with a conservative eye to avoid conclusions that go beyond what is appropriate considering the nature of the data and the accepted governing scientific principles.

## Human Population Studies: A Brief Review

A *haplotype* (also termed a *multilocus genotype*) is a distinct variant of a group of linked loci. Strictly speaking, a haplotype may be isolated for comparison by cutting homologous DNA sequences with restriction enzymes to identify restriction fragment length polymorphisms (RFLPs), amplifying length variants in satellite DNA using the polymerase chain reaction (PCR), sequencing a distinct region of DNA to reveal nucleotide variation, or any number of different techniques that distinguish derived genetic characters within a single linkage group. Groups of haplotypes that share prominent features are considered *monophyletic* (of a single origin) and are referred to as *haplogroups*.

Relative to human population studies, haplotype information has been gathered from many potential sources, including mitochondrial genomes, Y chromosomes, and autosomal chromosomes. Several correlations have been made between the molecular evolution of these genetic markers and the development of regional linguistics.[53] In fact, cross-referencing genetic and linguistic studies provides a rich context by which genetic information may be interpreted. However, certain assumptions must be taken into account when considering such a correlation, including the following: (1) once language families diverge, they never again exchange migrants—an idea that is not supported by genetic evidence[54]—and (2) genetic lineages diverge quickly in small populations and slowly in large populations such that a molecular clock cannot be invoked.[55] Not surprisingly, definite conclusions that explain all the observed genetic variations are few.[56] Characterizing the dynamics of human population genetics is a highly complex research pursuit and must be approached with a certain degree of conservatism and skepticism.[57]

*Mitochondrial haplotypes.* One of the first very important human population studies was performed in 1984 by a research group at the University of California at Berkeley using 12 restriction enzymes that produced polymorphisms relative to 441 cleavage sites in the human mitochondrial genomes of 112 people from 4 continents. Of these sites, 163 were polymorphic for cleavage, most likely due to a single-base mutation that was most probably under very little functional constraint. Although very few inferences regarding historical contact or migrations were drawn from these data, the enormous amount of genetic variation among humans, especially within the mitochondrial genome, was an obvious conclusion of the study. It also revealed a type of coevolution between the mitochondrial cytochrome oxidase subunit 2 and the nuclear cytochrome *c* genes, both of which are involved in cellular energy production (as part of the electron transport chain) and evolve roughly five times faster in primates (including humans) than in rodents or ungulates. This study represented the most comprehensive comparative study for closely related, complete mitochondrial genomes of that period, but—of importance to the topic of this essay—this study did not include any Native American samples.[58]

The group at Berkeley followed up the 1984 study with a paper published in the internationally prestigious scientific journal *Nature.* This paper, entitled "Mitochondrial DNA and Human Evolution," has since become the foundation for the study of human population genetics. It drew upon restriction-map data from 147 people from 5 geographic populations, once again not including Native Americans. The main conclusion of this study was that the common female ancestor of these sampled individuals lived about 200,000 years ago[59] —an individual who has since become known as "mitochondrial

Eve." This controversial study has since been confirmed multiple times, although the exact time frame and other details relative to our most recent common female ancestor remain unclear.[60] Other questions persist—most notably, To what extent does the history of a locus represent the history of a population?[61]

Some resolution has been achieved by correlating the results of population genetics, archaeology, and linguistics. For example, it has been suggested that one of the major routes of humans from Africa to Eurasia (the combined European and Asian continents) may have been across Saudi Arabia, through Iraq and Iran, dispersing to Pakistan and along the coasts of the Indian subcontinent to East Asia, and then on to the islands of Micronesia, including Australia and New Guinea. Archaeological evidence suggests that Australia has experienced continuous human occupation for about the past 60,000 years, and it is clear that people have inhabited New Guinea for at least 45,000 years.[62] These approximate dates may be used to calibrate the molecular clock emergent from genetic studies such that the timing of each event along the route of migration may be inferred.[63] This, however, is the approximate limit of the technique; only mass migrations may be inferred, and only with a degree of uncertainty, and only if there is corroborating evidence. Details relative to historical human migration may be achieved without correlating these three lines of support, but only at the cost of uncertainty as to absolute dates and unsubstantiated assumptions.

The historical population structure of Native Americans may be characterized by the four major haplogroups A, B, C, and D.[64] All have been associated with an Asian origin. There also are more rare haplotypes that do not appear to be part of haplogroups A–D. These "other" haplotypes[65] form a monophyletic haplogroup[66] that is curiously similar to the uncommon European and Druze (Israel) haplogroup X.[67] This haplogroup is currently endemic to Native American groups in North America—including the Ojibwa, Nuu-Chah-Nulth (Nootka), Sioux, Navajo, and Yakima[68]—and has also been identified among the Yanomami of the northern Amazon.[69] Accumulated fixed differences between the "other" haplotypes of Native Americans and the European/Druze haplogroup X indicate that they may have had a common ancestor between 12,000 and 36,000 years ago,[70] representing a fifth founding lineage of Native Americans.[71] However, this may be an overestimate if the original founding population was very small; as discussed above, population size and the probability of fixation have an inverse relationship, so small historical populations may appear to be older than they are if the assumption of constant, large population size is asserted when no evidence to the contrary is forthcoming. The recent discovery of a 9,300-year-old Caucasoid human skeleton buried near Kennewick, Washington—the so-called Kennewick man[72]—may provide an independent confirmation of molecular findings surrounding haplogroup X or, at the very least, allow for the possibility of Caucasoid habitation in the Americas.[73]

Subsequent research has identified haplogroup X among the Altaian people of south Siberia,[74] and some have suggested that this invalidates previous speculation of a Caucasoid ancestry for haplogroup X;[75] but this suggestion is based on the speculation that haplogroup X must originally have come from Asia because haplogroups A–D also originate in Asia.[76] This explanation, however, does not account for the fact that haplogroup X is found to be more widespread in Europe than in Asia, while haplogroups A–D are not found in Europe. Far from determining that there was a single place of origin for Native Americans, these new data underscore the possibility that X and A–D may be parts of completely separate lineages. In general, without a proper *outgroup* (DNA sequences that have a sister relationship to the study group DNAs) to polarize the relationships of the population network, it is nearly impossible to determine the point of origin.

Several possible conclusions may be consistent with these data, including the following: (1) as presented by Derenko et al., that Altaians represent the origin of the haplogroup[77] (which does not explain why Europeans and Israelis also possess it); (2) that haplogroup

X originated in Europe and migrated independently to south Siberia and North America; (3) that haplogroup X originated in Europe and migrated to Israel, south Siberia, and then on to North America;[78] or even (4) that haplogroup X originated somewhere central to Europe and Asia (perhaps near Israel) and migrated simultaneously in different directions at the same time, arriving in North America as part of the same dispersal (which is consistent with a scenario not unlike the diaspora). Given that fluctuations in population sizes may affect the rate at which variants become fixed in populations,[79] none of these hypotheses—or a host of other hypotheses that may or may not exhibit testable characteristics—can be verified. It is very possible that migrating populations originally represented only small subpopulations of a much bigger parent population; genetic drift may thus have had a great effect among founders, generating more fixed differences while at the same time ridding the population of a great percentage of its within-population variation than is expected by chance alone.

Another haplotype, C10,[80] is found only among the Cayapa people of Ecuador, who possess it in relatively high frequencies (30 percent). C10 does not appear to be closely related to any other extant human haplotype, although it appears that it may be loosely related to haplogroup C to the exclusion of haplogroups B and A. At best, haplotype C10 represents a lineage that has a questionable origin.

Mitochondrial studies have also been performed with the remains of ancient Maya from the Postclassic period of AD 900–1521, just prior to European colonization.[81] Findings include the identification of a single individual (1 out of 16) whose mitochondrial haplotype failed to correspond to any of the known extant haplogroups (A–D). Although another unidentified haplotype was isolated among contemporary Maya, it was discounted as the product of modern European admixture.[82] However, the presence of a similarly unidentified haplotype in ancient Maya may call this conclusion into question.

Although the preponderance of mitochondrial genome data supports the hypothesis that the Americas were originally peopled by humans from eastern Asia, the exact location of the source population and the number of migration waves remains controversial,[83] despite claims to the contrary.[84] The presence of haplotypes X and C10 and the "unknown" Maya haplotypes (both ancient and modern), however, emphasize the fact that much that has been discovered is yet to be explained. A hypothesis for the diversity of Native American mitochondrial genome haplotypes that relies exclusively on an out-of-Asia origin falls short of a complete explanation.

*Y-chromosome haplotypes.* Parallel to human studies of the matrilineal mitochondrial genome are studies of the Y chromosome, its patrilineal counterpart. However, unlike the mitochondrial genome, or even autosomal chromosomes, the Y chromosome exhibits very little polymorphism[85] yet is subject to a large measure of stochastic error.[86] The lack of genetic variation may be the result of episodic selective sweeps, but the exact mechanism for this evolutionary constraint remains unclear.[87] Nevertheless, great effort has been exerted to discover fixed differences that may act as diagnostic haplotypes that allow for the identification of human founder events. To date, these fixed differences have been found within several genes and noncoding regions such that the construction of compound haplotypes has been possible.[88] A positive correlation between Y-chromosome haplotypes and linguistic patterns has also been deduced.[89]

Since Y-chromosome markers lack much of the genetic diversity that mitochondrial genomes exhibit, the ambiguity arising in the data is somewhat compounded. It is very difficult to differentiate true ancient relationships from relatively recent and extensive European admixture resulting from colonization after the time of Columbus. One example of this problem is a recent study that examined Native American Y-chromosomal haplotypes and concluded that there may have been two separate lineages of migrating populations to the

Americas,[90] a conclusion that has been confirmed by independent evaluation.[91] Of the five Native American haplotypes, four (haplotypes 1, 10, 20, and 31) exhibited only 1–2 mutational differences among them, while the fifth haplotype (23) clusters tightly with other haplotypes to the exclusion of the first four. The fifth haplotype is more closely allied with Central East Asian, Evenki, and Mongolian haplotypes (7, 24, and 28); the first four were similar to these, as well as to Altai, Ket, Indian, and European haplotypes (4, 6, 13, and 32). When the data were analyzed using a different optimality criterion, however, these results converge on a single lineage emerging from Asia, largely discounting the strong relationship with European haplotypes (4 and 6 were exclusively European) and the presence of a single haplotype (31) that did not appear in any sample population outside the Americas.

Although I do not necessarily disagree with this study's conclusion that Native American Y-chromosome lineages originate largely from Asian source populations,[92] I do find that it fails to explain many aspects of the resulting data. For example, when the haplotypes shared by Europeans and either Native Americans or Siberians were excluded from the analysis, it did not appreciably change the ancestral relationships inferred from the data, indicating that modern European admixture is not a plausible explanation. Yet the most common European haplotype (1) also appears in Native Americans, suggesting that there has been modern admixture. The authors of the study then refer to studies involving Kennewick man[93] and haplogroup X[94] as evidence of a Native American–European connection, only to turn right around and explicitly state that a recent European admixture is likely. Needless to say, conclusions are far from definite.

*Differing results from mitochondrial DNA and Y-chromosome analysis.* The previous example points out the problem scientists have with ambiguity, especially the uncertainty emerging from human Y-chromosome data. One issue that can create ambiguity is the inherent difficulty of interpretation presented by inferring population dynamics from gene-based markers. The problem was defined clearly in a recent paper on New World Y-chromosome haplotypes:

> Gene trees [relationships inferred from gene variation] such as our Y-chromosome scaled coalescent tree . . . , the numerous mtDNA trees in the literature (Cann et al. 1987), and the recent global β-globin–analysis tree based on autosomal sequence data (Harding et al. 1997) are not equivalent to population trees [the true relationships of populations]. Inferences about population relationships derived from gene trees must be made very cautiously, especially since each gene has its own evolutionary history (Harpending et al. 1998).[95]

This difficulty is compounded when polymorphism levels are low, as is the case with much of the Y-chromosome data. Although many researchers acknowledge this to be the case,[96] some continue to use relationship-reconstruction techniques that ignore the problem, yet they freely draw seemingly unambiguous conclusions from their inferences.[97] This problem is further amplified with regard to the question of ancient colonization of the New World by the fact of extensive and prolonged gene flow from Asia,[98] which serves to confound the ability of scientists to reconstruct the historical population structure of Native Americans.[99]

Ambiguity notwithstanding, some authors of studies with multiple interpretations relative to possible recent European admixture in the Americas point out that the estimated dates of dispersal generally correspond to the estimated age of Kennewick man.[100] This acknowledgment suggests that at least some researchers have reason to be skeptical of the global acceptance of the prevailing "out-of-Asia" paradigm. As a recent commentary put it, "Genetic evidence derived from contemporary populations can only study lineages that survived. It is impossible to estimate the number of nonsurviving lineages"[101]—meaning that if a population is currently extinct due to war or some kind of natural disaster, we could never infer their existence from DNA data because they would have no descendants. Furthermore, this would be true independently for each genomic linkage group, which is the primary reason why mitochondrial DNA and Y-chromosome data may yield different analytical results.[102]

*Differing results from mitochondrial DNA and Y-chromosome analysis.* One factor that may potentially result in conflicting conclusions emerging from among unique human genetic data sets is the differing regional dispersal patterns of males and females. A good example of this is a recent study entitled "Mitochondrial and Nuclear Genetic Relationships among Pacific Island and Asian Populations." Among 745 samples collected throughout eastern Asia and major islands of the Pacific Ocean, mitochondrial data (190 bp) correlates closely with linguistic data, suggesting that peoples of remote Pacific islands originated from human populations of Southeast Asia. Nuclear data (17 short tandem-repeat [STR] loci) from these samples, on the other hand, fail to correlate with linguistic data but underscore a relationship between peoples of larger western islands and smaller eastern islands.[103] On the surface, these data appear to be in conflict, even to the point of supporting conflicting hypotheses for human dispersal in the islands of Melanesia, referred to as the "express train" and "entangled bank" hypotheses.[104] These differing results, however, may be reflective of different dispersal patterns among males and females, with females dispersing from southern China to the remote islands via primary expansion (the "express train"). In contrast, males probably dispersed secondarily without exterminating the local female population, whether by completely displacing the local males or by extrapair copulations while engaged in fishing or merchant ventures (thus resulting in an "entangled bank").[105] Although this is just one interpretation of these data and others may be possible, given additional data from other genetic loci, this article stresses the importance of considering multiple points of view in an effort to characterize a scenario that is consistent with all of the data, not just those that fit one's a priori assumptions.

As noted above, mitochondrial DNA and Y-chromosome data may have independent natural histories, resulting in inferential discrepancies. Recent findings confirm previous conclusions[106] that these discrepancies have a cultural basis.[107] The differing conclusions resulting from the analysis of these linkage groups are largely the product of either men remaining near their birthplace while women migrate to be near them (termed *patrilocality*)[108] or women remaining near their birthplace while men migrate (termed *matrilocality*).[109] Each scenario results in a different discrepancy among analytical results. Patrilocality would naturally produce a high rate of mitochondrial change and a low rate of Y-chromosome change, while matrilocality would naturally produce the opposite result. This is exactly what was found.[110] However, patrilocality prevails in the majority of peoples sampled to date,[111] resulting in Y-chromosome data that are less robust than mitochondrial data, thus yielding different inferences.[112]

## Conclusions

This review has produced several biologically meaningful conclusions relative to the question of whether it is possible to recover an ancient genetic signature of a small migrating group that lived 2,600 years ago—namely, the parties of Lehi and Mulek, who, the Book of Mormon claims, migrated to the Americas from Jerusalem just prior to the occupation of Judah by the Babylonians. Each of these conclusions is open to interpretation because each necessitates the application of scientific concepts and assumptions, which is largely a subjective endeavor. One of the most common misconceptions of science, especially among the lay public (and new biology students), is that it is a completely deterministic process. If experiments are performed correctly, they reason, the results will have no ambiguity. In reality, not only are the results highly ambiguous, but it is often difficult to come up with an appropriate experimental design when little is known of a topic. In practice, a lot of experimentation is exploratory in nature. If the dynamics of a system are unknown, experiments are designed that will allow the researcher to gain an intuition for how the components are related and interact. Thus, initial experimentation is largely for the purpose of probing a system such that a preliminary understanding of the applicable parameters may be ascertained.

Some of the students I train in laboratory research express frustration with my inability to answer their questions with confidence. Quite often I tell them that one conclusion would be most greatly supported under one set of circumstances, while another would be supported under another set of circumstances. Furthermore, I add, the set of assumptions—both explicitly stated and implicitly supposed—limit the conclusions that are possible given the data. These assumptions are frequently difficult to reveal or even understand unless the researcher has a great deal of experience with the system in question. Put plainly and simply, the more complex the system, the harder it is to interpret the data appropriately.

Such is the case with those who have attempted to draw conclusions regarding the validity of the Book of Mormon based on the current body of human genetic data.[113] They reveal their ignorance of scientific principles by drawing conclusions that are inappropriate. They ignore pertinent information because they do not know that it may be important, or they fail to probe the primary literature, opting instead to use summaries or popular scientific literature exclusively because they have a difficult time interpreting much of the data for themselves. They simply trust the speculative suggestions of scientists, when all the scientists were doing was offering a possible interpretive alternative—a hypothesis that may or may not be testable—rather than stating a definite conclusion that is emergent from the facts because such a conclusion may not be possible given the data.

This review first concluded that, regardless of the answer to the essential question under consideration, it is not possible to conclude logically that the Book of Mormon is not true based on its story line.

Nothing can be proven in science; hypotheses can only be rejected. Thus, if it is not possible to recover such a signature, it also is not possible to disprove the Book of Mormon based on genetic data. Conversely, if it is possible to recover a genetic signature like Lehi's or Mulek's, the mere fact that it has not been recovered means nothing with regard to the truthfulness of the Book of Mormon. Either way, the Book of Mormon does not present a testable hypothesis in terms of human population genetics.

Putting the philosophical ramifications of scientific method aside, I then attempted to test the hypothesis that it is possible to recover the ancient genetic signature of Lehi or Mulek. The story line of the Book of Mormon presents a great deal of information bearing on the conditions known to preserve genetic signatures (which would include the preservation of a suite of genetic alleles over evolutionary time):

- The Book of Mormon begins with the account of a familial migration and proceeds to describe a series of further migrations over land and sea, resulting in a multitude of new founding populations. Once they had arrived in the land of promise, the descendants of Lehi most probably experienced at least some degree of gene flow between themselves and indigenous populations that were largely Asian in origin. These accounts blatantly violate the assumption of no migration.

- Each migrating population had its beginning as a relatively small group of people. Constant wars and at least one major series of catastrophes prior to the coming of Christ to the Americas resulted in serial population bottlenecks, especially among the effective male population. These conditions constitute a blatant violation of the assumption of a constant, large effective population size.

- When populations migrate to dissimilar environments, some individuals find it easier to bear offspring than others. This differential reproductive success may have resulted in nonrandom fluctuations in allele frequencies contingent upon the genetic constitutions of those who bore the greatest number of children initially. It is plain from the Book of Mormon that times were tough, especially for colonizing populations. If these difficult conditions resulted in differential reproductive success, it constitutes another violation of equilibrium assumptions: the assumption of no natural selection.

• When the Nephites initially settled the New World, cousins were most probably forced to marry because of a lack of unrelated covenant-making peers. This circumstance would have resulted in the fixation of rare recessive alleles that would have not become fixed if the population had stayed behind in Jerusalem. Inbreeding, at least when the Nephites first founded their colony, would have resulted in a violation of the assumption of completely random mating.

• There is, however, no reason to suspect that the underlying mutation rate increased or decreased among Nephites, Lamanites, or Mulekites, although the gross number of mutations is fewer when there are fewer individuals. The rate of fixation of new alleles arising from mutation, however, generally increases in founding populations, making it appear as if the lineages to which populations belong diverged more anciently than in fact they did. If this had occurred, it would not have violated equilibrium assumptions, but it most definitely would have violated the assumption of a molecular clock, a basic assumption for reconstructing genetic relationships.

Thus, almost all the assumptions of Hardy-Weinberg equilibrium were violated by the Book of Mormon peoples. According to the specifics of the Book of Mormon story line, it may not be possible to recover the genetic signature of Lehi or Mulek. Too many influences would have resulted in too many violations of equilibrium-preserving conditions. In light of this information, a population geneticist would not even bother designing an experiment to test the hypothesis because there would be no reason to expect a successful result. Furthermore, if it were possible to recover the genetic signature, there would be no way to verify its source. One would expect that if Lehi's or Mulek's genetic signature was found, it would be categorized as "unknown" or "other" or "unrelated." Based on this information, and if I were forced to design an experiment that would produce evidence in support of the Book of Mormon, I would look for haplotypes that are not closely related to any extant ethnic group, but appear to be older—perhaps much older—than 2,600 years. Curiously, documentation of such haplotypes is exactly what is emerging in the literature (haplogroup X, haplotype C10, the "other" haplotypes from ancient and modern Maya, the unexplained Y-chromosome haplotypes, and so forth), but interpretation of these data is largely avoided in the individual studies because they do not correspond well to the current scientific paradigm. However, I will stop short of interpreting these "other" data as belonging to the Book of Mormon peoples because it is completely unverifiable. As indicated, one cannot prove anything; one can only reject hypotheses.

My next point builds on this: current human population genetic data produce many ambiguous results that are hard to interpret, so they must be interpreted conservatively. They also present more data than fit into the general conclusions of the paper, and that data must eventually be dealt with. If we read a human population genetics study that purports to have definite, ironclad conclusions drawn from data of questionable interpretation, we should feel fairly confident that the authors of the research article are going beyond what the data will realistically allow them to conclude. The leading experts in the field are currently urging their colleagues to avoid definite conclusions because of the lack of precision produced by conflicting data.[114] This professional skepticism, however, rarely makes its way into popular media or literature reviews because there are no definite conclusions to report. Those who question the truth of the Book of Mormon based on genetic data would be well advised to avoid these publications like the plague because they present only part of the story. They generally do not, however, present the part that tends to be the most pertinent to the critics' essential question—the ambiguous results.

The general conclusion of this essay, therefore, is that although it may be possible to recover the genetic signature of a small migrating family from 2,600 years ago, it is not probable. But either way, it would not allow the story line of the Book of Mormon to be rejected because the absence of a genetic signature means absolutely nothing.

That said, I feel compelled to voice my professional confidence in those that are actively researching human population genetics. I have read a large body of primary literature while compiling this review, and I have found the methods and interpretation of results to be consistent with scientific principles and current thought. I am convinced that there has been constant gene flow between Asia and the Americas, but I am also convinced that there has been a trickle of migrants from other source populations. Though far from verifying or proving the Book of Mormon, this observation allows for the plausibility of the Book of Mormon story line. It is very possible that a group or groups of people from the Middle East found their way to the New World in 600 BC. Others had made the trip from somewhere other than Asia at much earlier dates. Thus, a statement that the Book of Mormon account is absolutely impossible would be at the very least naïve, but most probably quite foolish. It would reveal the overall absence of scientific training, as well as an underlying agenda.

# Notes

1. Sandro L. Bonatto and Francisco M. Salzano, "A Single and Early Migration for the Peopling of the Americas Supported by Mitochondrial DNA Sequence Data," *Proceedings of the National Academy of Sciences, USA* 94 (1997): 1866–71.

2. See Matthew Roper, "Nephi's Neighbors: Book of Mormon Peoples and Pre-Columbian Populations," *FARMS Review* 15/2 (2003): 185–224 (also this volume pp. 217–56).

3. David A. McClellan, David F. Whiting, Ryan G. Christensen, and Joshua K. Sailsbery, "Genetic Codes as Evolutionary Filters: Subtle Differences in the Structures of Genetic Codes Result in Significant Differences in Patterns of Nucleotide Substitution," *Journal of Theoretical Biology* 226 (2004): 393–400.

4. Brent Ewing and Phil Green, "Analysis of Expressed Sequence Tags Indicates 35,000 Human Genes," *Nature Genetics* 25 (2000): 232–34; Feng Liang et al., "Gene Index Analysis of the Human Genome Estimates Approximately 120,000 Genes," *Nature Genetics* 25 (2000): 239–40.

5. J. Craig Venter et al., "The Sequence of the Human Genome," *Science* 291 (2001): 1304–51.

6. Michael Olivier et al., "A High-Resolution Radiation Hybrid Map of the Human Genome Draft Sequence," *Science* 291 (2001): 1298–1302.

7. Venter et al., "Sequence of the Human Genome," 1304–51.

8. Friderun Ankel-Simons and Jim M. Cummins, "Misconceptions about Mitochondria and Mammalian Fertilization: Implications for Theories on Human Evolution," *Proceedings of the National Academy of Sciences, USA* 93 (1996): 13859–63.

9. See, for example, D. R. Foran, J. E. Hixson, and W. M. Brown, "Comparisons of Ape and Human Sequences That Regulate Mitochondrial DNA Transcription and D-Loop DNA Synthesis," *Nucleic Acids Research* 16 (1988): 5841–61; Matthias Krings et al., "DNA Sequence of the Mitochondrial Hypervariable Region II from the Neandertal Type Specimen," *Proceedings of the National Academy of Sciences, USA* 96 (1999): 5581–85; Truls Moum, Ulfur Arnason, and Einar Árnason, "Mitochondrial DNA Sequence Evolution and Phylogeny of the Atlantic Alcidae, Including the Extinct Great Auk (*Pinguinus impennis*)," *Molecular Biology and Evolution* 19 (2002): 1434–39.

10. Thomas W. Murphy, "Lamanite Genesis, Genealogy, and Genetics," in *American Apocrypha: Essays on the Book of Mormon,* ed. Dan Vogel and Brent Lee Metcalfe (Salt Lake City: Signature Books, 2002), 64.

11. Marga Belle White et al., "A de Novo Cystic Fibrosis Mutation: CGA (Arg) to TGA (Stop) at Codon 851 of the CFTR Gene," *Genomics* 11 (1991): 778–79; Laura Cremonesi et al., "Detection of a de Novo R1066H Mutation in an Italian Patient Affected by Cystic Fibrosis," *Human Genetics* 98 (1996): 119–21.

12. Brunhilde Wirth et al., "De Novo Rearrangements Found in 2% of Index Patients with Spinal Muscular Atrophy: Mutational Mechanisms, Parental Origin, Mutation Rate, and Implications for Genetic Counseling," *American Journal of Human Genetics* 61 (1997): 1102–11.

13. See William B. Provine, *The Origins of Theoretical Population Genetics* (Chicago: University of Chicago Press, 2001), 132.

14. László Patthy, *Protein Evolution* (Oxford: Blackwell Science, 1999), 99.

15. Orlando J. Miller and Eeva Therman, *Human Chromosomes,* 4th ed. (New York: Springer, 2001), 176–78.

16. White et al., "De Novo Cystic Fibrosis Mutation," 778–79; Cremonesi et al., "Detection of a de Novo R1066H Mutation," 119–21; Wirth et al., "De Novo Rearrangements," 1102–11.

17. Motoo Kimura, *The Neutral Theory of Molecular Evolution* (Cambridge: Cambridge University Press, 1983).

18. Tomoko Ohta, "Evolutionary Rate of Cistrons and DNA Divergence," *Journal of Molecular Evolution* 1 (1972): 150–57.

19. For example, some evidence shows two complete genome duplications anciently in the lineage resulting in *Homo sapiens,* but not more recently than just after the origin of all vertebrates, over 400 million years ago. See, for example, Marie-Josèphe Pébusque et al., "Ancient Large-Scale Genome Duplications: Phylogenetic and Linkage Analyses Shed Light on Chordate Genome Evolution," *Molecular Biology and Evolution* 15 (1998): 1145–59; P. W. Holland, "More Genes in Vertebrates?" *Journal of Structural and Functional Genomics* 3 (2003): 75–84; A. C. Horton et al., "Phylogenetic Analyses Alone Are Insufficient to Determine Whether Genome Duplication(s) Occurred during

Early Vertebrate Evolution," *Journal of Experimental Zoology, Part B: Molecular and Developmental Evolution* 299 (2003): 41–53.

20.  John W. Drake et al., "Rates of Spontaneous Mutation," *Genetics* 148 (1998): 1667–86.

21.  J. L. Weber and C. Wong, "Mutation of Human Short Tandem Repeats," *Human Molecular Genetics* 2 (1993): 1123–28; Lynn B. Jorde, Michael Bamshad, and Alan R. Rogers, "Using Mitochondrial and Nuclear DNA Markers," *BioEssays* 20 (1998): 126–36.

22.  Masatoshi Nei, *Molecular Evolutionary Genetics* (New York: Columbia University Press, 1987), 34.

23.  Satoshi Horai et al., "Recent African Origin of Modern Humans Revealed by Complete Sequences of Hominoid Mitochondrial DNAs," *Proceedings of the National Academy of Sciences, USA* 92 (1995): 532–36; Jorde, Bamshad, and Rogers, "Using Mitochondrial and Nuclear DNA Markers," 126–36.

24.  Émile Zuckerkandl and Linus Pauling, "Evolutionary Divergence and Convergence in Proteins," in *Evolving Genes and Proteins*, ed. Vernon Bryson and Henry J. Vogel (New York: Academic Press, 1965), 97–166.

25.  Motoo Kimura, "Evolutionary Rate at the Molecular Level," *Nature* 217 (1968): 624–26; Tomoko Ohta and Motoo Kimura, "On the Constancy of the Evolutionary Rate of Cistrons," *Journal of Molecular Evolution* 1 (1971): 18–25; Ohta, "Evolutionary Rate of Cistrons," 150–57; Kimura, *Neutral Theory of Molecular Evolution*.

26.  Malaria Foundation International at www.malaria.org (accessed 23 October 2003).

27.  A. Ashley-Koch, Q. Yang, and R. S. Olney, "Sickle Hemoglobin (HbS) Allele and Sickle Cell Disease: A HuGE Review," *American Journal of Epidemiology* 151 (2000): 839–45; Wylie Burke, "Genomics as a Probe for Disease Biology," *New England Journal of Medicine* 349 (2003): 969–74.

28.  Lindell Bromham and David Penny, "The Modern Molecular Clock," *Nature Reviews: Genetics* 4 (2003): 216–24.

29.  Philip W. Hedrick, *Genetics of Populations*, 2nd ed. (Sudbury, Mass.: Jones and Bartlett, 2000), 64.

30.  For more on the hypothesis approach taken by science and how it applies to the Book of Mormon, see Michael F. Whiting, "DNA and the Book of Mormon: A Phylogenetic Perspective," *Journal of Book of Mormon Studies* 12/1 (2003): 24–35; D. Jeffrey Meldrum and Trent D. Stephens, "Who Are the Children of Lehi?" *Journal of Book of Mormon Studies* 12/1 (2003): 42–44.

31.  See Brian Stubbs, "Elusive Israel and the Numerical Dynamics of Population Mixing," *FARMS Review* 15/2 (2003): 165–82 (see this volume pp. 294–314).

32.  Nicolas Galtier, Frantz Depaulis, and Nicholas H. Barton, "Detecting Bottlenecks and Selective Sweeps from DNA Sequence Polymorphism," *Genetics* 155 (2000): 981–87; Rasmus Nielsen and John Wakeley, "Distinguishing Migration from Isolation: A Markov Chain Monte Carlo Approach," *Genetics* 158 (2001): 885–96.

33.  Rebecca L. Cann, "Genetic Clues to Dispersal in Human Populations: Retracing the Past from the Present," *Science* 291 (2001): 1742–48.

34.  G. Udny Yule, "Mendel's Laws and Their Probable Relations to Intra-racial Heredity," *New Phytologist* 1 (1902): 193–207; William E. Castle, "The Laws of Heredity of Galton and Mendel, and Some Laws Governing Race Improvement by Selection,"

*Proceedings of the American Academy of Arts and Sciences* 38 (1903): 535–48, reprinted as "Mendel's Law of Heredity," *Science* 18 (1903): 396–406; Karl Pearson, "On a Generalised Theory of Alternative Inheritance, with Special Reference to Mendel's Laws," *Philosophical Transactions of the Royal Society of London: Series A . . .* 203 (1904): 53–86.

35. Godfrey H. Hardy, "Mendelian Proportion in a Mixed Population," *Science* 28 (1908): 49–50.

36. Wilhelm Weinberg, "Über den Nachweis der Vererbung beim Menschen," *Jahreshefte des Vereins für Vaterländische Naturkunde in Württemberg, Stuttgart* 64 (1908): 368–82; English translation "On the Demonstration of Heredity in Man," in *Papers on Human Genetics*, ed. S. H. Boyer (Englewood Cliffs, N.J.: Prentice Hall, 1963), 4–15.

37. J. Arjan G. M. de Visser et al., "Diminishing Returns from Mutation Supply Rate in Asexual Populations," *Science* 283 (1999): 404–6; Antoine Giraud et al., "Costs and Benefits of High Mutation Rates: Adaptive Evolution of Bacteria in the Mouse Gut," *Science* 291 (2001): 2606–8.

38. See Roper, "Nephi's Neighbors." It is not even certain that the members of Lehi's party brought any distinctively Israelitish genetic markers with them when they arrived. See Matthew Roper, "Swimming in the Gene Pool: Israelite Kinship Relations, Genes, and Genealogy," *FARMS Review* 15/2 (2003): 129–64 (see this volume 257–94); John M. Butler, "A Few Thoughts from a Believing DNA Scientist," *Journal of Book of Mormon Studies* 12/1 (2003): 36–37.

39. For two strictly numerical studies of the rate at which human gene flow can progress, see Roper, "Nephi's Neighbors," and Stubbs, "Elusive Israel," both in this volume.

40. Cann, "Genetic Clues to Dispersal," 1742–48.

41. Pascal Gagneux et al., "Mitochondrial Sequences Show Diverse Evolutionary Histories of African Hominoids," *Proceedings of the National Academy of Sciences, USA* 96 (1999): 5077–82.

42. Cann, "Genetic Clues to Dispersal," 1742–48.

43. D. Posada, Keith A. Crandall, and Alan R. Templeton, "GeoDis: A Program for the Cladistic Nested Analysis of the Geographical Distribution of Genetic Haplotypes," *Molecular Ecology* 9 (2000): 487–88.

44. Alan R. Templeton, "Out of Africa Again and Again," *Nature* 416 (2002): 45–51.

45. Masatoshi Nei and Gregory Livshits, "Genetic Relationships of Europeans, Asians and Africans and the Origin of Modern *Homo sapiens*," *Human Heredity* 39 (1989): 276–81.

46. R. L. Dorit, Hiroshi Akashi, and W. Gilbert, "Absence of Polymorphism at the ZFY Locus on the Human Y-Chromosome," *Science* 268 (1995): 1183–85.

47. Jorde, Bamshad, and Rogers, "Using Mitochondrial and Nuclear DNA Markers," 126–36.

48. Templeton, "Out of Africa," 45–51; Rebecca L. Cann, "Tangled Genetic Routes," *Nature* 416 (2002): 32–33.

49. O. Rickards et al., "mtDNA History of the Cayapa Amerinds of Ecuador: Detection of Additional Founding Lineages for the Native American Populations," *American Journal of Human Genetics* 65 (1999): 519–30, quotation on 527–28.

50. Matthias Krings et al., "Neanderthal DNA Sequences and the Origin of Modern Humans," *Cell* 90 (1997): 19–30.

51.  Krings et al., "DNA Sequence of the Mitochondrial Hypervariable Region II," 5581–85.

52.  Russell G. Higuchi et al., "DNA Sequences from the Quagga, an Extinct Member of the Horse Family," *Nature* 312 (1984): 282–84; Russell G. Higuchi et al., "Mitochondrial DNA of the Extinct Quagga: Relatedness and Extent of Postmortem Change," *Journal of Molecular Evolution* 25 (1987): 283–87.

53.  Guido Barbujani, "DNA Variation and Language Affinities," *American Journal of Human Genetics* 61 (1997): 1011–14.

54.  Templeton, "Out of Africa," 45–51.

55.  Barbujani, "DNA Variation and Language Affinities," 1011–14.

56.  Cann, "Genetic Clues to Dispersal," 1742–48. For an illustration of this complexity specific to Native American origins, see Meldrum and Stephens, "Who Are the Children of Lehi?" 40–44.

57.  Rickards et al., "mtDNA History of the Cayapa Amerinds," 519–30.

58.  Rebecca L. Cann, Wesley M. Brown, and Allan C. Wilson, "Polymorphic Sites and the Mechanism of Evolution in Human Mitochondrial DNA," *Genetics* 106 (1984): 479–99.

59.  Rebecca L. Cann, Mark Stoneking, and Allan C. Wilson, "Mitochondrial DNA and Human Evolution," *Nature* 325 (1987): 31–36.

60.  Ibid.; Horai et al., "Recent African Origin of Modern Humans," 532–36; Thomas D. Kocher and Allan C. Wilson, "Sequence Evolution of Mitochondrial DNA in Humans and Chimpanzees: Control Region and a Protein-Coding Region," in *Evolution of Life: Fossils, Molecules, and Culture,* ed. Syozo Osawa and Tasuku Honjo (Tokyo: Springer-Verlag, 1991), 391–413; Linda Vigilant et al., "African Populations and the Evolution of Human Mitochondrial DNA," *Science* 253 (1991): 1503–7; Maryellen Ruvolo et al., "Mitochondrial COII Sequences and Modern Human Origins," *Molecular Biology and Evolution* 10 (1993): 1115–35; Yu-Sheng Chen et al., "Analysis of mtDNA Variation in African Populations Reveals the Most Ancient of All Human Continent-Specific Haplogroups," *American Journal of Human Genetics* 57 (1995): 133–49; Elizabeth Watson et al., "Mitochondrial Footprints of Human Expansions in Africa," *American Journal of Human Genetics* 61 (1997): 691–704; Yu-Sheng Chen et al., "mtDNA Variation in the South African Kung and Khwe—and Their Genetic Relationships to Other African Populations," *American Journal of Human Genetics* 66 (2000): 1362–83; Max Ingman et al., "Mitochondrial Genome Variation and the Origin of Modern Humans," *Nature* 408 (2000): 708–13; Jan Klein and Naoyuki Takahata, *Where Do We Come From? The Molecular Evidence for Human Descent* (Berlin: Springer-Verlag, 2002), 276–82; Darren Curnoe and A. Thorne, "Number of Ancestral Human Species: A Molecular Perspective," *Homo* 53 (2003): 201–24; Erika Hagelberg, "Recombination or Mutation Rate Heterogeneity? Implications for Mitochondrial Eve," *Trends in Genetics* 19 (2003): 84–90.

61.  Cann, "Genetic Clues to Dispersal," 1742–48.

62.  Richard G. Roberts, Rhys Jones, and M. A. Smith, "Beyond the Radiocarbon Barrier in Australian Prehistory," *Antiquity* 68 (1994): 611–16.

63.  Cann, "Genetic Clues to Dispersal," 1742–48.

64.  Theodore G. Schurr et al., "Amerindian Mitochondrial DNAs Have Rare Asian Mutations at High Frequencies, Suggesting They Derived from Four Primary Maternal

Lineages," *American Journal of Human Genetics* 46 (1990): 613–23; Antonio Torroni et al., "Native American Mitochondrial DNA Analysis Indicates That the Amerind and the Nadene Populations Were Founded by Two Independent Migrations," *Genetics* 130 (1992): 153–62; Satoshi Horai et al., "Peopling of the Americas, Founded by Four Major Lineages of Mitochondrial DNA," *Molecular Biology and Evolution* 10 (1993): 23–47; Rickards et al., "mtDNA History of the Cayapa Amerinds," 519–30.

65. Peter Forster et al., "Origin and Evolution of Native American mtDNA Variation: A Reappraisal," *American Journal of Human Genetics* 59 (1996): 935–45; Rosaria Scozzari et al., "mtDNA and Y Chromosome-Specific Polymorphisms in Modern Ojibwa: Implications about the Origin of Their Gene Pool," *American Journal of Human Genetics* 60 (1997): 241–44.

66. Antonio Torroni, "Mitochondrial DNA and the Origin of Native Americans," in *America Past, America Present: Genes and Languages in the Americas and Beyond,* ed. Colin Renfrew (Cambridge: McDonald Institute for Archaeological Research, 2000), 77–87.

67. Antonio Torroni et al., "Classification of European mtDNAs from an Analysis of Three European Populations," *Genetics* 144 (1996): 1835–50; Michael D. Brown et al., "mtDNA Haplogroup X: An Ancient Link between Europe/Western Asia and North America?" *American Journal of Human Genetics* 63 (1998): 1852–61.

68. Brown et al., "mtDNA Haplogroup X," 1852–61.

69. Ruth D. Easton et al., "mtDNA Variation in the Yanomami: Evidence for Additional New World Founding Lineages," *American Journal of Human Genetics* 59 (1996): 213–25.

70. Brown et al., "mtDNA Haplogroup X," 1852–61.

71. Torroni, "Mitochondrial DNA," 77–87.

72. Virginia Morell, "Kennewick Man's Trials Continue," *Science* 280 (1998): 190–92.

73. Virginia Morell, "Genes May Link Ancient Eurasians, Native Americans," *Science* 280 (1998): 520. I am not going to suggest that the Native American version of haplogroup X may be that of the tribe of Lehi; such a claim could not be substantiated, especially if there is a link with the confirmed age of Kennewick man. Nevertheless, the presence of haplogroup X and a Caucasoid skeleton in the Americas leaves open a possibility that other lineages besides those of Asian descent may have contributed to the ancient admixture of the Native American human population. Thus, far from suggesting otherwise, haplogroup X demonstrates that a migration such as Lehi's is not far-fetched but is actually consistent with current DNA evidence. However, as discussed above, this *proves* nothing.

74. Miroslava V. Derenko et al., "The Presence of Mitochondrial Haplogroup X in Altaians from South Siberia," *American Journal of Human Genetics* 69 (2001): 237–41.

75. Namely, Murphy, "Lamanite Genesis, Genealogy, and Genetics," 57–58.

76. Derenko et al., "Presence of Mitochondrial Haplogroup X," 237–41.

77. As presented in ibid.

78. Suggested by Murphy, "Lamanite Genesis, Genealogy, and Genetics," 57–58.

79. Barbujani, "DNA Variation and Language Affinities," 1011–14.

80. Rickards et al., "mtDNA History of the Cayapa Amerinds," 519–30.

81. Angélica González-Oliver et al., "Founding Amerindian Mitochondrial DNA Lineages in Ancient Maya from Xcaret, Quintana Roo," *American Journal of Physical*

*Anthropology* 116 (2001): 230–35.

82.  Torroni et al., "Native American Mitochondrial DNA Analysis," 153–62.

83.  James V. Neel, Robert J. Biggar, and Rem I. Sukernik, "Virologic and Genetic Studies Relate Amerind Origins to the Indigenous People of the Mongolia/Manchuria/ Southeastern Siberia Region," *Proceedings of the National Academy of Sciences, USA* 91 (1994): 10737–41; Connie J. Kolman, Nyamkhishig Sambuughin, and Eldredge Bermingham, "Mitochondrial DNA Analysis of Mongolian Populations and Implications for the Origin of New World Founders," *Genetics* 142 (1996): 1321–34; Bonatto and Salzano, "Single and Early Migration," 1866–71.

84.  Derenko et al., "Presence of Mitochondrial Haplogroup X," 237–41.

85.  Dorit, Akashi, and Gilbert, "Absence of Polymorphism at the *ZFY* Locus," 1183–85; Michael F. Hammer, "A Recent Common Ancestry for Human Y-chromosomes," *Nature* 378 (1995): 376–78.

86.  Nei and Livshits, "Genetic Relationships," 276–81.

87.  Dorit, Akashi, and Gilbert, "Absence of Polymorphism at the *ZFY* Locus," 1183–85; Hammer, "Recent Common Ancestry," 376–78; Peter A. Underhill et al., "A Pre-Columbian Y Chromosome-Specific Transition and Its Implications for Human Evolutionary History," *Proceedings of the National Academy of Sciences, USA* 93 (1996): 196–200; Simon Tavaré et al., "Inferring Coalescence Times from DNA Sequence Data," *Genetics* 145 (1997): 505–18.

88.  See, for example, B. M. Ciminelli et al., "Recurrent Simple Tandem Repeat Mutations during Human Y-Chromosome Radiation in Caucasian Subpopulations," *Journal of Molecular Evolution* 41 (1995): 966–73; Michael F. Hammer and S. Horai, "Y Chromosomal DNA Variation and the Peopling of Japan," *American Journal of Human Genetics* 56 (1995): 951–62; Amanda B. Spurdle and Trefor Jenkins, "The Origins of the Lemba 'Black Jews' of Southern Africa: Evidence from p12F2 and Other Y-Chromosome Markers," *American Journal of Human Genetics* 59 (1996): 1126–33.

89.  E. S. Poloni et al., "Human Genetic Affinities for Y-Chromosome P49a,F/*Taq*I Haplotypes Show Strong Correspondence with Linguistics," *American Journal of Human Genetics* 61 (1997): 1015–35.

90.  Fabricio R. Santos et al., "The Central Siberian Origin for Native American Y-chromosomes," *American Journal of Human Genetics* 64 (1999): 619–28.

91.  Maria-Catira Bortolini et al., "Y-Chromosome Evidence for Differing Ancient Demographic Histories in the Americas," *American Journal of Human Genetics* 73 (2003): 524–39; Tatiana M. Karafet et al., "Ancestral Asian Source(s) of New World Y-Chromosome Founder Haplotypes," *American Journal of Human Genetics* 64 (1999): 817–31; Andrés Ruiz-Linares et al., "Microsatellites Provide Evidence for Y-Chromosome Diversity among the Founders of the New World," *Proceedings of the National Academy of Sciences, USA* 96 (1999): 6312–17.

92.  Santos et al., "Central Siberian Origin," 619–28.

93.  Morell, "Kennewick Man's Trials Continue," 190–92.

94.  Morell, "Genes May Link Ancient Eurasians, Native Americans," 520.

95.  Karafet et al., "Ancestral Asian Source(s)," 829. The internal references refer to Cann, Stoneking, and Wilson, "Mitochondrial DNA and Human Evolution," 31–36;

Rosalind M. Harding et al., "Archaic African *and* Asian Lineages in the Genetic Ancestry of Modern Humans," *American Journal of Human Genetics* 60 (1997): 772–89; Henry C. Harpending et al., "Genetic Traces of Ancient Demography," *Proceedings of the National Academy of Sciences, USA* 95 (1998): 1961–67.

96. Dorit, Akashi, and Gilbert, "Absence of Polymorphism at the *ZFY* Locus," 1183–85; Hammer, "Recent Common Ancestry," 376–78; Karafet et al., "Ancestral Asian Source(s)," 817–31.

97. For example, Ruiz-Linares et al., "Microsatellites Provide Evidence," 6312–17.

98. Tatiana Karafet et al., "Y Chromosome Markers and Trans–Bering Strait Dispersals," *American Journal of Physical Anthropology* 102 (1997): 301–14.

99. Karafet et al., "Ancestral Asian Source(s)," 817–31.

100. Santos et al., "Central Siberian Origin," 619–28; Karafet et al., "Ancestral Asian Source(s)," 817–31.

101. Richard L. Jantz and Douglas W. Owsley, "Reply to Van Vark et al.: Is European Upper Paleolithic Cranial Morphology a Useful Analogy for Early Americans?" *American Journal of Physical Anthropology* 121 (2003): 185.

102. For example, J. Koji Lum et al., "Mitochondrial and Nuclear Genetic Relationships among Pacific Island and Asian Populations," *American Journal of Human Genetics* 63 (1998): 613–24; Karafet et al., "Ancestral Asian Source(s)," 817–31; Hiroki Oota et al., "Human mtDNA and Y-Chromosome Variation Is Correlated with Matrilocal versus Patrilocal Residence," *Nature Genetics* 29 (2001): 20–21; Bortolini et al., "Y-Chromosome Evidence," 524–39.

103. Lum et al., "Mitochondrial and Nuclear Genetic Relationships," 613–24.

104. For example, see Jared M. Diamond, "Express Train to Polynesia," *Nature* 336 (1988): 307–8, and John E. Terrell, Terry L. Hunt, and Chris Gosden, "The Dimensions of Social Life in the Pacific: Human Diversity and the Myth of the Primitive Isolate," *Current Anthropology* 38 (1997): 155–96, respectively.

105. For a more comprehensive review, see Cann, "Genetic Clues to Dispersal," 1742–48.

106. Lum et al., "Mitochondrial and Nuclear Genetic Relationships," 613–24.

107. Oota et al., "Human mtDNA and Y-Chromosome Variation," 20–21.

108. Mark T. Seielstad, Eric Minch, and L. Luca Cavalli-Sforza, "Genetic Evidence for a Higher Female Migration Rate in Humans," *Nature Genetics* 20 (1998): 278–80.

109. Oota et al., "Human mtDNA and Y-Chromosome Variation," 20–21.

110. Ibid.

111. Seielstad, Minch, and Cavalli-Sforza, "Genetic Evidence," 278–80.

112. For example, Karafet et al., "Ancestral Asian Source(s)," 817–31; Bortolini et al., "Y-Chromosome Evidence," 524–39.

113. For example, Murphy, "Lamanite Genesis, Genealogy, and Genetics," 47–77.

114. For example, Templeton, "Out of Africa," 45–51; Rickards et al., "mtDNA History of the Cayapa Amerinds," 519–30.

# Who Are the Children of Lehi?

*D. Jeffrey Meldrum and Trent D. Stephens*

The questions Who are the children of Lehi? and How can we reconcile Book of Mormon perspectives with modern DNA data? are issues of great importance to a number of Latter-day Saints and other people. We present this essay in an attempt to facilitate some reconciliation. Our perspective is that of active members of the Church of Jesus Christ of Latter-day Saints who view the Book of Mormon as an accurate, correct account of actual historic events that occurred on the American continent. We are also biologists. Although we are both involved in research outside the immediate field of human genetics, our backgrounds and training include firm foundations in genetics, including human and population genetics. As biologists we accept the published data dealing with Native American origins and view those data as reasonably representing American-Asian connections. Only by understanding the nature of inheritance, however, can one reconcile a written record with a genetic profile of an individual or group.

We propose that the Abrahamic covenant, by which all the families of the earth would be blessed through Abraham (see Abraham 2:11), applied to the children of Lehi in much the same way that it applied to the children of Israel, as leaven within bread. The leaven is, of necessity, only a small ingredient in bread, not the bread itself. We propose that the children of Lehi are the leaven of the Abrahamic covenant in the New World, unlikely to be detected by genetic analysis of modern New World inhabitants.

## A Covenant People

The Judeo-Christian Bible recounts Jehovah's relationship with his chosen people up to the New Testament era. Through the patriarchs, the God of the Old Testament established a covenant with the believing posterity of Adam. That covenant was in turn established with Abraham, promising that his seed would be as numerous as the sands of the sea and that through his seed all families and all nations of the earth would be blessed (see Genesis 12:2–3; 22:18). It was written that, before the foundations of the world were laid, the inheritance of nations was set according to the number of the children of Israel (see Deuteronomy 32:8).

The prophet Isaiah, whose vision seemed to penetrate the veil of time, marked history largely by the scattering and gathering of the house of Israel. The Lord said of him: "Great are the words of Isaiah. For surely he spake as touching all things concerning my people, which are of the house of Israel" (3 Nephi 23:1–2). He and others saw Israel sifted throughout the nations of the world much like leaven in a loaf of bread, dispersing the promises of the covenant and the hope for a Redeemer to the four quarters of the earth (see Isaiah 5:13; Amos 9:9). Isaiah saw the people of Israel eventually gathered and reestablished as a people in the latter days (see Isaiah 11:10–16).

From the Hebrews' own ethnocentric perspective, they occupied center stage in the world drama as God's covenant people. However, from the point of view of their immediate neighbors, let alone the rest of the world, they were a minor, clannish people who happened to occupy a strategic geographic nexus between two centers of civilization, Egypt and Mesopotamia, but were otherwise of little historical consequence. The two greatest kings of Israel, David and Solomon, left hardly a trace in the archaeological record. And yet, rather surprisingly, much of the world has been and continues to be influenced by Israel's history. Perhaps most significantly, the person regarded by an important fraction of the world populace as the Savior of humankind, Jesus of Nazareth, was born through the house of Israel.

Calendars now pivot upon that event. Not long after his crucifixion by the hands of the Romans, many Jews were scattered, as the kingdoms of Israel and of Judah had been before them. The reckoning of time by Christians throughout the world since then has pointed to the day when the Lord would stretch forth his arm to once again gather in his people, the lost sheep of Israel, in prelude to his return.

In spite of the perception of ethnocentricity and elitism among historical and modern Jews, the original notion of a covenant people was a spiritual and religious concept rather than a strictly ethnic or genealogical identity. The covenant binds together all those who have accepted the terms of belief and behavior. Those not born into the house of Israel were not of necessity excluded; they could be partakers of the covenant through "adoption." For Christians, "they which are of faith . . . are the children of Abraham" (Galatians 3:7). The biblical book of Ruth tells the story of a woman of Moabite descent who was the great-grandmother of David. She declared these immortal words to her mother-in-law, Naomi: "Whither thou goest, I will go; and where thou lodgest, I will lodge; thy people shall be my people, and thy God my God" (Ruth 1:16). The gene pool of the house of Israel was, from its earliest history, a melting pot of ethnicities and nationalities. For example, Joseph, the favored son of Jacob, who, according to the Hebrew records, became second only to Pharaoh, took an Egyptian wife. Therefore all of his children, including Ephraim and Manasseh, and their descendants were of "mixed blood." It seems very likely that considerable mixing with the Egyptian gene pool occurred during the several centuries that the Israelites were enslaved in Egypt. Interestingly, this enslavement, so important in the Hebrew lineage record, is not at all mentioned in Egyptian records.

This Joseph, son of Jacob, foretold that a remnant of his seed would be preserved and inherit a land of promise. The principal characters in the Book of Mormon are said to be that remnant, "branches run[ning] over the wall," the "other sheep" of which Christ himself spoke (Genesis 49:22; John 10:16). By their account they heard the voice of the Shepherd and made record of it. The Book of Mormon asserts to be another testament of Christ, bearing record, as a voice from the dust, of his dealings with this American branch of the house of Israel, transplanted to the Western Hemisphere.

The Book of Mormon explicitly relates an account of the exodus of a small band of Israelites, consisting of two families led by father Lehi, out of the doomed city of Jerusalem soon after the year 600 BC This remnant of Joseph journeyed through the wilderness and across the sea to make a new home in a promised land, a place within the lands we now refer to as the Americas. From the children of Lehi arose two principal cultures, the Nephites and the Lamanites, who play out a drama fraught with wars and contentions. Notice we have said two cultures, not lineages. These were cultural-political-religious groups, not necessarily restricted to particular lineal descent, that soon encompassed varied populations, some made mention of and, very likely, some that went largely or completely unmentioned in Mormon's abridged record of the Nephites.[1] What is curious is the occasional pointed declaration by a prominent character that he is a direct descendant of Lehi. This would seem to be stating the obvious, unless there were an implicit acknowledgement of extensive intermingling with other people in the region who were not the children of Lehi. Ultimately, the Nephite culture was corrupted from within and overpowered from without and the Nephites were hunted virtually to extinction, but not before hiding up a record and a testament that would one day come forth, in part to convince the remnant of the Lamanites that Jesus is the Christ (see Book of Mormon title page). And yet this brief synopsis, so familiar to Latter-day Saints, does little to convey the convoluted history and complexities of the cultural, political, and genealogical relationships of the Book of Mormon peoples. It fails to acknowledge the subtle but persistent allusions to the more expansive stage and cast that fall just beyond the immediate purview of the record keepers, who lacked the benefit of modern transportation and telecommunication that we in today's modern world so easily take for granted.

A superficial consideration of the Book of Mormon account has led to misconceptions about its scope and context. A tradition apparently has persisted in the Latter-day Saint community, from the time the Book of Mormon first appeared in print in the 19th century, that all Native Americans are Lehi's direct descendants. This assumption seems to have been held by many early members of the Church of Jesus Christ of Latter-day Saints and is still held by most today. Although the idea that Native Americans are exclusively descended from the remnant of the "Lamanites" is not required by the scriptures, in the face of modern scientific research it has caused some to question the credibility of the Book of Mormon.

The modern era of molecular biology has ushered in new approaches to the study of human populations that some have hoped may shed light on Book of Mormon historicity. The notion has arisen that modern DNA research will either vindicate or refute the Book of Mormon as a record of some or all the ancient inhabitants of the Americas, whether to bolster one's own faith, to persuade the nonbeliever, or, conversely, to justify one's own rejection of the document as an ancient historical record and evidence of the restoration of the gospel through the prophet Joseph Smith.

## The Science of Native American Origins

The question of North American origins emerged soon after it became clear that the Americas were not the eastern shores of the Orient. As early as 1589, José de Acosta, a Jesuit missionary in South America, proposed that so-called Native Americans had migrated to the Americas from Siberia thousands of years ago.[2] Georges Louis Leclerc, Comte de Buffon, one of the leading early naturalists, proposed in 1749 that Asians and American Indians shared a common origin and that the New World was populated by people who had migrated from Asia.[3] Later in the same century, Johann Friedrich

Blumenbach proposed that the American Indians were descended from Mongols of northeast Asia. He suggested that the colonization occurred in several waves of migration.

Michael Crawford, from the Department of Anthropology at the University of Kansas, who has conducted extensive human population genetic research in the islands of the Bering Strait, argues that these "waves of migration" continued until the mid-20th century. He states: "Up to World War II, Alaskan Eskimos crossed the winter ice pack into Siberia to obtain wives. It is my contention that social contacts persisted in the Norton Sound region between the Eskimo groups of both sides of the Bering Strait and that complete reproductive isolation between the Old and New Worlds is a myth."[4]

Crawford is a major contributor to work in the field of Native American origins. He published an excellent book in 1998 in which he reviewed the voluminous history of research concerning those origins (his book has been cited by several researchers in the field as a recommended review of the subject, and we highly recommend it to anyone who is looking for more detailed information concerning these issues). Crawford reviewed the genetic data from human blood groups, serum proteins, red-blood-cell proteins, immunoglobulins, histocompatibility proteins, DNA polymorphisms—including mitochondrial DNA (mtDNA) and both coding and noncoding regions of nuclear DNA—and Y-chromosome markers. He pointed out that, by 1998, population genetic studies had been conducted for 341 different proteins.[5] In some cases, polymorphisms were either insufficient between populations or too great within populations to be useful in human population studies. There were several genetic markers, however, that provided powerful tests of hypotheses concerning human populations. Crawford concluded that "a considerable body of scientific evidence has been compiled about the origins of these [New World] populations. This evidence indicates extremely strong biological and cultural affinities between New World and Asian populations and leaves no doubt that the first migrants into the Americas were Asians, possibly from Siberia."[6]

Since the publication of Crawford's book, well over 40 additional papers have appeared in the literature addressing issues of Native American origins. Most are essentially consistent with the findings published before 1998. The data accumulated to date indicate that 99.6 percent of Native American genetic markers studied so far exhibit Siberian connections.

But what about the so-called X haplotype? Could that be evidence for a European or Middle Eastern connection to Native Americans? The term *haplotype* is a contraction of the phrase *haploid genotype*. Haplotypes are commonly used in population genetics to compare individuals within and among populations. A haplogroup is a set of related haplotypes that share the same group of alleles or DNA polymorphisms. It is usually assumed that the members of a haplogroup, sharing a common haplotype, form a single lineage; that is, they are all descended from a common ancestor from which the haplotype is derived. Antonio Torroni and Douglas Wallace stated in 1995 that 718 of 743 (96.6 percent) Native American mtDNA polymorphisms studied to that date fell into one of four haplogroups: A, B, C, and D. The remaining 25 exhibited other mtDNA variations.[7] Anne C. Stone and Mark Stoneking examined the nuclear and mtDNA from 20 individuals buried in a 700-year-old cemetery in Illinois.[8] They found that the population exhibited all four of the major modern Native American haplogroups (A, B, C, D), as well as a fifth (probably X; see discussion to follow). They concluded that no major mtDNA markers were lost between 1300 AD and the present, in spite of the severe population decline. They also proposed that the major markers were not introduced into the population by modern Europeans.

Graciela Bailliet and coworkers in 1994 proposed that as many as ten possible mtDNA founder haplotypes gave rise to Native American populations.[9] Four of those ten would have given rise to the four major haplogroups, whereas the other six haplotypes would exist among the 3.4 percent of the population not among the major haplogroups. In 1996 Torroni and coworkers identified ten haplogroups (designated H, I, J, K, M, T, U, V, W, and X) among three European populations.[10] Haplogroup X was present in 4 percent of the population. Peter Forster and others stated in 1996 that they would call the major Native American haplogroup, which was previously referred to as "other," haplogroup X.[11] They proposed that this haplogroup was Siberian in origin. In 1998 Michael Brown and others asserted that the X haplotype of the Forster study was the same as the X haplotype in the Torroni European study. They noted, "Our analysis confirmed that haplogroup X is present in both modern Native Americans and European populations."[12] The Brown study also demonstrated that haplogroup X was clearly of ancient origin. Moreover, they concluded, "Overall, these data exclude the possibility that the occurrence of haplogroup X in Native Americans is due to recent European admixture and, instead, provide a rigorous demonstration that this haplogroup represents an additional founding mtDNA lineage in Native Americans."[13]

The antiquity of haplogroup X in the Americas was confirmed in 2002 when R. S. Malhi and David Smith identified a 1,300-year-old person discovered along the Columbia River near Vantage, Washington, as belonging to haplogroup X. Their finding "confirms the hypothesis that haplogroup X is a founding lineage."[14]

The implications were interesting, to say the least: an ancient European haplogroup in Native American populations? Brown and his colleagues asked the obvious question: "Where did this haplogroup originate? Thus far, haplogroup X has not been detected in numerous Asian/Siberian populations."[15] They went on to say, "Haplogroup X is remarkable in that it has not been found in Asians, including Siberians, suggesting that it may have come to the Americas via a Eurasian migration."[16] The possibility that one of the five founding groups had ancient European connections was exciting, and controversial. Even the popular press picked up on it. Some Latter-day Saint scholars hoped that this was evidence of the long-awaited link to the Middle East, ignoring the fact that Brown and his associates proposed that haplotype X arrived in North America 20,000 to 30,000 years ago. The controversy was largely put to rest in 2001 when Miroslava Derenko and his fellow researchers found haplogroup X in south Siberia (although in only 3.5 percent of the population).[17]

Haplogroup X accounted for 3 percent of the Native American population studied to date. Added to the 96.6 percent accounted for by haplogroups A, B, C, and D, that left only 0.4 percent of Native Americans so far studied unaccounted for. As expressed by Smith and his colleagues, most researchers believe that the origins of 99.6 percent of Native Americans are accounted for now by five haplogroups: A, B, C, D, and X.

The limited data garnered from studies so far of human populations, in concert with archaeological and anthropological studies, have largely confirmed the scientific hypothesis that northeast Asia is the primary source of the majority of the early inhabitants of the Americas. This conclusion has led to the establishment of a paradigm of Native American origins. There has been little if any evidence seriously considered by the mainstream scientific community that would indicate a Middle East origin, or any other source of origin, for the majority of contemporary Native Americans. What are the implications of this lack of accepted empirical support for the claim of the Book of Mormon?

## Hypotheses of Native American Origins

At least three major hypotheses can (and have) been advanced concerning Native American origins:

1. All Native Americans are of Asian origin. (This has been the predominant hypothesis of mainstream science since the late 16th century.)

2. All Native Americans are of Middle Eastern origin. (This hypothesis is that advocated by people who accept the Book of Mormon account.)

3. Most Native Americans are of Asian origin, whereas some small subset is of Middle Eastern origin. This latter hypothesis has two subservient hypotheses:

a. No genetic evidence of the Middle Eastern subset has been found, but will eventually

b. No genetic evidence of the Middle Eastern subset has been found, and probably never will be found.

Hypotheses 1 and 2 are testable by direct, scientific methods. The genetic constitution of the extant Native American population has been extensively tested. The data support hypothesis number 1 and refute hypothesis 2. Hypothesis 3 is more problematic and may not be testable. Why? Because a very small population introduced into a larger population may or may not be identifiable, depending on whether any specific genetic markers for that population were transferred to the main population. The X haplotype is an example of such a potential genetic marker. Because haplotype X had not been found in Asian populations prior to 2001, it remained as a possible marker brought into the population from Europe or the Middle East. The discovery that haplotype X existed in south Siberia ended most inquires into its source. This observation was consistent with the hypothesis that all Native Americans originated in Asia. The X haplotype, however, was present in only 3.5 percent of the south Siberian population, an area from which the other four haplotypes were not proposed to have originated. Although the observation was consistent with the hypothesis, the prospect that the Native American X haplotype was actually derived from the Siberian X haplotype, and not from the European X haplotype, has never been, and probably never can be, established.

Although the principle of parsimony in science states that the simplest explanation is preferred, that explanation is not necessarily the correct one. It is, however, the explanation accepted by science until additional data refute it. The data collected to date, when considered in the context of the principles of population genetics, do not exclude the possibility of other gene sources not detected in the limited sampling of extant populations. One or more relatively small populations, now extinct or genetically swamped out in the gene pool of the Western Hemisphere, could have existed but are no longer apparent. The limitations on the potential for data collection mean that some hypotheses of Native American origins cannot be tested by DNA research.

While the singular assumption or interpretation that all modern Native Americans are direct lineal descendants of the dominant Book of Mormon peoples may be set aside by modern molecular evidence, it is a very different matter to take the additional step to assert that the DNA data refute the claim of the Book of Mormon to be a historical document. Such a conclusion ignores the complex relationships described in the Book of Mormon and the limitations of the sampled genetic data. Nor is it likely that any scientific data will be forthcoming to resolve the question empirically one way or the other. The necessary experiment simply cannot be designed that would refute the historicity of the Book of Mormon, as the record of a small, isolated population, on the basis of DNA studies and population genetics.

We propose that the Book of Mormon is the account of a small group of people who lived on the American continent, interacting to some degree with the indigenous population but relatively isolated from the general historical events occurring elsewhere in the Americas. What DNA evidence might exist today of such a group? What are the implications if no molecular evidence ever emerges that such a group ever existed? How small does a population have to be before it is swamped out or killed off by a larger population, leaving no genetic trace? Does the absence of such evidence compel us to assume that no such group existed? Do the sciences of population genetics and molecular biology give us any direction for addressing questions such as these?

## Heredity and Heritage

Although it has been more than 100 years since Gregor Mendel's foundational work in heredity was discovered, most people do not understand all the implications of inheritance. Many people still adhere to the old concept of "bloodlines," the notion that in some small way we all carry some tiny bit of organic information from each and every one of our ancestors. According to this concept, popular in the 19th century, bloodlines are mixed through matings, much as one would mix a cocktail, so that although a given ancestral line may be faint, it should still be detectable in the blood of the descendant.

To describe ancestral lines and inheritance patterns, we present here, as an example, one of our family histories, that of Trent Stephens, presented in first person: Julia Ann Buchanan was my mother's mother. Her great-grandfather, John Buchanan III, came to America in 1800 from Ramelton, Donegal, Ireland. His third great-grandfather, George Buchanan (b. 1648) of Blairlusk, Scotland, was a Presbyterian Covenanter who fought against James Scott, Duke of Monmouth and contender for the English crown, at the Battle of Bothwell Bridge in the summer of 1680. After the Scottish defeat, George gave all his holdings in Scotland to his brother William and fled to Ireland. Ten generations separate me from this George Buchanan, a Presbyterian patriot or Scottish rebel, depending on which side of the bridge you stood.

I have, as does everyone else, 1,024 ancestor slots in the 10th generation back. The actual number of ancestors filling those slots is often not quite 1,024 because of multiple descent from the same ancestor. For example, I am descended through two lines from Alexander Stephens (my second great-grandfather on one line and third great-grandfather on another line). To my knowledge, however, my descent from George Buchanan is by only one line. The progenitors of Alexander Stephens, from whom I am descended by two lines, would each occupy two slots rather than one in the 10th generation. However, someone like George Buchanan, from whom only one line descends to me, would still occupy only one slot of the 1,024. The size of the genome in the euchromatin of every living human, or for any human that has ever lived, is approximately 30,000 genes, with at least two alleles for each gene (some genes have multiple copies in the genome, and additional genes may yet be discovered in the heterochromatin). Considering a minimum of 60,000 alleles, there are 61,440,000 allelic slots in the 10th generation, from which my 60,000 alleles were randomly selected. The chance, therefore, of my inheriting any single allele from George Buchanan is 60,000 in 61,440,000 or 1 in 1,024. The probability of my inheriting any single allele from the 10th generation in the line of Alexander Stephens, from whom I descend twice, is twice as great, or 1 in 512.

The same probability applies to inheriting any one of George Buchanan's 44 autosomal chromosomes. Of 45,056 chromosomal slots in the 10th generation back, the probability of my inheriting any one of George Buchanan's chromosomes is 44 in 45,056, or 1 in 1,024.

The same probability, however, does not apply to the sex chromosomes, the X and Y chromosomes. My Y chromosome, derived from my paternal line only, comes directly from Thomas Stephens (b. 1610) of England, in the 10th generation. My X chromosome comes from my mother, who obtained it from either her father or mother. Each woman carries two X chromosomes, one inherited from her maternal line and one from her father's maternal line. Each man inherits only one X chromosome, which comes from his mother. Therefore, the ancestry of the X chromosome is less certain than that of the Y chromosome, or for that matter of mtDNA, but more certain than that of the autosomal chromosomes. Every male and female alike inherit their mtDNA strictly from their maternal line. My mtDNA comes from a Mrs. Vandenberg, 10 generations ago, born about 1657 in New York.

Ten more generations back along the Buchanan line takes me to Walter, 11th laird of Buchanan, born in 1338. The probability of my inheriting any one allele or chromosome from Walter is 1 in 1,048,576.

Ten more generations back brings me to Anselan Buey O'Kyan, 1st laird of Buchanan, who was born in Ireland in AD 980. He came to Scotland to escape the Viking raids in Ireland, then helped Malcolm II, king of Scotland, fight against the Vikings in Scotland. (Some of the Vikings he fought against may have also been my ancestors because I am descended, through several lines, from the Normans.) For his service to the king, Anselan was given, in AD 1016, the hand of Dennistoun, heiress to the Buchanan lands on the east bank of Loch Lomen. My chances of inheriting an allele or chromosome from Anselan or Dennistoun, 30 generations and 1,000 years ago, is 1 in 10,737,417,000, about as much chance as winning the lottery!

The Buchanan family is neither on my direct paternal line nor on my direct maternal line, so the chance of finding any genetic fingerprint linking me to Anselan Buey O'Kyan is about 1 in 11 billion. The chance of finding a genetic fingerprint linking me to Walter Buchanan is 1 in 1 million; and to George Buchanan, 10 generations and a little more than 300 years ago, is 1 in 1,000. Those are not good odds if I am trying to identify genetic connections to even the most recent of these ancestors.

Do all these data indicate that the lairds of Buchanan are not my ancestors? Not at all! I am a direct lineal descendent of Anselan Buey O'Kyan as much as I am from any other of my ancestors of that era. My genealogy can be traced back, in this one line, to Anselan Buey O'Kyan, and for seven more generations beyond, to Fargallus, who was born in Ireland in AD 680. These lines are well established and documented, with dates and places. There is less than 1 chance in 10 billion, however, that my descent from Anselan can be confirmed genetically.

My paternal family line goes back only 13 generations before reaching a dead end, to Henry Stephens, born in England in 1497.

My Y chromosome, therefore, says that my ancestry is English, with no mention of my Scottish, Irish, French, or German heritage. My maternal line goes back only 10 generations to a Mrs. Vandenberg, born about 1657 in New York. I don't know where her maternal line originated. For the sake of argument, let's say that Jan Hendrichse Vandenberg married a Native American, not uncommon for that place and time. My mtDNA would show me descended from a Native American line, with no mention of my English, Scottish, Irish, French, or German heritage, even though Mrs. Vandenberg is only 1 of 1,024 ancestors in that generation.

Mitochondrial DNA and Y chromosome DNA reveal just a tiny slice of family history. Only 1 out of 4 great-grandfathers is represented in the Y chromosome, and only 1 great-grandmother in the mtDNA. Go back just five generations and only 1 of 16 forefathers is revealed. But am I not more closely related to my Stephens ancestors than to my Buchanan ancestors because that's my family name? No. With the exception of my Y chromosome, which came from my father, and my mtDNA and X chromosome, which came from my mother, all chromosomes and associated genes have an equal chance. One-half of my autosomal chromosomes came from my father, and one-half came from my mother. Half of each of their autosomal chromosomes came from each of their parents, but I did not get an equal mix from my four grandparents. I received approximately one-fourth of my chromosomes from each grandparent, but only approximately. For example, I may have inherited more Buchanan chromosomes from my mother than Behunin chromosomes (her paternal line), and I may have inherited more Stone chromosomes (my father's maternal line) from my father than Stephens chromosomes. Thus, although my name is Stephens, each of my cells could contain more Buchanan autosomal chromosomes than Stephens autosomal chromosomes. Such is the random nature of inheritance.

As a result of this random nature of inheritance and the extremely small probabilities that exist for inheriting any identifiable genetic material from a distant ancestor, we predict that finding a genetic marker for some given ancestor such as Father Israel or Father Lehi will be very unlikely. The spreading of Israelite genes throughout the world is apparently part of God's plan. Other than his promise to Abraham, however, we have little insight as to the reason. In light of what we now know about inheritance, we can be quite certain that finding the leaven in the bread will be next to impossible. It is extremely unlikely that we will ever identify the children of Lehi using genetic techniques.

### No More Strangers or Foreigners

It turns out, however, that genes are not the only things we inherit from our ancestors; they may not even be the most important things. The apostle Paul addressed the gentile converts to the fledgling apostolic church saying, "Now therefore ye are no more strangers and foreigners, but fellow citizens with the saints, and of the household of God" (Ephesians 2:19). This was not a genealogical relationship based on lineage or DNA. It made reference to the spiritual rebirth of the individual into the family of Christ. King Benjamin, from the Book of Mormon, spoke similarly to his people: "And now, because of the covenant which ye have made ye shall be called the children of Christ, his sons and his daughters; for behold, this day he hath spiritually begotten you; for ye say that your hearts are changed through faith on his name; therefore, ye are born of him and have become his sons and his daughters" (Mosiah 5:7).

In other words, lineage is not the only mechanism by which God's purposes on earth are to be accomplished, or his blessings realized. Lineage and genetics are a consequence of the means by which the human family fulfills its divine charge to multiply and replenish the earth. Genetics has tremendous influence on the individual and on the course of history, but it does not solely dictate one's potential in realizing the things of eternity. There are nongenetic factors that also exert tremendous influence on people's lives.

"What, after all, is so special about genes?" asks Richard Dawkins in his book *The Selfish Gene.* He continues:

> The answer is that they are replicators. The laws of physics are supposed to be true all over the accessible universe. Are there any principles of biology that are likely to have similar universal validity? . . . Obviously I do not know but, if I had to bet, I would put my money on one fundamental principle. This is the law that life evolves by the differential survival of replicating entities. The gene, the DNA molecule, happens to be the replicating entity that prevails on our planet. There may be others. . . .
>
> . . . I think that a new kind of replicator has recently emerged on this very planet. It is staring us in the face. It is still in its infancy, still drifting clumsily about in its primeval soup. . . .
>
> The new soup is the soup of human culture. We need a name for the new replicator, a noun that conveys the idea of a unit of cultural transmission, or a unit of imitation. 'Mimeme' comes from a suitable Greek root, but I want a monosyllable that sounds a bit like 'gene.' I hope my classicist friends will forgive me if I abbreviate mimeme to meme. If it is any consolation, it could alternatively be thought of as being related to 'memory,' or to the French word même. It should be pronounced to rhyme with 'cream.' Examples of memes are tunes, ideas, catch-phrases, clothes fashions, ways of making pots or of building arches.[18]

Susan Blackmore wrote in October 1998, in the preface to her book *The Meme Machine,* "I had read Dawkins' *The Selfish Gene* many years before but, I suppose, had dismissed the idea of memes as nothing more than a bit of fun." At least she took note of the term many others apparently skipped right over. "Suddenly [during a prolonged illness, while reading Dennett's *Darwin's Dangerous Idea* and a student's paper on memes] I realized that here was a powerful idea, capable of transforming our understanding of the human mind—and I hadn't even noticed it."[19] Blackmore continues:

> When you imitate someone else, something is passed on. This "something" can then be passed on again, and again, and so take on a life of its own. We might call this thing an idea, an instruction, a behaviour, a piece of information, . . . but if we are going to study it we shall need to give it a name. Fortunately, there is a name. It is the "meme."[20]

We present here an example of the importance of memes in the family of Trent Stephens, again in first person: My wife is adopted. She has two older brothers who are her full genetic siblings. All three of them were adopted by the Browns shortly after birth. The Browns were incapable of bearing children. Their obstetrician/gynecologist worked with an adoption agency to arrange for them to adopt a child. Arrangements were made with a woman who was expecting and who wanted to have the baby adopted. Everything was worked out before the baby was born, so the Browns were able to take their new little baby boy home from the hospital. About a year later, the Browns' doctor called to say that the same two people who were the genetic parents of their little boy were expecting another child. Did they want to adopt it? Yes, if it was a girl. It wasn't, but that no longer mattered. The happy parents took the new little baby boy home to grow up with his older brother. About a year later the circumstance was repeated. The Browns had planned to adopt only two children, but when they learned that the same couple was having another baby, they didn't even qualify their answer. "Yes, we'll take it." They brought the future Mrs. Kathleen Stephens home to meet her two older brothers.

All my wife knows about her biological parents is that they were of northern European stock, they were Catholic, and their three children were born in Portland, Oregon. That's all she wants to know. Her adoptive parents are Ray and June Brown. They are the most wonderful parents a girl, or son-in-law, for that matter, could have. My wife's older brother, Rocky, is an avid, active genealogist, doing research on the Brown family lines. We have all been to the temple doing work for their deceased ancestors.

Kathleen's father was not a member of the Church of Jesus Christ of Latter-day Saints when the children were born. Her mother was. When the children were still very young, her father joined the church. A year later the family went to the Idaho Falls Temple and was sealed for time and all eternity. Kathleen knows no more about the Catholic Church than most any other Latter-day Saint. She grew up with a strong Latter-day Saint heritage and is a devout member of the church. I know of few women who are stronger in the faith. It is her belief, and mine, that she was meant from the premortal existence to be with her brothers and her parents. Because her parents were not able to have children, she and her siblings came by another means to live with their loving parents.

My wife's patriarchal blessing tells her that she is "wellborn." She was blessed with a strong body, keen mind, and natural graces. She was also told that she is of the house of Israel, descended from Ephraim. She was told to be thankful to her Heavenly Father and to her earthly parents for "the wonderful things that have come to you because of your training and your upbringing." She was admonished to pass these things on to the next generation. Her being well-born, with a strong body and a keen mind, and being blessed with natural graces are her genetic heritage from unknown parents. Her training and upbringing, for which she is so grateful, are the heritage from her adoptive parents, as are the cultivation of her keen mind and the development of her natural graces. I see a number of mannerisms in her facial expressions and behaviors that remind me of her brothers. Her abilities to cook and sew, maintain a beautiful, cozy, comfortable home, and to raise her children with a strong sense of security and faith, come from her upbringing. Her natural grace and her ability to make and keep friends, which can lead to long telephone conversations, even with a stranger who has dialed the wrong number, probably come from a combination of her genetic background and her upbringing.

In my wife's case, and mine, I believe, memes are stronger than genes. The many wonderful things most important to her to pass on to the next generation, and the next, come from her upbringing. They are linked to her undying faith in her Savior Jesus Christ and her belief in the restored gospel. Our children's genes, a mixed heritage from my wife and me, as well as their upbringing, have made them strong willed and independent (probably my fault in both the genes and upbringing). That heritage has sometimes made it difficult for them to readily accept the wonderful things their mother has had to offer them. But, as her patriarchal blessing promised her, she has been able to hold her children close and teach them the gospel. The gospel is the strongest of all memes in our lives. After all, it was that meme that brought my wife's genes and mine together. We met on the front row of a Pearl of Great Price class at Brigham Young University. How much more strongly can memes influence genes than deciding what genes come together to produce the next generation?

President Boyd K. Packer recently spoke about patriarchal blessings. Quoting Elder John A. Widtsoe, he said:

> "In giving a blessing the patriarch may declare our lineage—
> that is, that we are of Israel, therefore of the family of
> Abraham, and of a specific tribe of Jacob. In the great majority
> of cases, Latter-day Saints are of the tribe of Ephraim, the tribe
> to which has been committed the leadership of the Latter-day
> work. Whether this lineage is of blood or adoption does not
> matter. . . . This is very important, for it is through the lineage
> of Abraham alone that the mighty blessings of the Lord for His
> children on earth are to be consummated." . . .
>
> Since there are many bloodlines running in each of us,
> two members of one family might be declared as being of different tribes in Israel.[21]

D. Jeffrey Meldrum is of the declared lineage of Ephraim, as are the remainder of his family with the exception of one sibling whose patriarchal blessing states that he is of the tribe of Benjamin.

Do Latter-day Saints whose patriarchal blessings state that they are of the tribe of Ephraim have any Israelite genetic markers? Would we expect them to? How would one identify such a marker without a standard of comparison? The tribe of Ephraim as a discrete population marched off the stage of history more than two and one-half millennia ago. There is no recognized population that would represent the gene pool of Ephraim from the time of the Assyrian conquest (722 BC). Each of us certainly has numerous "bloodlines," but the realization of the promises to Abraham and Israel has less to do with genetics and more to do with the transmission from one generation to the next of spiritual blessings and opportunities that transcend bloodlines.

Language is another example of the principle of memes. There is often poor correlation between the ordering of populations on the basis of language as compared to the ordering based on genetic traits. Frequently, populations that share a common or closely related language are not similarly closely related genetically. Nephi states that he was educated in the learning of the Jews and in the language of the Egyptians. Later we learn that the Book of Mormon records were kept in "reformed Egyptian." This written language had been handed down through the generations and altered according to the Nephites' manner of speech (see Mormon 9:32). It appears that only men of learning could read the records. The language of common usage by the Nephites was Hebrew, but it had been altered by them as well (see Mormon 9:33). King Benjamin had his three sons "taught in all the language of his fathers, that thereby they might become men of understanding" (Mosiah 1:2). Zeniff stated that he had been taught "in all the language of the Nephites" (Mosiah 9:1). Why would he have made that statement if there were no alternatives? Who among us, raised in the United States, would say in opening our autobiography, "I was taught English when I was young." Zeniff and his people lived for a time in close contact with the Lamanites, thus perhaps raising his perspective on a different language.

One way a language can be altered in a relatively short period of time is through extended contact and interaction with speakers of another language or languages and the incorporation of native words. This is especially true when the speakers of the original language find themselves in a foreign setting at a loss for words to describe unfamiliar objects and places. Of course, the influence works in both directions, and the native languages would be expected to quickly incorporate foreign words as well. It is therefore interesting to note the repeated observation of parallels to Hebrew in a number of Native American languages. Most recently, Brian Stubbs, a specialist in Near Eastern and Native American languages, has investigated parallels between Hebrew and Uto-Aztecan, a family of languages spoken in Mesoamerica. He proposes two hypotheses to explain the relationship between these two languages: (1) Uto-Aztecan was originally at its core a Near Eastern language but later was heavily influenced by non-Hebrew ("native") tongues, or (2) Uto-Aztecan began as the result of a Creole, or mix of languages, in which Hebrew was a significant to dominant component.[22]

In the history of the British Isles there is a striking parallel. The invaders who set themselves up as the overlords were Normans, Vikings from France who spoke an altered form of French. The commoners, the Britons, spoke the native Old English. The language of the commoners became altered by interactions with the French-speaking Normans. The language of the priests and the sacred records, the Bible, was Latin, accessible only to the learned. In the end it was the language of the common populace that won out—English. But in the process, the Old English of 1,200 years ago lost 85 percent of its vocabulary, leaving only 15 percent of the original Old English intact 1,000 years later.[23] Likewise, in Central America it appears to have been the language of the common populace that survived, although considerably altered, while the language of the elite, Hebrew, and the sacred language of the scriptures, a form of Egyptian, became extinct.

Evidence of contact, influence, or cultural legacy need not rely on genetic mechanisms of replication and transmission from one generation to the next or from one populace to another. Memes are an example of a nongenetic form of transmission. The Lamanite legacy of rejecting the covenant is unlikely to have left an obvious trail of genetic markers, but it is quite historical, and its influence will likely be found to extend across the generations.

### Divine Kinship

The principle of covenant was familiar—in fact, central—to the clannish ancient Israelites. The types and symbolisms are perhaps less apparent to us in today's society, except perhaps in a nationalistic sense, as in one's patriotism to homeland. The covenant originated, according to Frank Moore Cross, not only as a social means to regulate kin relationships but also as a legal means by which the duties and privileges of *kinship* may be extended to another individual or group.[24] Through a covenant with God, ancient Israel became the "kindred of Yahweh." Israel was converted or adopted into the family of God, with each person taking on mutual obligations. The principle of covenant was acknowledged in the Book of Mormon account as well. The prophet Alma, in recounting his conversion experience, said, quoting the Lord, "Marvel not that all mankind, yea, men and women, all nations, kindreds, tongues and people, must be born again; yea, born of God, . . . being redeemed of God, becoming his sons and daughters" (Mosiah 27:25).

Cross examines the relationship between the concepts of covenant and kinship further: "The social organization of the West Semitic tribal groups was grounded in kinship. Kinship relations defined the rights and obligations, the duties, status and privileges of tribal members. . . . Kinship was conceived in terms of one blood flowing through the veins of the kinship group. Kindred were of one flesh, one bone."[25]

The apostle Paul, in his famous letter to the gentile Christians of Galatia, made it plain that all people who are of the faith in Christ Jesus and baptized unto his name become the adopted seed of Abraham and heirs to the mission and joint heirs to the promise inherent in the Abrahamic covenant with God. It is the acceptance of and commitment to the binding terms of this covenant that justify the recognition of kinship. And yet what is on the surface a legalistic arrangement of kinship is considered by the kinsman as a blood kinship and treated accordingly.

The Lord declared to Abraham,

> I will make of thee a great nation, and I will bless thee above measure, and make thy name great among all nations, and thou shalt be a blessing unto thy seed after thee, that in their hands they shall bear this ministry and Priesthood unto all nations; and I will bless them through thy name; for as many as receive this Gospel shall be called after thy name, and shall be accounted thy seed, and shall rise up and bless thee, as their father. (Abraham 2:9–10)

But where is the archaeological or genetic evidence of Abraham? "Was there ever, thousands of years ago, a personage named Abraham," asked Tad Szulc, "whom more than three billion people—more than half of humanity—venerate as the father, patriarch, and spiritual ancestor of their faiths [2 billion Christians, 1.5 billion Muslims, 15 million Jews]?"[26] Neither in Babylon nor Egypt is an archaeological trace of Abraham to be found. Manfred Bietak, chairman of the Institute of Egyptology at the University of Vienna, said, "Absolutely blank. . . . As far as the Egyptians are concerned, . . . it's as if Abraham never set foot in the delta."[27] The study of the DNA of male Jews and Middle Eastern Arabs—among them Syrians, Palestinians, and Lebanese—shows to date that they share a common set of ancestors, but none can be specifically identified as Abraham. Bietak continued, "Today he still stands out as a unique spiritual figure, transcending the frontiers of great religions. However questionable the accuracy of the scriptures, however thin the archaeological and historical evidence, Jews, Christians, and Muslims still revere him as the patriarch."[28] The Abrahamic covenant is an example of a meme. That meme—Abraham's testimony of God—changed the world forever.

Ultimately, in a modern era of mobility and diversity, the matter comes down to one of personal commitment to values and beliefs, and participation in the fellowship of believers, while living among a broader community. It has less to do with genealogy or bloodlines or tribal affiliations. The Abrahamic covenant, reestablished as the new and everlasting covenant of the gospel of Jesus Christ, is extended to all. Those who embrace it become God's "people."

These concepts of kinship bear directly on the Book of Mormon account of a branch of Israel "run[ning] over the wall." The data suggest that a small colony under the leadership of Nephi established a kinship within the fabric of a larger resident population. In effect, it was a situation of "them and us"—Lamanites and Nephites. The Nephites were the believers, while the Lamanites were everyone else (see, for example, Jacob 1:14; Alma 3:11). This perception differs little from the concept of "Jew and Gentile," the latter term encompassing all non-Jews. With final destruction of the Nephite kinship, all who remained in the Americas were "Lamanites." If this interpretation is correct, then the statement from the introduction to the Book of Mormon, "After thousands of years, all were destroyed except the Lamanites, and they are the principal ancestors of the American Indians" is fully justified. All Native Americans are in fact descended from these "Lamanites"—these "Gentiles" of the record of Nephi's people. Lehi's prophecy to Laman and Lemuel was realized: their heritage of dissension continued, and their legacy never died out—in the Abrahamic sense or in the Buchanan context, even if their genetic markers may have.

According to God's promise to Abraham, remnants of the house of Israel have been scattered among all nations of the earth, like leaven in bread. Whereas leaven adds to the quality of the bread, too much leaven, to the point where it can be tasted in the bread, decreases the quality. We all benefit from our genetic and memic heritage from the house of Israel, but we probably will never find genetic traces of the leaven in most nations of the world. We probably will never find a genetic marker for the children of Lehi, for the children of Abraham, or even for the "Children of God." Ultimately we are impressed by the realization that the fundamental question of the veracity of the claims of the Book of Mormon lies beyond the ken of modern DNA research. The final implications of the book, as a witness of the prophetic calling of Joseph Smith and as another testament of the divinity of Jesus Christ, remain within the realm of faith and individual testimony.

# Notes

1. See John L. Sorenson, "When Lehi's Party Arrived in the Land, Did They Find Others There?" *Journal of Book of Mormon Studies* 1/1 (1992): 1–34.

2. See Sasha Nemecek, "Who Were the First Americans?" *Scientific American*, Sept. 2000, 81.

3. See Michael H. Crawford, *The Origins of Native Americans: Evidence from Anthropological Genetics* (Cambridge: Cambridge Univ. Press, 1998), 3.

4. Crawford, *Native Americans*, 88.

5. Crawford, *Native Americans*, 122.

6. Crawford, *Native Americans*, 3.

7. See Antonio Torroni and Douglas C. Wallace, "mtDNA Haplotypes in Native Americans," *American Journal of Human Genetics* 56/5 (1995): 1234–36.

8. Anne C. Stone and Mark Stoneking, "Analysis of Ancient DNA from a Prehistoric Amerindian Cemetery," in *Philosophical Transactions of the Royal Society of London*, series B, 354/1379 (1999): 153–59.

9. Graciela Bailliet et al., "Founder Mitochondrial Haplotypes in Amerindian Populations," *American Journal of Human Genetics* 55/1 (1994): 27–33.

10. Antonio Torroni et al., "Classification of European mtDNAs from an Analysis of Three European Populations," *Genetics* 144/4 (1996): 1835–50.

11. Peter Forster et al., "Origin and Evolution of Native American mtDNA Variation: A Reappraisal," *American Journal of Human Genetics* 59/4 (1996): 935–38.

12. Michael D. Brown et al., "mtDNA Haplogroup X: An Ancient Link between

Europe/ Western Asia and North America?" *American Journal of Human Genetics* 63/6 (1998): 1857.

13. Brown, "mtDNA Haplogroup X," 1853.

14. R. S. Malhi and D. G. Smith, "Haplotype X Confirmed in Prehistoric North America," *American Journal of Physical Anthropology* 119/1 (2002): 84–86.

15. Brown, "mtDNA Haplogroup X," 1857.

16. Brown, "mtDNA Haplogroup X," 1859.

17. Miroslavia V. Derenko et al., "The Presence of Mitochondrial Haplogroup X in Altaians from South Siberia," *American Journal of Human Genetics* 69/1 (2001): 237–41.

18. Richard Dawkins, *The Selfish Gene* (1976; reprint, Oxford: Oxford Univ. Press, 1989), 191–92.

19. Susan Blackmore, *The Meme Machine* (Oxford: Oxford Univ. Press, 1999), xix.

20. Blackmore, *Meme Machine*, 4.

21. Boyd K. Packer, "The Stake Patriarch," *Ensign*, Nov. 2002, 44–45.

22. John L. Sorensen, "Was There Hebrew Language in Ancient America? An Interview with Brian Stubbs," *Journal of Book of Mormon Studies* 9/2 (2000):54–63.

23. Albert C. Baugh and Thomas Cable, *A History of the English Language*, 4th ed. (Eaglewood Cliffs, N.J.: Prentice-Hall, 1993), 53.

24. Review of "God as Divine Kinsman: What Covenant Meant in Ancient Israel," by Frank Moore Cross, *Biblical Archaeology Review* (July/August 1999): 32ff.; and Frank Moore Cross, *From Epic to Canon: History and Literature in Ancient Israel* (Baltimore: Johns Hopkins University Press, 1998), 8.

25. Cross, *Epic to Canon*, 3.

26. Tad Szulc, "Abraham: Journey of Faith," *National Geographic*, Dec. 2001, 96.

27. Szulc, "Abraham," 118.

28. Szulc, "Abraham," 129.

# Nephi's Neighbors: Book of Mormon Peoples and Pre-Columbian Populations

*Matthew Roper*

The Book of Mormon describes the migration of three colonies from the Old World to the New. Two of these were small Israelite groups that migrated to an American land of promise around 600 BC. Many Latter-day Saint scholars interpret the Book of Mormon as a record of events that occurred in a relatively restricted region of ancient Mesoamerica. During and after those events, according to this view, peoples from this area—including some descendants of Book of Mormon peoples—may have spread to other parts of the Americas, carrying with them some elements of Mesoamerican culture. These Latter-day Saint scholars also believe that pre-Columbian populations of the Americas include within their ancestry many groups other than those small colonies mentioned in the Book of Mormon.[1]

A recent critic of the Church of Jesus Christ of Latter-day Saints has complained that "some LDS scholars, especially those associated with FARMS, . . . reinterpret Lamanite identity in the later part of the twentieth century"[2] and thereby "implicitly reject long-standing popular Mormon beliefs, including those held by Joseph Smith, about Lamanites being the ancestors of today's American Indians."[3] Of course, popular beliefs, longstanding or otherwise, are not crucial to the foundations of the faith of Latter-day Saints, which are based on revealed scripture.[4] In regard to the ancestry of the Amerindians, the central issue for Latter-day Saints is not whether Native Americans are in some measure descendants of Israel but whether their ancestors are *exclusively* Israelite. Latter-day scriptures speak of a remnant of those people described in the Book of Mormon and of their prophetic destiny, suggesting that this remnant may be found among Native American groups known perhaps to Joseph Smith and others. While these revelations affirm an Israelite component to Native American ancestry, they never claim that all the Native Americans' ancestors were Israelite, nor do they deny the presence of other peoples in pre-Columbian America.

In 1993, Elder Dallin H. Oaks of the Quorum of the Twelve Apostles made the following statement:

> Speaking for a moment as one whose profession is advocacy, I suggest that if one is willing to acknowledge the importance of faith and the reality of a realm beyond human understanding, the case for the Book of Mormon is the stronger case to argue. The case against the historicity of the Book of Mormon has to prove a negative. You do not prove a negative by prevailing on one debater's point or by establishing some subsidiary arguments.
>
> For me, this obvious insight goes back over forty years to the first class I took on the Book of Mormon at Brigham Young University. . . . Here I was introduced to the idea that the Book of Mormon is not a history of all of the people who have lived on the continents of North and South America in all ages of the earth. Up to that time I had assumed that it was. If that were the claim of the Book of Mormon, any piece of historical, archaeological, or linguistic evidence to the contrary would weigh in against the Book of Mormon, and those who rely exclusively on scholarship would have a promising position to argue.
>
> In contrast, if the Book of Mormon only purports to be an account of a few peoples who inhabited a portion of the Americas during a few millennia in the past, the burden of argument changes drastically. It is no longer a question of all versus none; it is a question of some versus none. In other words, in the circumstance I describe, the opponents of his-

toricity must prove that the Book of Mormon has no historical validity for any peoples who lived in the Americas in a
particular time frame, a notoriously difficult exercise. One
does not prevail on that proposition by proving that a particular . . . culture represents migrations from Asia. The op-
ponents of the historicity of the Book of Mormon must prove
that the people whose religious life it records did not live
anywhere in the Americas.[5]

Elder Oaks's observations, though made more than a decade
ago, underscore a fatal weakness in some recent arguments against
the Book of Mormon. Critics assume that genetic evidence—any genetic evidence—taken from any Native American population must
be shown to be Israelite, or the Book of Mormon's claims are false.
But there is no good reason to assume that Native American lineages
and ancestors must be *exclusively* Israelite. In regard to the nature
and identity of Lehi's people, Latter-day Saints have held a variety
of opinions and expressed several interpretations historically, but
whether *some* Native Americans, or *many* Native Americans, or even
*all* Native Americans have Lehi as an ancestor, it does not follow that
they did not have others.[6]

Although a few statements made by Joseph Smith are sometimes
used to justify the critics' complaints, they are not inconsistent with
the idea that other people came to the Americas in pre-Columbian
times. Also, a review of the development of Latter-day Saint ideas
about pre-Columbian peoples as they relate to the Book of Mormon
makes it clear that the idea that others resided in Lehi's promised
land is not a recent revisionist conclusion or a ploy to deflect recent
criticism. While not the only view, it is, in fact, an interpretation that
has been discussed and entertained in Latter-day Saint literature in
both the nineteenth and twentieth centuries. The very few scriptur-
ally based potential objections that critics have raised against this interpretation are overwhelmed by the countering scriptural evidence
presented below, all of which, I am persuaded, makes the best sense

under the assumption that there were other pre-Columbian peoples in the American land of promise.

## Joseph Smith and Indian Ancestry

In 1833 Joseph Smith penned a letter to the editor of the *American Revivalist and Rochester Observer* in which he described the Book of Mormon as follows:

> The Book of Mormon is a record of the forefathers of our western tribes of Indians; having been found through the ministration of an holy Angel, translated into our own language by the gift and power of God, after having been hid up in the earth for the last fourteen hundred years, containing the word of God which was delivered unto them. By it, we learn that our western tribes of Indians, are descendants from that Joseph that was sold into Egypt, and that the land of America is a promised land unto them.[7]

The Book of Mormon may indeed be said to be a record of the forefathers of the American Indians, but Joseph Smith never claimed that it was the only one, nor need we believe from this statement that the Book of Mormon accounts for all the ancestors of Native Americans.

In another statement made in 1835, Joseph Smith described the visit of an angel to him twelve years earlier: "He told me of a sacred record which was written on plates of gold. I saw in the vision the place where they were deposited. He said the Indians were the literal descendants of Abraham."[8] This statement affirms the claim that Native Americans are descendants of Abraham, but it does not follow that this is the whole story. My great-great-grandfather is John Whetten, but it would not be reasonable to assume that in making this statement I am declaring that I have no other ancestors. Joseph Smith's statement plainly allows for Abraham to be one ancestor among many others.

In his 1838 account of Moroni's visit, the Prophet recounted: "He said there was a book deposited, written upon gold plates, giving an account of the former inhabitants of this continent, and the source from whence they sprang; he also said that the fulness of the everlasting Gospel was contained in it, as delivered by the Savior to the ancient inhabitants" (Joseph Smith—History 1:34). Does this mean that the Book of Mormon tells us everything about Native American history and ancestry? Certainly not. While helping my family to move recently, I found a book giving an account of my ancestors who formerly inhabited this land and telling me where they came from. This book, which I had never seen before, gives an account of John Whetten, his family, and the Whetten line in my ancestry, but it says very little about my other ancestors: the Ropers, Mellors, Smiths, Van Wagonens, Gillespies, Hamblins, and so forth. While significant, that book tells only a small part of my family history. Similarly, one can accept Joseph Smith's description of the Book of Mormon as an account of the ancient inhabitants of the promised land without insisting that it tells about all of them.

In 1842, at the request of John Wentworth, Joseph Smith prepared a brief outline of the events surrounding the early history of the Church of Jesus Christ of Latter-day Saints. As part of this account, the Prophet described the visit of the angel Moroni in 1823.

> I was also informed concerning the aboriginal inhabitants of this country, and shown who they were, and from whence they came; a brief sketch of their origin, progress, civilization, laws, governments, of their righteousness and iniquity, and the blessings of God being finally withdrawn from them as a people was made known to me.[9]

Neither the Wentworth letter nor any other Joseph Smith account gives us a transcription of Moroni's actual words to Joseph Smith. Since Moroni offered Joseph Smith only a "brief sketch," it is unlikely that he revealed to Joseph a comprehensive knowledge of Native American origins. Within the context of introducing the plates, a more likely interpretation is that Moroni simply gave Joseph Smith a general description of the Book of Mormon story of Lehi's people who *came from* the land of Jerusalem. There is no need to read into this statement any more than this.

After giving an account of the visitation of Moroni, the Prophet provided a description of the Book of Mormon as follows:

> In this important and interesting book the history of ancient America is unfolded, from its first settlement by a colony that came from the tower of Babel, at the confusion of languages to the beginning of the fifth century of the Christian era. We are informed by these records that America in ancient times has been inhabited by two distinct races of people. The first were called Jaredites and came directly from the tower of Babel. The second race came directly from the city of Jerusalem, about six hundred years before Christ. They were principally Israelites, of the descendants of Joseph. The Jaredites were destroyed about the time that the Israelites came from Jerusalem, who succeeded them in the inheritance of the country. The principal nation of the second race fell in battle towards the close of the fourth century. The remnant are the Indians that now inhabit this country. . . . For a more particular account I would refer to the Book of Mormon.[10]

Does this statement discredit the idea of other people coming to the Americas because Joseph Smith only mentions two groups? Since Joseph Smith refers to the Jaredite colony as the "first settlement" of ancient America, are Latter-day Saints required to believe that no other people came to the Americas before that time? First, it is important to note that in the Wentworth letter, Joseph Smith starts with what the angel told him and then provides his own description of the Book of Mormon narrative for the press. Consequently, his words about the Jaredite and Israelite migrations do not come from the angel Moroni. In fact, this wording, for the most part, did not even originate with Joseph Smith but is essentially adapted from Orson Pratt's 1840 pamphlet on the Book of Mormon,[11] as the comparison below shows.

| Pratt 1840 | Wentworth Letter 1842 |
| --- | --- |
| In this important and most interesting book, we can read the history of ancient America, from its early settlement by a colony who came from the tower of Babel, at the confusion of languages, to the beginning of the fifth century of the Christian era. | In this important and interesting book the history of ancient America is unfolded, from its first settlement by a colony that came from the tower of Babel, at the confusion of languages to the beginning of the fifth century of the Christian era. |
| By these Records we are informed, that America, in ancient times, has been inhabited by two distinct races of people. The first, or more ancient race, came directly from the great tower, being called Jaredites. | We are informed by these records that America in ancient times has been inhabited by two distinct races of people. The first were called Jaredites and came directly from the tower of Babel. |
| The second race came directly from the city of Jerusalem, about six-hundred years before Christ, being Israelites, principally the descendants of Joseph. | The second race came directly from the city of Jerusalem, about six hundred years before Christ. They were principally Israelites, of the descendants of Joseph. |
| The first nation, or Jaredites, were destroyed about the time that the Israelites came from Jerusalem, who succeeded them in the inheritance of the country. | The Jaredites were destroyed about the time that the Israelites came from Jerusalem, who succeeded them in the inheritance of the country. |
| The principal nation of the second race, fell in battle towards the close of the fourth century. | The principal nation of the second race fell in battle towards the close of the fourth century. |
| The remaining remnant, having dwindled into an uncivilized state, still continue to inhabit the land, although divided into a "multitude of nations," and are called by Europeans the "American Indians." | The remnant are the Indians that now inhabit this country. |

Second, the Jaredite migration is the earliest migration to America mentioned in the Book of Mormon, but the Book of Mormon itself does not claim that the Jaredites were the first human beings in the New World. When Joseph Smith's statement is read within its context of the Wentworth letter, it is clear that he was actually, at that point, offering a general description of the time span of the book, indicating that the Book of Mormon narrative stretches from the Jaredite settlement to the beginning of the fifth century AD. In so doing, he was not necessarily designating the Jaredite settlement as the oldest in the land, but merely as the oldest mentioned in the Book of Mormon account. Perhaps, like many other Latter-day Saints, he assumed that the Jaredites were the first settlers of ancient America, but this goes beyond what the Book of Mormon says. It specifically mentions three migrations to the Americas but never claims that they were the only ones or the earliest.

Finally, Joseph Smith's description of the contents of the Book of Mormon in the Wentworth letter gives a brief overview of the text and not a comprehensive account. For instance, Joseph did not say that America was inhabited by *only* two races of people in pre-Columbian times, although presumably he could have said so. In the course of the letter, he directed the reader to the contents of the Book of Mormon three different times and on the third time advised, "For a more particular account I would refer to the Book of Mormon." In other words, Joseph Smith considered the Book of Mormon itself, rather than his letter to Wentworth, to be the authoritative word on the subject.

## Latter-day Saint Views on Other Pre-Columbians

Latter-day Saints have long been open to the idea that peoples not mentioned in the Book of Mormon may have migrated to the Americas either before, during, or after the events described in the Book of Mormon and that these various peoples intermingled with those of Israelite or Jaredite descent.[12] The idea of other pre-Columbian migrations to the Americas has a long history and can be traced back to the earliest Latter-day Saints. In the 15 September 1842 issue of the *Times and Seasons,* the editor—Joseph Smith, according to the paper's masthead—cited favorably an account of Don Juan Torres, grandson of the last king of the Quiché Maya, which affirmed that

> the Toltecas themselves descended from the house of Israel, who were released by Moses from the tyranny of Pharaoh, and after crossing the Red Sea, fell into Idolatry. To avoid the reproofs of Moses, or from fear of his inflicting upon them some chastisement, they separated from him and his brethren, and under the guidance of Tanub, their chief, passed from one continent to the other, to a place which they called the seven caverns, a part of the kingdom of Mexico, where they founded the celebrated city of Tula.[13]

"Whether such a migration ever took place or not," states Hugh Nibley, "it is significant that the Prophet was not reluctant to recognize the possibility of other migrations than those mentioned in the Book of Mormon."[14]

Interest in the possibility of additional migrations to the Americas seems to have persisted among Latter-day Saints. In 1852, the *Deseret News* cited with interest an account of a purported Welsh migration to America "three hundred yeeres before Columbus."[15] Orson Pratt of the Quorum of the Twelve Apostles interpreted the promises found in the book of Ether regarding other nations inheriting the land as referring to pre-Columbian migrants to the Americas after the Nephite destruction at Cumorah.

> Now, these same decrees, which God made in relation to the former nations that inhabited this country, extend to us. "Whatever nation," the Lord said, "shall possess this land, from this time henceforth and forever, shall serve the only true and living God, or they shall be swept off when the fullness of his wrath shall come upon them." *Since* this

ancient decree there are *many nations* who have come here. And *lastly* Europeans have come from what is termed the old world across the Atlantic.[16]

It is significant that Pratt, one of the earliest converts to Mormonism, who did much to popularize the hemispheric model of Book of Mormon geography in the nineteenth century, apparently had no difficulty simultaneously asserting that many other nations came to the Americas in the interval between the Nephites' destruction and the European arrival.

Other Latter-day Saints of the time agreed with Elder Pratt. In an article published in 1875, George M. Ottinger, a faculty member at the University of Deseret (later the University of Utah), explored the idea advanced by some scholars of the day suggesting that the Phoenicians may have helped to colonize the Americas in pre-Columbian times. After surveying this literature, he concluded "that the Phoenicians at one time held intercourse with Jared's people."[17] Another Latter-day Saint author, in or about 1887, surmised that Lehi's people and the Jaredites "were contemporary co-workers in the work of civilizing the aborigines of the promise[d] land."[18] He viewed the account of Mosiah's union with the people of Zarahemla as evidence for the existence of indigenous peoples already in the land when they arrived. Mosiah "had to teach the Nephite language to the Zarahemlans, for though the parents of both people had come from Jerusalem at about the same time, and must have then the same verbiage, their off-spring took rather to their mothers, as it was but natural. Probably those Aborigines mothers were more numerous and influential, than their Hebrew husbands." Such intermarriages may not have been confined to the Mulekites. "Were most of those who helped Nephi to build that great temple Hebrews, and the many wives and concubines who caused the reprimand of Jacob from within the walls of the very same temple, aborigines?"[19] He argued the need for Latter-day Saints to preach the gospel among the Maya and other peoples of the region since, in his view, "most of the descendants of the genuine race of Lamanites, possibly live in Yucatan and Central America."[20]

Thus, the sentiments of B. H. Roberts of the First Council of the Seventy, expressed in 1909, were not entirely unfamiliar to Latter-day Saints: "It cannot possibly be in conflict with the Book of Mormon to concede that the northeastern coast of America may have been visited by Norsemen in the tenth century; or that Celtic adventurers even at an earlier date, but subsequent to the close of the Nephite period, may have found their way to America. It might even be possible that migrations came by way of the Pacific Islands to the western shores of America." He also thought it "indisputable" that there have been at least some migrations from northeast Asia to North America over the Bering Strait.[21] He continued, "It is possible that Phoenician vessels might have visited some parts of the extended coasts of the western world, and such events receive no mention in the Jaredite or Nephite records known to us." While the Book of Mormon text does not specifically mention such migrations, Roberts conceded that "the records now in hand, especially that of the Jaredites, are but very limited histories of these people." Transoceanic contacts may in fact have gone both ways: "It is not impossible that between the close of the Nephite period and the discovery of the western world by Columbus, American craft made their way to European shores."[22] Thus, "even in Jaredite and Nephite times voyages could have been made from America to the shores of Europe, and yet no mention of it be made in Nephite and Jaredite records now known."[23]

In 1902, Anthony W. Ivins, then president of the Juarez Stake in Mexico, suggested in an article published in the *Improvement Era* that Coriantumr may have taken wives and fathered children before his death among the Mulekites, a position with which Roberts was inclined to agree.[24] One of the most influential writers on the Book of Mormon in the early twentieth century, Janne M. Sjodahl, went even further; in 1927 he asked, "Have the Lamanites Jaredite blood in their veins?" and answered the question in the affirmative.[25] Sjodahl

interpreted the account in the book of Ether as "an epitome princi-
pally of the history of [the land of] Moron, where the Jaredites first
established themselves." He postulated that, over time, "the Jaredites
gradually settled in favorable localities all over the American continents, and that both Nephites and Lamanites came in contact with
them, and that an amalgamation took place everywhere as in the case
of the Nephites and Mulekites in Zarahemla."[26] During their long history, descendants of the original Jaredite colony, according to Sjodahl,
could have become widely dispersed throughout the Americas at
various times and would not have been directly involved in events associated with Coriantumr, Shiz, and their people. Under this interpretation, Ether's prophecy of Jaredite destruction (Ether 13:20–21)
concerned only those associated with Coriantumr's kingdom near the
narrow neck of land and not the entire northern hemisphere.[27]

In 1921, in an article published in the *Improvement Era*, Sjodahl
observed:

> The Book of Mormon has nothing to say about the occupation
> of America by man before the arrival of the Jaredites. If scien-
> tists find, beyond controversy, that there were human beings
> here before the building of the tower; in fact, before the flood
> and way back in glacial ages, the authors of that volume offer
> no objection at all. They do not touch that question. They only
> assert that the Lord led the brother of Jared and his colony
> to this country shortly after the dispersion, and they give the
> briefest possible outline of the political and ecclesiastical his-
> tory of their descendants until their final overthrow. This has
> never been, and cannot be, disputed on scientific grounds. If
> America was occupied by any race of people—pre-Jaredites,
> we may call them—information concerning them must be
> gathered, not from the Book of Mormon, but from geological
> strata, or from archaeological remains extant. . . .

Are there in this country any Indians that are not descendants of these first Hebrew settlers? That is a question
for the scientist to answer.

The Book of Mormon gives no direct information on that
subject. It confines itself strictly to the history of the descendants of Lehi and Mulek. If science, after a careful investigation of the physical characteristics of the present-day Indians;
their languages, their religious ideas, their myths and traditions, and their social institutions, should declare that there
are evidences of other influences . . . that would not affect the
authenticity of the Book of Mormon in the least.[28]

In another article published in 1927 that discusses four divergent models of Book of Mormon geography—including two that
placed the setting exclusively in the region of Central America—
Sjodahl advised, "Students of the Book of Mormon should be cau-
tioned against the error of supposing that all the American Indians
are the descendants of Lehi, Mulek, and their companions, and
that their languages and dialects, their social organizations, religious conceptions and practices, traditions, etc., are all traceable
to those Hebrew sources. . . . Nor is it improbable," he continued,
"that America received immigrants from Asia and other parts of
the globe, who may have introduced new creeds and institutions,
although not mentioned in the Book of Mormon."[29] He also suggested that "long before [the so-called Classic Maya period], the
descendants of Lehi had invaded this region and assimilated with the
people preceding them."[30]

In 1928, Latter-day Saint engineer Jean Driggs published a brief
but cogently argued pamphlet suggesting that the Book of Mormon
was the "record of a minority people." Looking at the matter from
the vantage point of his profession, he said, "It should not be expected that a study of the Book of Mormon lands will account for
all the ancient monuments and cultural phases on this continent any

more than that the Bible should account for all the civilizations of the Eastern Continent."[31]

It was not only scholars and professionals from within the rank and file of the church who expressed this note of caution. In the April 1929 general conference of the church, Anthony W. Ivins, who had become a counselor in the First Presidency, admonished the Saints, "We must be careful in the conclusions that we reach. The Book of Mormon teaches the history of three distinct peoples, or two peoples and three different colonies of people, who came from the old world to this continent. *It does not tell us that there was no one here before them. It does not tell us that people did not come after.* And so if discoveries are made which suggest differences in race origins, it can very easily be accounted for, and reasonably, for *we do believe that other people came to this continent.*"[32]

Nor was President Ivins alone among the General Authorities in this belief. In 1937, Elder John A. Widtsoe of the Quorum of the Twelve and Franklin S. Harris Jr. noted: "Three separate and distinct settlements of America are reported by the Book of Mormon. The first, the Jaredites, dates from the Tower of Babel, the other two, the Nephites and Mulekites, from the time of Zedekiah, King of Judah. There may also have been others not recorded in the Book or not known to the ancient authors."[33]

In 1938, the idea of others in the promised land entered the formal church curriculum when the church's Department of Education published a study guide for the instruction of Latter-day Saint students and teachers that explained: "Indian ancestry, at least in part, is attributed by the Nephite record to the Lamanites. However, the Book of Mormon deals only with the history and expansion of three small colonies which came to America and it does not deny or disprove the possibility of other immigrations, which probably would be unknown to its writers. Jewish origin may represent only a part of the total ancestry of the American Indian today." The study guide further stated: "A parallel is found in the Bible writings which mention only a small portion of the Old World geographical areas and its people, even though Palestine was the land bridge of ancient civilizations. The Hebrew writers mentioned other lands and people only when they came in contact with them."[34] Two years later, the same department published another study guide that affirmed:

> There is a tendency to use the Book of Mormon as a complete history of all pre-Columbian peoples. The book does not claim to be such an history, and we distort its spiritual message when we use it for such a purpose. The book does not give an history of all peoples who came to America before Columbus. There may have been other people who came here, by other routes and means, of which we have no written record. If historians wish to discuss information which the Book of Mormon does not contain but which is related to it, then we should grant them that freedom. We should avoid the claim that we are familiar with all the peoples who have lived on American soil when we discuss the Book of Mormon.
>
> . . . There is safety in using the book in the spirit in which it was written. Our use of poorly constructed inferences may draw us far away from the truth. In our approach to the study of the Book of Mormon let us guard against drawing historical conclusions which the book does not warrant.[35]

In this second publication, "the student is reminded again of the possibility of still other groups, ethnically unrelated to the Nephites or Lamanites, inhabiting portions of the Americas."[36]

Other publications of the Church of Jesus Christ of Latter-day Saints have offered similar counsel. In a 1950 article for the *Relief Society Magazine*, Elder Antoine R. Ivins, a member of the First Council of the Seventy and a son of President Anthony W. Ivins, observed that terms such as *Nephite* and *Lamanite* often referred to classifications other than the strictly biological. "We are in the habit of thinking," he said, in mild chastisement of the human tendency to adhere to popular tradition, "of all of the indigenous groups who were upon the land of the Americas when Christopher Columbus landed here, as Lamanites. I wonder if we are justified in this assumption." He pointed out that over a thousand years had elapsed between the final destruction of the Nephites and the arrival of Columbus to the Americas. "During this time great changes may have taken place in the populations of the Americas and among these changes may have been migrations of other groups to America." While the Book of Mormon tells of the migrations of the Jaredites, Mulekites, and Lehites, he continued, Latter-day Saints need not suppose that there were no others. "There may have been other peoples whom the Nephites never discovered living then on this great land. Or, as suggested, others may have come later. The very wide differentiation in the languages of the native races of the Americas would seem to indicate this possibility." Elder Ivins added that these thoughts did not disturb his faith in the truthfulness of the Book of Mormon, concluding, "Whether all of these indigenous peoples were descended from Lehi matters little."[37]

Seven years later, in a statement approved for publication by the First Presidency of the church in a comparative work on American religions, Elder Richard L. Evans of the Quorum of the Twelve Apostles described the Book of Mormon as "part of a record, both sacred and secular, of prophets and peoples who (with supplementary groups) were *among* the ancestors of the American 'Indians.'"[38] This article was subsequently reprinted in 1963 and 1975. Although the 1975 edition expressly stated that the article had been slightly modified and then reapproved for publication by the First Presidency of the church, this portion of Elder Evans's article was left unchanged. It seems reasonable that language such as this, written by an apostle and twice approved by the First Presidency for publication in a work intended to represent the Church of Jesus Christ to the scholarly community, could be considered reliable.

This same view was, at the same time, being disseminated to members of the church as well. In 1961, Latter-day Saint writer and Book of Mormon scholar Ariel Crowley thought it "beyond any question true" that the Americas had received periodic migrations across the Bering Strait at various times. It would be incorrect, he argued, for one to say "that *all* American Indians are descended from Israel. Neither is it proper to say that no American Indians are descended from Mongolian sources. It is equally improper to assert that Indians may not be descended from both sources, and very probably others as well." The mixture of populations in the Americas and throughout the world makes "definitive boundaries of descent very difficult to trace, and in most cases truly impossible." Crowley insisted that past statements by church leaders were never "intended to be critical analyses of racial ancestries, nor intended to exclude migrations from other nations and intermarriages with Nephite or Lamanite people."[39] The Book of Mormon "is no more the history of all peoples and doings of past ages on the American continents than the Bible is a history of all the peoples and nations of the East. Each covers its own time and provenance and makes no pretense beyond that." Native Americans "are of mixed blood, very much like the mixtures produced in modern America, the 'melting pot' of nations. The Book of Mormon attests the presence of the blood of Israel. It is not in the least impugned by extraneous proof that other blood, by other migrations, found this land and mingled with the peoples there."[40]

Latter-day Saint anthropologists shared Crowley's opinion. In 1976, in an article for the church's *Liahona* magazine, archaeologist Ross T. Christensen noted that the diversity in Native American languages makes it clear that "the original forefathers of the Indians came from diverse ethnic groups from many distant lands in the Old World. For this reason it is impossible to declare with certainty that *all* American Indians are Lamanites. The Book of Mormon does not make this claim, although it is affirmed by some members of the Church."[41] In this he concurred with his colleague M. Wells Jakeman, who had stated two years before Elder Evans's article that "the Nephite record does not purport to give the history of *all* the New World for *all* the time before Columbus" nor "claim to give the origin of *all* the American Indian peoples found inhabiting the New World at the coming of the Europeans."[42]

A year before Christensen's article appeared, the *Ensign* responded to the question "Who and where are the Lamanites?" Its author, Lane Johnson, noted that latter-day "Lamanites," in addition to being descended from Lehi, Ishmael, Zoram, and Mulek, "may also be descended from other groups of whom we have no record. Certainly they have mixed with many other lineages at the far reaches of their dispersal in the Americas and most of the islands of the Pacific since the time when Moroni bade them farewell in AD 421." Yet notwithstanding the mixed nature of these groups, they all "have a legitimate claim to the blessings of the Abrahamic covenant."[43]

Hugh Nibley had broached this idea of claim upon the covenant as early as 1952 when he wrote of the possibility that these others in the land were not accidental arrivals but had been led to it by the hand of God for his own purposes, as the Book of Mormon colonists had.

> Just because Lehi's people had come from Jerusalem by special direction we are not to conclude that other men cannot have had the same experience. And by the same token the fact that the Jaredites were led to the land of promise at the time of the dispersion gives us no right to conclude that no one else was ever so led, either earlier or later than they. It is nowhere said or implied that even the Jaredites were the first to come here, any more than it is said or implied that they were the first or only people to be led from the tower.
> . . . Now there is a great deal said in the Book of Mormon about the past and future of the promised land, but never is it described as an empty land. The descendants of Lehi were never the only people on the continent, and the Jaredites never claimed to be.[44]

Fifteen years later he noted: "The Book of Mormon offers no objections whatever to the free movement of whatever tribes and families choose to depart into regions beyond its ken, so it presents no obstacles to the arrival of whatever other bands may have occupied the hemisphere without its knowledge; for hundreds of years the Nephites shared the continent with the far more numerous Jaredites, of whose existence they were totally unaware."[45] In fact, he added, "The idea of other migrations to the New World is taken so completely for granted that the story of the Mulekites is dismissed in a few verses (Omni 1:14–17)."[46]

One of the most prominent proponents of the idea that Native American populations were not confined to those of Israel is anthropologist John L. Sorenson. His views on how the Book of Mormon relates to ancient Mesoamerica actually began circulating in preliminary form as early as 1955.[47] In 1985, an expanded version of his work was published, and since then he has published additional works relating to the question.[48] Sorenson argued that the Book of Mormon was not intended as a history of all the American Indians but is primarily a "lineage history," or a "record of the people of Nephi" written by the elite of that people.[49] He also contended that many elements found in the Book of Mormon text can best be accounted for under the assumption that Nephites and Lamanites included other people in addition to those descended from the original founding colony. For example, Lehi's son Jacob's condemnation of the Nephites having "'many wives and concubines' . . . seems to call for a larger population of females," which could not have been the case with Lehi's party just one or two generations after their arrival. Male casualties in battles involving such tiny numbers could hardly have been very many. This would suggest the incorporation of "'other' people."[50]

The activities and words of Sherem also support this view. Jacob says that "there came a man among the people of Nephi, whose name was Sherem" (Jacob 7:1). In his conversation with Jacob, Sherem indicates that he had "sought much opportunity that I might speak unto you; for I have heard and also know that thou goest about much, preaching that which ye call the gospel, or the doctrine of Christ" (Jacob 7:6). Sorenson estimated that the population of actual descendants of the Nephite colony "could not have exceeded fifty by that time," hardly "enough to populate one modest-sized village. . . . Jacob, as head priest and religious teacher, would routinely have been around the Nephite temple in the cultural center at least on all holy days (see Jacob 2:2). How then could Sherem never have seen him, and why would he have had to seek 'much opportunity' to speak to him in such a tiny settlement? And where would Jacob have had to go on the preaching travels Sherem refers to, if only such a tiny group were involved? Moreover, from where was it that Sherem 'came . . . among the people of Nephi' (Jacob 7:1)?"[51] Sorenson also noted references to wars, flocks, and domesticated corn as suggesting the presence of other people.[52] Even more recently, Brant Gardner has marshaled additional evidence suggesting that the Nephites were a minority people in the midst of many other Mesoamerican groups with whom they interacted.[53]

The idea that people other than the Book of Mormon colonists also inhabited the pre-Columbian Americas is not a new or revisionist concept. It has a well-documented history that began in the early generations of the restored Church of Jesus Christ and has carried on uninterrupted to the present day. It has been presented, discussed, and published openly and in authorized contexts throughout that history. It has been promoted and defended by some of the church's most distinguished leaders and scholars, and it continues to inform the work of faithful Book of Mormon researchers today. As ever more scientific evidence arises in support of it, one can hope that it will in time fully supersede the erroneous but "long-standing popular Mormon beliefs" defended by the Book of Mormon's critics.[54]

## Possible Scriptural Objections to the Presence of Others

In seeking possible scriptural objections to the proposition that there were others in the land, some have suggested that two Book of Mormon passages (Ether 2:5 and 2 Nephi 1:8) require an empty hemisphere previous to the arrival of Jaredites, Lehites, and Mulekites.[55] However, it is evident that the passage from Ether 2:5, stating that the Jaredites were "commanded . . . that they should go forth into the wilderness, yea, into that quarter where there never had man been," when taken in context, actually refers to the wilderness through which the Jaredites were to travel in the Old World and says nothing about the populations of the New World at that time. The second reference, from Lehi's prophecy, reads as follows:

> And behold, it is wisdom that this land should be kept as yet from the knowledge of other nations; for behold, many nations would overrun the land, that there would be no place for an inheritance. Wherefore, I, Lehi, have obtained a promise, that inasmuch as those whom the Lord God shall bring out of the land of Jerusalem shall keep his commandments, they shall prosper upon the face of this land; and they shall be kept from all *other nations,* that they may possess this land unto themselves. And if it so be that they shall keep his commandments they shall be blessed upon the face of this land, and there shall be none to molest them, nor to take away the land of their inheritance; and they shall dwell safely forever. (2 Nephi 1:8–9)

One reading of this statement could be that Lehi's people inherited an empty promised land when their ship arrived, but the Book of Mormon allows for other interpretations.[56] Is there a distinction, for example, between "nations" and other social groups? Lehi would have been familiar with nations such as Babylon and Egypt that had well-organized armies capable of waging sophisticated warfare and extending their power over large distances. Lehi's prophecy could allow for smaller societies that did not yet merit the description "nations." For instance, Sorenson's model of Book of Mormon geography places the land of Nephi in highland Guatemala near the site of Kaminaljuyú. At the time Nephi and his people separated from Laman's followers to found their own settlement in the early sixth century BC, archaeological evidence shows that that region had only scattered, sparsely populated villages.[57] Also, to "possess this land unto themselves" does not necessarily mean to be the only inhabitants but can also mean—as it often does in Book of Mormon contexts—that a group has the ability to control and exercise authority over the land and its resources (see, for example, Mosiah 19:15; 23:29; 24:2; Alma 27:22, 26).[58] Significantly, however, even Lehi's statement about "other nations" is conditional. Lehi indicates that the promised protection from threatening nations would be removed when his children dwindled in unbelief. Sorenson has observed that the Lamanites, at least, dwindled in unbelief from the beginning.

> How then could Lehi's prophecy about "other nations" being brought in have been kept long in abeyance after that? Furthermore, the early Nephites generally did the same thing within a few centuries. Their wickedness and apostasy culminated in the escape of Mosiah and his group from the land of Nephi to the land of Zarahemla (see Omni 1:13–14). And if the Lord somehow did not at those times bring in "other nations," then surely he would have done so after Cumorah, 1100 years prior to Columbus. Even if there were no massive armed invasions of strange groups to be reported, we need not be surprised if relatively small groups of strange peoples who were neither so numerous nor so organized as to be rivals for control of the land could have been scattered or infiltrated among both Nephites and Lamanites without their constituting the "other nations" in the threatening sense of Lehi's prophecy. Thus in the terms of Lehi's prophecy, "others" could and probably even should have

been close at hand and available for the Lord to use as instruments against the straying covenant peoples any time after the arrival of Nephi's boat.[59]

## Scriptural Support for the Presence of Others

### Prophecies about the Scattering

The scriptural evidence against the presence of others, then, is sparse and unimpressive. The scriptural evidence for the presence of others, however, is abundant. For instance, prophecies from the Old Testament would have led Lehi's people to expect to be placed in a new land in the midst of other people. The prophets of ancient Israel had foretold that the tribes of Israel would be "scatter[ed] . . . among all people" (Deuteronomy 28:64) and "removed to all the kingdoms of the earth" (Jeremiah 29:18) and that they would become "wanderers among the nations" (Hosea 9:17). Further, Moses informed them, "The Lord shall scatter you among the nations, and ye shall be left few in number among the heathen, whither the Lord shall lead you" (Deuteronomy 4:27). These prophecies make plain that the whole house of Israel was subject to being scattered among non-Israelite peoples who would be more numerous than they.[60] Lehi taught his children that they should consider themselves to be a part of this scattering: "Yea, even my father spake much concerning the Gentiles, and also concerning the house of Israel, that they should be compared like unto an olive-tree, whose branches should be broken off and should be scattered upon all the face of the earth. Wherefore, he said it must needs be that we should be led with one accord into the land of promise, unto the fulfilling of the word of the Lord, that we should be scattered" (1 Nephi 10:12–13).

The allegory of the olive tree, as recounted by Jacob, spells their fate out even more plainly. Branches broken off the tame tree, which represents historical Israel (Jacob 5:3), are to be grafted onto the roots of wild trees, meaning non-Israelite groups. In other words, there is to be a demographic union between two groups, with "young and tender branches" from the original tree, Israel, being grafted onto wild rootstock in various parts of the vineyard or the earth (Jacob 5:8; see also 14). Jacob 5:25 and 43 clearly identify Lehi's people as such a broken-off branch. That branch is to be planted in the choicest spot of the vineyard. In that prime location, the Lord has already cut down "that which cumbered this spot of ground" (Jacob 5:44)—clearly a reference to the destruction of the Jaredites.[61] In addition, the statement that one part of the new hybrid tree "brought forth good fruit," while the other portion "brought forth wild fruit," is an obvious reference to the Nephites and Lamanites respectively (Jacob 5:45).

So the Lehite "tree" of the allegory consists of a population geographically "transplanted" from the original Israelite promised land and "grafted" onto a wild root—or joined with non-Israelite people. Note that the Lord considers the new root to be "good" despite its being wild (Jacob 5:48). This allegorical description requires that a non-Israelite root—other peoples, in terms of this discussion—already be present on the scene where the "young and tender branch," Lehi's group, would be merged with them.

### Open-ended Promises concerning the Land

Book of Mormon prophets describe for latter-day readers the responsibilities that rest upon those who inherit the land of promise. But these conditions did not begin with Lehi's family or even with the Jaredites; this land has been one of promise from its beginning (Ether 13:2).[62] Those conditions specify that the people and nations who inhabit the land are to be free from bondage, captivity, and "all other nations under heaven" *if* they will serve God (Ether 2:12). The reverse is also implicit in Moroni's statement: those who do not serve God have no promised protection and may expect to be subjected to bondage, captivity, and affliction by other nations who will come to the land and exercise God's judgment upon them. Some people, then, are brought to the land for their righteousness, and others are brought to scourge the inhabitants. Moroni also states that unrighteous nations or people may be swept off the face of the land, but "it is not until the fulness of iniquity among the children of the land, that they are swept off" (Ether 2:10), suggesting that those peoples who do not reach a "fulness of iniquity" may yet remain in the land.

"And he raiseth up a righteous nation, and destroyeth the nations of the wicked. And he leadeth away the righteous into precious lands, and the wicked he destroyeth, and curseth the land unto them for their sakes" (1 Nephi 17:37–38). Nephi's statement in the context of his own family's journey to a New World land of promise suggests that their experience is not unique but indicative of the activities of other groups. Upon his family's arrival, Lehi explained the nature of the covenant by which they would inherit the land. The Lord had led them out of the land of Jerusalem, "but, said he, notwithstanding our afflictions, we have obtained a land of promise, a land which is choice above all other lands; a land which the Lord God hath covenanted with me should be a land for the inheritance of *my seed*. Yea, the Lord hath covenanted this land unto *me*, and to *my children* forever, and *also all those who should be led out of other countries by the hand of the Lord*" (2 Nephi 1:5). We know that the Mulekites were, like the Lehites, led out of the land of Jerusalem "by the hand of the Lord" (Omni 1:16). Lehi's reference to "other countries" suggests countries other than the land of Jerusalem. Modern readers may correctly include in that category gentile peoples who migrated to this hemisphere during historic times, yet Lehi does not limit the application to post-Columbian gentile groups. Their identity is left open and unspecified.

> Wherefore, this land is consecrated unto *him whom he shall bring*. And if it so be that they shall serve him according to the commandments which he hath given, it shall be a land of liberty unto them; wherefore, they shall never be brought down into captivity; if so, it shall be because of iniquity; for if iniquity shall abound cursed shall be the land for

their sakes, but unto the righteous it shall be blessed forever. (2 Nephi 1:7)

Lehi's words parallel similar promises in both the Book of Mormon and latter-day revelation:

Cursed shall be the land, yea, this land, unto *every* nation, kindred, tongue, and people, unto destruction, which do wickedly, when they are fully ripe. (Alma 45:16)

And thus the Lord did pour out his blessings upon this land, which was choice above all other lands; and he commanded that *whoso* should possess the land should possess it unto the Lord, or they should be destroyed when they were ripened in iniquity; for upon such, saith the Lord: I will pour out the fulness of my wrath. (Ether 9:20)

And I said unto them, that it should be granted unto them according to their faith in their prayers; yea, and this was their faith—that my gospel, which I gave unto them that they might preach in their days, might come unto their brethren the *Lamanites,* and also *all that had become Lamanites because of their dissensions.* Now, this is not all— their faith in their prayers was that this gospel should be made known also, if it were possible that *other nations should possess this land;* and thus they did leave a blessing upon this land in their prayers, that *whosoever should believe in this gospel in this land* might have eternal life; yea, that it might be free unto *all of whatsoever nation, kindred, tongue, or people they may be.* (D&C 10:47–52)

In both the Book of Mormon and modern-day scripture, the language of the scriptural promises concerning the land is open-ended. It refers to "*whoso* should possess the land" (Ether 2:8), "*whatsoever* nation" (Ether 2:9, 12), "he that doth possess it" (Ether 2:10), "all men . . . who dwell upon the face thereof" (Ether 13:2), "*whosoever* should believe in this gospel in this land" (D&C 10:50), "*all of whatsoever nation, kindred, tongue, or people they may be*" (D&C 10:51). The covenant conditions under which blessings may be inherited are explained, while the identification of who may inherit them is left unspecified in terms of both identification and time. Whoever they are, whenever they come, whatever their origins, the Book of Mormon makes clear that "this land is consecrated unto him whom he shall bring" (2 Nephi 1:7).

### The People of Nephi

After telling us that "Laman and Lemuel and the sons of Ishmael were angry with me because of the admonitions of the Lord" (2 Nephi 4:13) and were planning to kill him (2 Nephi 5:3), Nephi then relates:

> And it came to pass that the Lord did warn me, that I, Nephi, should depart from them and flee into the wilderness, *and all those who would go with me.* Wherefore, it came to pass that I, Nephi, did take my family, and also Zoram and his family, and Sam, mine elder brother and his family, and Jacob and Joseph, my younger brethren, and also my sisters, *and all those who would go with me. And all those who would go with me were those who believed in the warnings and the revelations of God;* wherefore, they did hearken unto my words. (2 Nephi 5:5–6)

At the time the Nephites and the Lamanites separated, then, Nephi was accompanied by his own family, Zoram and Sam and their respective families, his younger brothers Jacob and Joseph, and his sisters, in addition to "all those who would go with me." Who were these others who "believed in the warnings and the revelations of God"? The most likely answer seems to be other people living in the land, not of Lehi's family. Significantly, at this point in the text Nephi introduces the term *people of Nephi* for the first time in reference to his followers (2 Nephi 5:9), a term that may be suggestive of a larger society including more than his immediate family.

It is also at this point that the term *Lamanite* first appears. Nephi explains that he made preparations to defend his people "lest by any means the people *who were now called Lamanites* should come upon us and destroy us; for I knew their hatred towards me and my children and those who were called my people" (2 Nephi 5:14). As demographer James Smith observes, "One reading of the latter phrase is that 'Lamanites' is a new name for the family and followers of Laman, Nephi's brother-enemy from whom Nephi fled. Another possible reading is that some people not previously called 'Lamanites' were now so called, presumably because of Laman's affiliation with them."[63]

After explaining how he and his people separated themselves from Laman, Lemuel, the sons of Ishmael, and their people and having told how the people of Nephi became established in the land, Nephi quotes a prophecy of the Lord. "And cursed shall be the seed of *him that mixeth with their seed; for they shall be cursed even with the same cursing. And the Lord spake it, and it was done*" (2 Nephi 5:23). This prophecy anticipates future mixing and intermarriage with the Lamanites, but the immediacy of Nephi's personal observation that "the Lord spake it, and it was done" suggests that the process was already underway at the time Nephi left or very shortly after the separation. That is, unidentified people had, at this early period, already joined with the Lamanites in their opposition to Nephi and his people and had become like them, and Nephi saw this event as a fulfillment of the Lord's prophecy. Since Nephite dissensions are not explicitly mentioned until several generations later,[64] Nephi's statement about unidentified peoples intermarrying with the Lamanites seems to indicate the presence of other non-Lehite peoples who had joined or were joining the Lamanites.

### Being Numbered with the People of God

In light of the possibility that additional non-Lehite peoples had united with both the Nephites and the Lamanites, the teachings of

Nephi and Jacob relating to Isaiah take on greater significance. After explaining that "we had already had wars and contentions with" the Lamanites (2 Nephi 5:34), Nephi inserts a lengthy sermon delivered by his brother Jacob (2 Nephi 6–10). Jacob indicates that he has previously spoken about "many things" (2 Nephi 6:2) but that Nephi now wants him to preach from Isaiah. In fact, Jacob says that Nephi had even selected the scriptural passages he was to discuss: prophecies of Isaiah that concerned the relationship between scattered Israel and the Gentiles (2 Nephi 6:4). Further, Jacob asks his people to *liken* these passages from Isaiah to their present situation (2 Nephi 6:5) and suggests that the application of these teachings concerns "things which *are*" as well as things "which are to come" (2 Nephi 6:4). As Latter-day Saints, we quite appropriately focus on the latter, but what was the context that made likening Isaiah's words to themselves meaningful to the Nephites?

Jacob prophesies that in the latter days some Jews will reject the Messiah and be destroyed, while others will believe and be saved (2 Nephi 6:14–15). Jacob also interprets Isaiah as referring to two distinct groups of Gentiles: those who nourish and unite with Israel (2 Nephi 6:12; 10:18–19), and those who fight against Zion (2 Nephi 6:13; 10:16). In the latter days, both groups of Gentiles will play an active role in the drama of Israel's gathering and redemption. "Wherefore, he that fighteth against Zion, both *Jew* and *Gentile*, both bond and free, both male and female, shall perish; for they are they who are the whore of all the earth; for they who are not for me are against me, saith our God" (2 Nephi 10:16). Certainly, Jacob's sermon looks to the future, but I am persuaded that in likening Jacob's teachings to themselves, Nephite contemporary listeners would have drawn the obvious parallel with their own situation. As a branch of scattered Israel in a new land of promise, they sought to establish Zion but were opposed, hated, and persecuted by their former brethren. Even when Jacob applies these prophecies to the latter days, his words have immediate relevance to his contemporary listeners, who would likely have seen their Lamanite persecutors as the "Jews" of Jacob's prophecy and the "Gentiles" as those non-Lehite peoples who had joined with the Lamanites against the people of Nephi. However, in his application of Isaiah to the Lehites, Jacob explains that not all Gentiles would oppose Zion and that some would be joint heirs with the people of Lehi in the blessings of the land: "But behold, this land, said God, shall be a land of thine inheritance, and the Gentiles shall be blessed upon the land" (2 Nephi 10:10). How would the Gentiles in the land be blessed? By being numbered among the children of Lehi.

> Wherefore, my beloved brethren, thus saith our God: I will afflict thy seed by the hand of the Gentiles; nevertheless, I will soften the hearts of the Gentiles, that they shall be like unto a father to them; wherefore, the Gentiles shall be blessed and numbered among the house of Israel. Wherefore, I will consecrate this land unto *thy seed,* and *them who shall be numbered among thy seed,* forever, for the land of their inheritance; for it is a choice land, saith God unto me, above all other lands, wherefore I will have *all men* that dwell thereon that they shall worship me, saith God. (2 Nephi 10:18–19)

The Lord's promise, delivered to the people of Nephi by Jacob, is a perpetual one, having application from their own time forward. In the context of its time, Jacob's sermon can be read as addressing the immediate question of how Lehite Israel was to relate to and interact with non-Lehite peoples in the promised land.[65] The answer was that they might, if they so chose, join with the people of God in seeking to build up Zion as joint inheritors of the land. Once they did so, they too became Israel and were numbered with Lehi's seed. Some have wondered why, if other people were present in the land during Book of Mormon times, they were not mentioned more frequently in the record. The precedent of making no distinction between Lehi's descendants and converts from the rest of the population, introduced by the Nephites' first priest, would have been foundational to the unity of Nephite society, would have influenced the words of later Nephite prophets, and may have set the additional precedent of viewing all peoples in the land in polar terms, such as *Zion/Babylon* or *Nephite/Lamanite*. Previous cultural identity would have been swallowed up in this polarized frame of reference. An example of this process can be seen in the case of Nephi's righteous brother Sam. When Lehi blesses Sam, he promises, "Blessed art thou, and thy seed; for thou shalt inherit the land like unto thy brother Nephi. And thy seed shall be numbered with his seed; and thou shalt be even like unto thy brother, and thy seed like unto his seed; and thou shalt be blessed in all thy days" (2 Nephi 4:11). Lehi blesses all his children, but only Sam is promised that his seed will be numbered with Nephi's. Interestingly, when Lehite tribal designations are mentioned, there is no tribe of Sam (Jacob 1:13; 4 Nephi 1:35–38). Why? Apparently because when one is numbered with a people, one takes upon oneself the name and identity of that people. Similarly, Gentiles, once numbered with Israel or Lehi, are thereafter identified with their covenant fathers without respect to biological origin. From then on, they too are simply Israel.

Nephi's emphasis on the universal nature of God's love is even more meaningful if written and taught to a people grappling with issues of ethnic and social diversity. "And he inviteth them all to come unto him and partake of his goodness; and he denieth none that come unto him, black and white, bond and free, male and female; and he remembereth the heathen; and all are alike unto God, both Jew and Gentile" (2 Nephi 26:33). Nephites would understand Jews to be those who came out from Jerusalem, yet the additional reference to Gentiles and heathen would only make sense to a Nephite if there were others in the land.

## Likening Isaiah unto the Nephites

If there were others in the land, it would also help explain why many of Nephi's people had difficulty understanding Isaiah, although not all of them did (2 Nephi 25:1–6). Converts who had never lived in the ancient Near East would have lacked the historical and cultural background that made the words of Isaiah "plain" to Nephi. It is also apparent that some Isaiah passages cited by Nephite prophets would make better sense to a Nephite if there were others in the land. Here we will mention just three.

• *Strangers join the house of Israel.* "For the Lord will have mercy on Jacob, and will yet choose Israel, and set them in their own land; and the strangers shall be joined with them, and they shall cleave to the house of Jacob" (2 Nephi 24:1). Such prophecies may quite properly be applied to latter-day readers of the Book of Mormon as we liken the scriptures to ourselves, but they need not refer to us exclusively. How would the Nephites have likened this scripture to their own situation, as their prophets invited them to do? They would no doubt recognize the great mercy of the Lord in bringing them out from Jerusalem and saving them from destruction, and they would also see the Lord's hand in setting them in a new land of promise where they could establish Zion. Significantly, this prophecy would also suggest to the ancient audience that there were "strangers" in the land who had joined or would join with them in accepting the teachings of Nephi and could be numbered with the house of Jacob.

• *Temples and people.* "And it shall come to pass in the last days, when the mountain of the Lord's house shall be established in the top of the mountains, and shall be exalted above the hills, and all nations shall flow unto it. And many people shall go and say, Come ye, and let us go up to the mountain of the Lord, to the house of the God of Jacob; and he will teach us of his ways, and we will walk in his paths; for out of Zion shall go forth the law, and the word of the Lord from Jerusalem" (2 Nephi 12:2–3, quoting Isaiah 2:2–3). While there are several ways of reading this passage, the Nephites would likely have thought about their own temple, recently constructed at the direction of Nephi "after the manner of the temple of Solomon" (2 Nephi 5:16). This was the temple at which Jacob taught (Jacob 1:17; 2:11) and likely the one at which Nephi's own teachings to his people and his quotations of Isaiah were presented. Isaiah's reference to "many people" coming up to be taught would evoke the idea of people joining the Nephites and accepting their traditions and beliefs.

- *A confederacy against Zion.* Nephi cites Isaiah's prophecy concerning the alliance of Rezin, king of Syria, and Pekah, king of Israel, against Ahaz, king of Judah (2 Nephi 17–22, quoting Isaiah 7–12). Ephraim, Judah's brother-tribe, has allied itself with a non-Isaelite nation (Syria), and they seek to depose Ahaz and replace him with someone of their choosing (2 Nephi 17:1–6, quoting Isaiah 7:1–6). Responding to the crisis and the fears of the king and the people of Judah, Isaiah prophesies that the conspiracy of their enemies "shall not stand, neither shall it come to pass" (2 Nephi 17:7, quoting Isaiah 7:7) and urges Ahaz simply to have faith and be faithful (2 Nephi 17:9, quoting Isaiah 7:9). The application to Nephi's day is plain: In his ambition to gain power and assert his claims to rulership, Laman, leader of the brother-tribe of "the people who were now called Lamanites" (2 Nephi 5:14), has very possibly, like Pekah of Israel, acquired non-Israelite allies and made war on another ruler of Israelite descent, Nephi, and his people (2 Nephi 5:1–3, 14, 19, 34). Perhaps frightened by the superior numbers of their enemies, the people are counseled to trust in the Lord.

Although, as Sorenson posits, the Book of Mormon may be a lineage history with an accordingly narrow focus, scriptural evidences hinting at the presence of other peoples in the New World are abundant within the Book of Mormon and other scriptures. Many of these passages, in fact, take on a clearer meaning when their wording, content, and context are considered with the possibility in mind that Lehi's family and the Mulekites were merely two groups among many others in the land of promise.

## Conclusion

It is true that the assumption that Native Americans are of exclusively Israelite heritage has been around for a number of years.

Unfortunately for those who would like to use it to denounce the Book of Mormon, it is neither revelatory nor canonical. Regardless of who may have believed or propounded it in the past or under what circumstances they may have done so, it has never been anything more than an uncanonized, unscriptural assumption.

On the other hand, many Latter-day Saints over the years, including a number of church leaders, have acknowledged the likelihood that before, during, and following the events recounted in the Book of Mormon, the American hemisphere has been visited and inhabited by nations, kindreds, tongues, and peoples not mentioned in the text. They also concede that these groups may have significantly impacted the populations of the Americas genetically, culturally, linguistically, and in many other ways. Latter-day Saint interest in historical and scientific evidence for such migrations began early in the history of the restored church and has not waned appreciably since then.

Finally, neither in the Book of Mormon itself nor in the scriptural revelations concerning it is there anything to contradict the view that Nephi had neighbors in his New World land of promise. There is, on the other hand, much within these sources that seems to support this idea. Like the God whose gospel they proclaim, these scriptures and revelations are not respecters of persons. They insist upon a place for Israel in the ancestral heritage of Native Americans, but they do not insist upon an exclusive one.

## Notes

1. See, for example, John L. Sorenson, *An Ancient American Setting for the Book of Mormon* (Salt Lake City: Deseret Book and FARMS, 1985), 81–95; John L. Sorenson, "When Lehi's Party Arrived in the Land, Did They Find Others There?" *Journal of Book of Mormon Studies* 1/1 (1992): 1–34.

2. Thomas W. Murphy, "Lamanite Genesis, Genealogy, and Genetics," in *American Apocrypha: Essays on the Book of Mormon,* ed. Dan Vogel and Brent Lee Metcalfe (Salt Lake City: Signature Books, 2002), 62.

3. Ibid., 66.

4. See Matthew Roper, "Swimming in the Gene Pool: Israelite Kinship Relations, Genes, and Genealogy," *FARMS Review* 15/2 (2003): 225–62.

5. Dallin H. Oaks, "The Historicity of the Book of Mormon," in *Historicity and the Latter-day Saint Scriptures,* ed. Paul Y. Hoskisson (Provo, Utah: BYU Religious Studies Center, 2001), 238–39. This talk was first given at the annual dinner of the Foundation for Ancient Research and Mormon Studies in Provo, Utah, on 29 October 1993.

6. See Roper, "Swimming in the Gene Pool."

7. "Mormonism," *American Revivalist and Rochester Observer,* 2 February 1833. The letter was written by commandment, but the Prophet never claimed that the words of the letter were inerrant, as some critics imply. See editors' introduction to *American Apocrypha,* vii.

8. Quoted in *An American Prophet's Record: The Diaries and Journals of Joseph Smith,* ed. Scott H. Faulring (Salt Lake City: Signature Books, 1989), 51.

9. *Autobiographical and Historical Writings,* vol. 1 of *The Papers of Joseph Smith,* ed. Dean C. Jessee (Salt Lake City: Deseret Book, 1989), 431.

10. Ibid., 431–32.

11. Orson Pratt, *Interesting Account of Several Remarkable Visions, and of the Late Discovery of Ancient American Records* (Edinburgh: Ballantyne and Hughes, 1840), 14–15.

12. For details, see John L. Sorenson and Matthew Roper, "Before DNA," *Journal of Book of Mormon Studies* 12/1 (2003): 11–13.

13. "Facts Are Stubborn Things," *Times and Seasons* 3 (15 September 1842): 922.

14. Hugh Nibley, *Lehi in the Desert, The World of the Jaredites, There Were Jaredites* (Salt Lake City: Deseret Book and FARMS, 1988), 250. While Joseph Smith was nominal editor of the paper, John Taylor was likely the acting editor at this time. For our present purpose the identity of the author is of less concern than the idea of additional migrations to the New World not specifically mentioned in the Book of Mormon.

15. "Discovery of America, above three hundred yeeres before Columbus, by Madoc ap Owen Gwyneth," *Deseret News,* 3 April 1852, 44.

16. Orson Pratt, in *Journal of Discourses,* 12:343 (27 December 1868), emphasis added.

17. George M. Ottinger, "Old America: The Phoenicians," *Juvenile Instructor* 10 (6 February 1875): 33.

18. *Plain Facts for Students of the Book of Mormon, with a Map of the Promised Land* (n.p., [ca. 1887]), 3. Although the document is undated, the writer speaks of President John Taylor as being alive and cites a letter from President Taylor to an unnamed member in Logan City, Utah, dated 20 November 1886 (ibid., 4). John Taylor died on 25 July 1887.

19. Ibid., 4n.

20. Ibid., 4.

21. B. H. Roberts, *New Witnesses for God* (Salt Lake City: Deseret News Press, 1909), 2:356. Years later, Bruce R. McConkie of the Quorum of the Twelve Apostles spoke in similar terms: "The American Indians . . . as Columbus found them," he said, "also had other blood than that of Israel in their veins. . . . It is quite apparent that groups of orientals found their way over the Bering Strait and gradually moved southward to mix with the Indian peoples. We have records of a colony of Scandinavians attempting to set up a settlement in America some 500 years before Columbus. There are archeological

indications that an unspecified number of groups of people probably found their way from the old to the new world in pre-Columbian times. Out of all these groups would have come the American Indians as they were discovered in the 15th century." Bruce R. McConkie, *Mormon Doctrine* (Salt Lake City: Bookcraft, 1973), 33. McConkie seems to have felt that these non-Israelite influences were minimal compared to those of Israel. As noted in this article, however, other Latter-day Saint leaders have believed that the non-Israelite influences in American Indian ancestry were more substantial.

22. Roberts, *New Witnesses for God*, 2:357.

23. Ibid., 2:359.

24. Anthony W. Ivins, "Are the Jaredites an Extinct People?" *Improvement Era*, November 1902, 44; Roberts, *New Witnesses for God*, 3:137–38 note k.

25. Janne M. Sjodahl, "Have the Lamanites Jaredite Blood in Their Veins?" *Improvement Era*, November 1927, 56–57.

26. Janne M. Sjodahl, "Suggested Key to Book of Mormon Geography," *Improvement Era*, September 1927, 986–87.

27. Janne M. Sjodahl, "The Jaredite Lands," *Improvement Era*, June 1939, 371; Sjodahl, "Have the Lamanites Jaredite Blood in Their Veins?" 57. Other Book of Mormon researchers also considered Sjodahl's hypotheses viable. "It is possible that companies of Jaredites broke away from the parent colony, journeying down the western coast as far as the southern point of South America." M. H. Morgan, "Of Interest to Book of Mormon Students," *Saints Herald* 84 (19 June 1937): 781. In 1939, J. A. and J. N. Washburn suggested, "There may have been many [descendants of the original Jaredite colony] in other parts of the land, to the far north and the far south. These may not have gathered to the central place at the time of the destruction. They may have had governments of their own in other localities." In later times these descendants could have been few or potentially have numbered in the "millions." J. A. Washburn and J. N. Washburn, *An Approach to the Study of Book of Mormon Geography* (Provo, Utah: New Era, 1939), 73; see also 200, 202. Subsequent Latter-day Saint scholars have noted further evidence for the survival of some Jaredites. See Nibley, *Lehi in the Desert*, 237–52; Sorenson, "When Lehi's Party Arrived," 19–22. Elder Bruce R. McConkie was also willing to grant the possibility that "isolated remnants of the Jaredites may have lived through the period of destruction in which millions of their fellows perished." McConkie, *Mormon Doctrine*, 33.

28. Janne M. Sjodahl, "The Book of Mormon and Modern Research," *Improvement Era*, December 1921, 154–55, 156.

29. Sjodahl, "Suggested Key to Book of Mormon Geography," 986–87. Washburn and Washburn also suggested in 1939 that "there were other people in the land than those of whom the Book of Mormon is a record." Washburn and Washburn, *Approach to the Study of Book of Mormon Geography*, 33.

30. Janne M. Sjodahl, *An Introduction to the Study of the Book of Mormon* (Salt Lake City: Deseret News Press, 1927), 341.

31. Jean Russell Driggs, *The Palestine of America* (Salt Lake City: n.p., 1928), [1].

32. Anthony W. Ivins, Conference Report, April 1929, 15, emphasis added.

33. John A. Widtsoe and Franklin S. Harris Jr., *Seven Claims of the Book of Mormon: A Collection of Evidences* (Independence, Mo.: Zion's Printing and Publishing, [1937]), 87.

34. William E. Berrett, Milton R. Hunter, Roy A. Welker, and H. Alvah Fitzgerald, *A Guide to the Study of the Book of Mormon* (Salt Lake City: LDS Department of Education, 1938), 47–48.

35. Roy A. West, *An Introduction to the Book of Mormon: A Religious-Literary Study* (Salt Lake City: LDS Department of Education, 1940), 11. "Inspiration and encouragement were offered by Albert E. Bowen [a member of the Quorum of the Twelve Apostles] who read the manuscript and offered constructive appraisal upon the contents of the study" (ibid., 4).

36. West, *Introduction to the Book of Mormon*, 63 n. 27.

37. Antoine R. Ivins, "The Lamanites," *Relief Society Magazine* 37 (August 1950): 507–8.

38. Richard L. Evans, "What Is a 'Mormon'?" in *Religions of America*, ed. Leo Rosten (London: Heinemann, 1957), 94, emphasis added; reprinted as *Religions of America: Ferment and Faith in an Age of Crisis: A New Guide and Almanac* (New York: Simon and Schuster, 1975).

39. Ariel L. Crowley, *About the Book of Mormon* (Idaho City, Idaho: n.p., 1961), 142.

40. Ibid., 145.

41. Ross T. Christensen, "¿Son lamanitas todos los indios americanos?" Preguntas y Respuestas, *Liahona*, November 1976, 9.

42. M. Wells Jakeman to Dr. R. E. C., 12 November 1955, quoted in *Progress in Archaeology: An Anthology*, comp. and ed. Ross T. Christensen (Provo, Utah: University Archaeological Society, Brigham Young University, 1963), 141.

43. Lane Johnson, "Who and where are the Lamanites?" I Have a Question, *Ensign*, December 1975, 15.

44. Nibley, *Lehi in the Desert*, 249–50.

45. Hugh Nibley, *Since Cumorah* (Salt Lake City: Deseret Book and FARMS, 1988), 218–19.

46. Ibid., 219.

47. See John L. Sorenson, "Where in the World? Views on Book of Mormon Geography," unpublished paper, 1955, revised 1974.

48. Sorenson, *Ancient American Setting;* Sorenson, "When Lehi's Party Arrived," 1–34.

49. Sorenson, *Ancient American Setting*, 50–56.

50. Sorenson, "When Lehi's Party Arrived," 3–4.

51. Ibid., 4.

52. Ibid., 4–6. "Maize is so totally domesticated a plant that it will not reproduce without human care. In other words, the Zeniffites or any other of Lehi's descendants could only be growing corn/maize because people already familiar with the complex of techniques for its successful cultivation had passed on the knowledge, and the seed, to the newcomers. Notice too that these passages in Mosiah [7:22; 9:14] indicate that corn had become the grain of preference among the Lamanites, and perhaps among the Zeniffites. That is, they had apparently integrated it into their system of taste preferences and nutrition as a primary food, for which cooks and diners in turn would have had familiar recipes, utensils, and so on" (ibid., 5).

53.  Brant Gardner, "The Other Stuff: Reading the Book of Mormon for Cultural Information," *FARMS Review of Books* 13/2 (2001): 35–37.

54.  Murphy, "Lamanite Genesis, Genealogy, and Genetics," 66.

55.  "What about the claim that the Jaredite migration from the Middle East was to 'that quarter where never had man been' (Ether 2:5)? Or, Lehi's claim between 588 and 570 BC that 'it is wisdom that this land should be kept as yet from the knowledge of other nations' (2 Ne 1:8)?" Thomas Murphy, open e-mail to Michael Whiting, 25 January 2003.

56.  George Reynolds followed this interpretation, noting, however, that this would not apply to the Jaredites, since "we have no account in the sacred records that God shut them out from the knowledge of the rest of mankind when he planted them in America." George Reynolds, "History of the Book of Mormon VI: The Contents of the Records," *Contributor* 5 (April 1884): 242. See also George M. Ottinger, "Old America: The Phoenicians," *Juvenile Instructor* 10 (6 February1875): 33.

57.  Sorenson, *Ancient American Setting,* 85. For an overview of the argument for a limited Book of Mormon geography, see Sorenson and Roper, "Before DNA," 7–10. For an overview of the evidence of archaeology and other sciences for population diversity in the New World, see ibid., 18–23.

58.  See also John L. Sorenson, *Nephite Culture and Society: Collected Papers,* ed. Matthew R. Sorenson (Salt Lake City: New Sage Books, 1997), 205–7.

59.  Sorenson, "When Lehi's Party Arrived," 7–8. For an earlier but similar view, see Gareth W. Lowe, "The Book of Mormon and Early Southwest Cultures," *U.A.S. [University Archaeological Society] Newsletter,* no. 19 (12 April 1954): 3.

60.  D. Jeffrey Meldrum and Trent D. Stephens, "Who Are the Children of Lehi?" *Journal of Book of Mormon Studies* 12/1 (2003): 38, 46–51.

61.  The previous tree, or at least that part which cumbered the ground, is said to have been "cut down," not uprooted. Younger olive branches can be planted or grafted into an older rootstock or stump. For pictures of such hybrid olive trees, see *The Allegory of the Olive Tree,* ed. Stephen D. Ricks and John W. Welch (Salt Lake City: Deseret Book and FARMS, 1994), 536, 539.

62.  I interpret the "waters" in this passage to refer to the waters of creation (Genesis 1:9–10) rather than to the waters of the flood of Noah.

63.  James E. Smith, "How Many Nephites? The Book of Mormon at the Bar of Demography," in *Book of Mormon Authorship Revisited: The Evidence for Ancient Origins,* ed. Noel B. Reynolds (Provo, Utah: FARMS, 1997), 272.

64.  Although wars and contentions are mentioned by nearly every chronicler who wrote on Nephi's small plates, most of these conflicts are specified as being between Lamanites and Nephites. It is not until Amaleki, the last of these chroniclers, begins his account that dissent among the Nephites themselves is implied. He records in Omni 1:12–13 that Mosiah, "being warned of the Lord that he should flee out of the land of Nephi," departed into the wilderness with "as many as would hearken unto the voice of the Lord" and eventually encountered the people of Zarahemla. This exodus, reminiscent of Nephi's departure from the land of first inheritance generations earlier due to family contention, is estimated to have occurred sometime between 279 and 130 BC.

65. For a similar perspective, see Brant Gardner, "A Social History of the Early Nephites, Part 1," *Meridian Magazine,* 2003, www.meridianmagazine.com/sci_rel/030731fair .html (accessed 16 October 2003).

# Swimming in the Gene Pool: Israelite Kinship Relations, Genes, and Genealogy

*Matthew Roper*

The Book of Mormon claims an ancient Israelite heritage for the American Indian, and since identifiable genetic evidence that might connect contemporary Native Americans with modern Jews is lacking, critics of the Book of Mormon assert that this contradicts the revelations of Joseph Smith and long-held traditional views about the Book of Mormon. Further, the critics suggest Latter-day Saints should abandon their belief that the Book of Mormon is an authentic account of an ancient American people and concede it to be an anachronistic specimen of nineteenth-century racist ideology.[1]

Several assumptions underlie these arguments against the Book of Mormon, and these are not always made clear. For example, what do we really know about the hereditary background of Israel and the ancient Near East? Were they a uniform genetic group? What genetic characteristics would distinguish an ancient Israelite population from other Asiatic groups of the same era? Are modern Jewish populations hereditarily the same as ancient Israelite populations? Are modern Asiatic populations hereditarily the same as ancient Asiatic populations? Those who wish to demonstrate on the basis of DNA studies that Native American populations do not have Israelite roots should first establish what an ancient Israelite source population should be like. When one examines the biblical account and later Jewish history, however, it becomes clear that Israel was never a genetically homogeneous entity. Further, examination of the nature of ancient Israel raises similar questions about the genetic heritage of the "people of Lehi" (3 Nephi 4:11) as described in the Book of Mormon. Were all Book of Mormon peoples literally descended from Israel? Are all Amerindians descendants of Laman? Is the term *Lamanite* an exclusively genetic classification? The text of the Book of Mormon makes it clear that Lehite Israel was not confined to literal descendants, but also included many of other origins who, under different conditions and circumstances, came to be numbered among Israel. Finally, to what extent might the present-day Native American population plausibly have any Israelite genetic heritage? Could one reasonably expect it to be identifiable? Does a lack of genetic evidence negate the possibility of an authentic genealogical descent? In fact, population studies have shown that the notion of Lehi as an ancestor of the majority of the current Amerindian population is not as far-fetched as some may assume.[2]

## Who Is an Israelite?

One key assumption made by some recent critics of the Book of Mormon is that ancient Israel was a genetically identifiable group with a common set of markers that can still be found in modern Jewish populations. They conclude that it is a simple matter of testing Jewish DNA against Native American DNA to see if there are genetic ties.[3] But terms like *Israelite* or *Jew* can denote various kinds of identities, including sociocultural and political, as well as genetic relationships. In order to determine who is most likely to be a literal descendant of Israel or of Lehi, one must look in the right places. The Bible and the Book of Mormon are the primary sources of information concerning these people. As we review what these scriptures tell us about the biblical patriarchs and their descendants, we must bear in mind that most of the DNA studies performed using samples from Native Americans have been of *mitochondrial* DNA (mtDNA), which is passed directly from a woman to each of her offspring, with no input from the father.[4]

Before DNA sampling from the Old and New Worlds can be used to argue for or against the historical authenticity of the Book of Mormon, a number of factors must be considered. For example, from whom must DNA samples be taken in order to be relevant? While some Latter-day Saints may have assumed that everyone inhabiting the New World prior to the arrival of European explorers was a descendant of Lehi's party, the Book of Mormon makes no such claim. Indeed, on a number of occasions the Nephite text indicates that others were in the land.[5] Given the likelihood that some of Lehi's descendants intermarried with indigenous peoples, an interpretation held by many Latter-day Saints, we are faced with the difficulty of identifying who might plausibly be expected to carry Lehite DNA. The same problem exists with regard to Old World Israelites. Can one merely take DNA samples from people who currently identify themselves as Jewish and expect them to match Nephite or Lamanite DNA?

### Children of Abraham and of Israel

In order to understand what *Israel* meant anciently in terms of kinship relations, it is necessary to review the history and development of that people as described in the biblical account. Abraham is the first person to be called a "Hebrew" in the Bible (Genesis 14:13), though his grandson Jacob, who lived in Syria for a time, is termed a "Syrian" (Deuteronomy 26:5). The Bible gives us the names of Abraham's patrilineal male ancestors, but we know nothing about the origin of his mother or his wife Sarah. This poses a problem for a researcher hoping to trace the Abrahamic genetic heritage using mtDNA.

In addition to Sarah's son, Isaac, Abraham had sons by two other wives: an Egyptian named Hagar, who bore Ishmael (Genesis 16:1, 3; 21:9; 25:12); and a woman of unknown origin named Keturah, who bore six sons (Genesis 25:1–4). Besides his own children and immediate family, Abraham's house included men and women servants and people he had converted to his faith (Genesis 12:5; Abraham 2:15). Among these were his chief steward, Eliezer (Genesis 15:2), and 318 "trained servants, born in his own house," who could be mustered for battle (Genesis 14:14). All of these, according to the custom of the time, would have been considered "Hebrews," though they may have had no biological relationship to Abraham. This presents a second problem for those who hope to use the Bible as documentation of genetic connections.

Abraham's son Ishmael married an Egyptian woman (Genesis 21:21), while Isaac married his cousin Rebekah. Isaac's son Esau had two Hittite wives (Genesis 26:34) and another who was a daughter of Ishmael (Genesis 28:8–9). Esau's brother, Jacob, who came to be known as Israel, fathered twelve sons and one daughter by four wives (Genesis 29:28–35; 30:1–24; 35:15–19). Each of Jacob's children would have carried the mtDNA of his or her mother. While two of these wives, Leah and Rachel, were Jacob's cousins, the Bible tells us nothing of the origins and background of the other two, Zilpah and Bilhah.

Likewise, little is known of the women who married the sons of Jacob, though we know that Joseph married an Egyptian, Asenath, who bore him Manasseh and Ephraim (Genesis 41:45, 50–52).[6] Joseph's half-brother Judah had three sons by a Canaanite wife named Shuah and twin sons by Tamar, whose ancestry is unknown (Genesis 38:2–30). Of the half-Canaanite sons, only one (Shelah) lived long enough to have posterity, but his mtDNA would be unlike that of his half-brothers, Pharez and Zarah, unless their mothers were sisters (Genesis 46:12; Numbers 26:19–21). From Pharez descended Salmon, who married the Canaanite woman Rahab, who had been spared with her father's household during the Israelite destruction of the city of Jericho in Joshua's day. Their son was Boaz, who married the Moabitess Ruth, who became the great-grandmother of King David and, consequently, of all the kings of Judah and of Jesus Christ himself (Ruth 4:18–22; Matthew 1:2–16). While most of the kings of Judah from whom Christ is descended married women of the same tribe or of other Israelite tribes, this is not true of all of them. For example, Rehoboam, son of Solomon, was born of a woman named Naamah, who was an Ammonitess (1 Kings 14:21, 31; 2 Chronicles 12:13). Genesis 40:10 informs us that Simeon had a Canaanite wife, but nothing is said of the other wives of Jacob's sons or their origins, although it seems likely that they also married outside Abraham's kin group. The children and grandchildren of Jacob who are mentioned in the biblical account number seventy, but this does not include daughters and granddaughters. Although nothing is specifically said on the matter, it is not unreasonable to assume that Jacob's people included servants and their families as well.[7] One thing, however, seems certain: all of Jacob's grandchildren inherited their mtDNA from their mothers, who were likely non-Israelite.

We know very little about Israelite marriage practices in Egypt during the four-hundred-year sojourn there; however, there is some indication that intermarriage with non-Israelite peoples was not uncommon (see, for example, Leviticus 24:10). Moses married a Midianitess (Exodus 2:21). When the Israelites left Egypt, it is said that a "mixed multitude" went with them (Exodus 12:38; Numbers 11:4).[8] Whatever its size, the exodus group included many who were not descended from Jacob's original family.[9] We have no details about the ancestry of these other people, but we know from Leviticus 24:10 that at least one of the men who fled into the wilderness with Moses had an Israelite mother and an Egyptian father.

### Israel in the Promised Land

According to prominent Jewish scholar Raphael Patai, "It seems quite certain that the Israelite tribes which settled in Canaan in the thirteenth century BC contained, in addition to the original Aramaean stock of Abraham and his half-sister Sarah, also Amorite and Hittite, as well as Canaanite and Egyptian, racial elements."[10] Following their war with the Midianites, the Israelites "took all of the women of Midian captives, and their little ones" (Numbers 31:9). When Moses learned of this, he ordered them to slay the males and all the women who were not virgins but allowed his people to marry the virgins (Numbers 31:15–18). This would have had a substantial impact on the mtDNA of the various tribes, yet we know very little or nothing about the genetic inheritance of the Midianites.

Some Bible scholars believe that the Jerahmeelites, Kenizzites, and Calebites associated with the tribe of Judah in the Bible were non-Israelite peoples adopted or absorbed into that tribe.[11] The Kenites, descendants of Moses' Midianite father-in-law, assisted the tribe of Judah in conquering the region of Arad during the Israelite invasion of Canaan (Judges 1:16). One of their number, Heber, moved to the northern part of the land, where his wife, Jael, slew the Canaanite general Sisera (Judges 4:11–22). Several generations later, Jehonadab, son of Rechab, another Kenite living in the same region, took part in the overthrow of the house of Ahab (2 Kings 10:15–17; 1 Chronicles 2:55). Some of the Rechabites were later taken into the temple in Jerusalem by the prophet Jeremiah, who praised them for their faithfulness (Jeremiah 35). It is likely that there was some inter-marriage between Israel and these people. Also during the conquest, the Gibeonites, who controlled four cities, were incorporated into the people of Israel (Joshua 9). Again, we know very little about the background and origin of this people.

The Lord's instruction to the Israelites was to destroy the people of the land of Canaan ("the Hittites, and the Amorites, the Canaanites, and the Perizzites, the Hivites, and the Jebusites") but to make peace with more distant cities when possible. When not possible, they were to slay the men but keep the women and children for themselves (Deuteronomy 20:10–17). Following subsequent wars with the Syrians, Ammonites, Moabites, and Edomites, the Israelites would also have married women of those nations, thus introducing new mtDNA into the Israelite gene pool.

As it turned out, the Israelites did not destroy all the people of the land of Canaan.[12] They were unable to expel the Canaanite residents of Beth-shean, Taanach, Dor, Ibleam, Megiddo, Gezer, Kitron,

Nahalol, Accho, Zidon, Ahlab, Achzib, Helbah, Aphik, Rehob, Beth-shemesh, and Beth-anath, among others, all of whom were made to pay tribute and remained among the Israelites (Judges 1:27–36).

After the Israelites settled in Canaan, they intermarried with the indigenous inhabitants of the land. "And the children of Israel dwelt among the Canaanites, Hittites, and Amorites, and Perizzites, and Hivites, and Jebusites: And they took their daughters to be their wives, and gave their daughters to their sons, and served their gods" (Judges 3:5–6). Patai writes:

> We know too little about the racial identity of the Israelites and the nations enumerated above in this early period to be able to assess the racial significance of these intermarriages. There can, however, be little doubt that several nations were racially quite different from the Israelites. Thus the Philistines had come, in all probability, from the island of Crete ("Caphtor"). The Hivites, generally identified with the Hurrians, were a non-"Semitic" people whose original home seems to have been in Eastern Anatolia. The Hittites had come from Central Anatolia where they had a powerful empire in the second millennium BC. The Canaanites and Zidonians seem to have been of a racial stock similar to that of the Israelites. The racial identity of the Amorites, Perizzites, and Jebusites is unknown.[13]

Consequently, from the beginning, Israel came to incorporate many non-Israelite peoples into its tribal structure, even though they were originally neither a part of the exodus group nor of the house and family of Abraham, Isaac, and Jacob. The story of Lehi's own tribe, Manasseh, is typical:

> Although the earliest Israelite population of Manasseh was rural, the tribal territory remained under the dominance of a number of towns in its heartland that only gradually became Israelite. Shechem, for instance, was already of

importance to the oldest Israelites in the Bronze Age, but in the period of the Judges it still had a predominantly non-Israelite population (Judges 9). Like Tirzah and Hepher, Shechem was ultimately included in the tribal genealogy (Num 26:28–34; Josh 17:2–3). Other former Canaanite towns like Ibleam, Dothan, Beth-shan, Taanach, and Megiddo were more peripheral. Gradually all of these towns became Israelite.[14]

Lehi's genetic heritage, then, is likely to have been as diverse as that of any other descendant of Israel. Indeed, the very fact that Lehi was still in Judah after his tribe had gone into captivity and subsequently disappeared, as well as the fact that he was unaware of his tribal affiliation until he read the brass plates, indicates that genetic relationships were by no means the sole ties binding Israelite society together. And, of course, the mtDNA passed on to Lehi's children would not in any case have been his own.[15]

"In a small country such as biblical Israel," observes Patai, "with non-Hebrew ethnic elements interspersed with the Hebrews and surrounding them on all sides within a few miles of their main urban population centers, and with lively commercial, cultural, and often also hostile contacts across the borders (all of which is amply attested in the books of Samuel and Kings), there can be no question but that interbreeding was an everyday occurrence."[16] The ever-increasing genetic complexity of this mixture of interbred peoples can be illustrated using just a few examples from the time of King David, which we can assume were typical of other contemporary Israelite relationships at the time. As noted by Patai,

> David had a Hittite officer in his army, Uriah, whose wife was an Israelite woman. Tyrian carpenters and masons lived for years in Jerusalem while they built a palace for David. David himself had numerous concubines, some of whom must have been alien slave girls. His servants, too, had such

handmaids. Among his slaves were Moabites. After he smote Hadadezer, king of Zobah in Syria, he brought back thousands of prisoners of war. Part of his own army consisted of Cherethites and Pelethites who were, in all probability, foreign troops. He also had troops from the Philistine city of Gath. Among his servants there was a Cushite; and among the thirty "mighty men" of David, who seem to have been commanders of élite troops, there were several foreigners. The commander of his camel corps was Obil the Ishmaelite. His flocks were under the control of Jaziz the Hagrite; the Hagrites were, like the Ishmaelites, nomadic, tent-dwelling tribes located east of Gilead in the Syrian Desert. The presence of so many foreign men could not help but lead to interbreeding with the Israelite women.[17]

Patai adds that "toward the end of this period, the mixed origin of the Judaites must have been common knowledge."[18]

Hiram, the architect of Solomon's temple, was a resident of the Canaanite city of Tyre; his father was a Tyrian, but his mother was of the Israelite tribe of Naphtali (1 Kings 7:13–14). The king of Tyre, whose name was also Hiram, in payment for his assistance in providing materials and workmen for the temple, received from Solomon control over some twenty Galilean cities (1 Kings 9:11).

Solomon married an Egyptian princess (1 Kings 3:1; 7:8; 9:16, 24). "But king Solomon loved many strange [foreign] women, together with the daughter of Pharaoh, women of the Moabites, Ammonites, Edomites, Zidonians, and Hittites; of the nations concerning which the Lord said unto the children of Israel, Ye shall not go in to them, neither shall they come in unto you: for surely they will turn away your heart after their gods: Solomon clave unto these in love" (1 Kings 11:1–2). A few generations later, Ahab, king of Israel, married Jezebel, daughter of the king of the Canaanite city of Zidon (1 Kings 16:30–31). According to 1 Chronicles 2:34–35, Sheshan, of the tribe of Judah, married his daughter to an Egyptian servant named Jarha. We also know that Samson, of the tribe of Dan, preferred Philistine women (Judges 14:1–3; 16:1–20). So the intermarriage of Israelites with their neighbors is well attested in the Bible and may have been even more widespread than these few examples illustrate. Indeed, through the prophet Ezekiel the Lord said to the Jewish city of Jerusalem, "Thy birth and thy nativity is of the land of Canaan; thy father was an Amorite, and thy mother an Hittite" (Ezekiel 16:3).

After the time of David and Solomon, ethnic groups within the land came to be included by biblical writers under the label *Israel* even though at one time they had been seen as socially distinct. "By the end of the united monarchy," notes Ziony Zevit, "they were either wiped out (completely or partially) or they were absorbed into the fabric of the tribal organizations (cf. 1 Sam. 27:8; Deut. 21:10–13; Josh. 9:26–27 [an apologetic etiology]). If absorbed, they were no longer 'others.'"[19] They were now simply *Israel*.

In his seminal history of Israel, historian John Bright argues that

> we are not to suppose that the entity we call Israel was formed and held together in the face of adversity exclusively, or even primarily, through ties of blood kinship. True, the Bible traces the descent of all the tribes to the ancestor Jacob (Israel), and this might lead one to suppose that Israel was in fact a kinship unit. But kinship terminology is often employed in the Bible to express a social solidarity, a feeling of closeness, that actually arose from other factors. Seldom in all of history has blood kinship, or common racial stock or language, been the determinative factor in the formation and preservation of larger social and political units. What is more to the point, there is abundant evidence that not all Israelites were in fact related one to another by blood. . . . As the Bible itself makes clear, Israel—both those parts of it that had come from the desert and those parts already present in Palestine who entered into its structure—included elements of the most heterogeneous origin who could not possibly

have descended from a single family tree. Even the various tribes doubtless represented territorial units, rather than familial ones (though, naturally, through intermarriage, ties of real kinship were doubtless strong within the tribes). And, on the other hand, it was never her bloodstream, her racial stock or her language, that set Israel off from her immediate neighbors (Canaanites, Moabites, Ammonites, Edomites, etc.), but rather the tradition (or, if one prefers, the ideology) to which she was committed. Speaking theologically, one might with justice call Israel a family; but from a historical point of view neither her first appearance nor her continued existence can be accounted for in terms of blood kinship.[20]

Even in preexilic times, Israel was a mixture of diverse groups, many of whose exact origins are unknown. In addition to actual descendants of Abraham, "Israel" always included many others who became attached to that body in various ways.

By 722 BC, the northern kingdom of Israel had been carried into captivity by the Assyrians. Assyrian records report that 27,290 inhabitants of Samaria were taken captive by Sargon,[21] but we can assume that previous Assyrian invasions would have taken away many more. Shortly after the fall of Samaria, Sennacherib invaded Judah, conquered many of its cities, and drove out of them 200,150 men, women, and children.[22] Assyrian captives were forcibly resettled in northern Mesopotamia, where many would have intermarried with the peoples of that land, eventually losing their identity as Israel and becoming "lost" to history. Other remnants of the northern kingdom remained in the land and intermarried with non-Israelite peoples whom the Assyrians had brought in to replace the Israelites who had been carried away. Given how little we know of the details of such events, it is difficult to measure the genetic effect that such intermarriages had upon subsequent Israelites. Because Lehi and Laban were descendants of the tribes of Joseph (1 Nephi 5: 14, 16), whose lands of inheritance were in the kingdom of Israel, it is possible that their ancestors had been displaced during the war with Assyria and had relocated in Judah.[23] Did any of Lehi's ancestors marry non-Israelites? What effect would such relationships have had upon Lehi's genetic inheritance? We don't know.

## Who Is a Jew?

Although the kingdom of Judah endured for 134 years longer than the kingdom of Israel, it underwent genetic changes as sweeping as those that overwhelmed its brother nation. In addition to the regular intermarriages recorded in the Bible as normal in everyday Judaic life, inhabitants of Judah who refused to heed Jeremiah, Lehi, and their contemporary prophets experienced the Babylonian conquest and captivity, which meant new infusions of DNA from captors and fellow captives. The subsequent conquest of Babylon by the Medes and Persians brought new intermarriages (the most famous of which is chronicled in the biblical book of Esther), as well as the opportunity for Jews to choose whether to remain in Babylon or to return to Judah and rebuild it. Since some chose to leave and others to remain, the genetic heritage of the Jews became divided at that point into many streams of genetic history.

In time, the returned inhabitants of Judah suffered conquest and occupation by first the Greeks and then the Romans, with further intermarriage as the almost inevitable result. The Jews to whom Jesus came to teach his gospel were genetically a very mixed group, and the Savior knew it. His apparent reluctance to heal the Syro-Phoenician woman's daughter (Matthew 15:21–28; Mark 7:24–30) stemmed not from racist feeling but from his sense of mission toward *covenant* Israel; genetically, the woman may have had every right to claim Israelite heritage.

The final great historical blow to the already compromised purity of Jewish DNA came about with the expulsion of the Jews from the land of their inheritance soon after the death and resurrection of Christ. In the Diaspora that followed, Jews spread from Spain to

China, separating their genetic heritage into innumerable divergent streams. Depending on the tolerance level of their host cultures, perceived needs for alliances, conversion rates, types of contact in the course of everyday life, and a myriad of other influences, intermarriage has been more or less a factor in Jewish genetic heritage ever since.

## Later Criteria for Jewishness

To whom, then, does the term *Jewish* refer? In ancient Israel, one was considered a member of one's father's tribe and clan. This changed in postbiblical Judaism, when it was decided that one born of a Jewish mother is Jewish, while one born of a gentile mother is not Jewish, even if the father is (Babylonian Talmud *Kiddushin* 68b). While this would seem to make easier the task of tracing genetic background through mtDNA, there is no evidence of what the mtDNA of a "typical" Jewish woman was like at the time this criterion developed in the second and third centuries AD. This fact, combined with the certainty of new mtDNA introduction due to intermarriages and conversions before and since, means that the problem remains as it began in Abraham's day, with no known, distinctive strain of mtDNA from which to begin.

Certain lineages continue to be designated through the father, such as the *cohanim,* or priests, who are descended from Aaron's tribe. The Y chromosome passes from father to son virtually intact,[24] and there is indeed a distinctive *haplotype* (genetic complex) on the Y chromosome of *cohanim* that sets them apart; more will be said about this below. Even in these cases, though, for the tribal association to count in modern Judaism, one's mother must still be Jewish. However, since Judaism accepts converts, the Jewishness of one's mother is not necessarily traceable to one of the ancient tribes of Israel. In the tenth century AD, for example, the king of the Khazars, a group living in Central Asia, converted to Judaism and was followed by his people. So an entire nation with no Israelite genetic inheritance suddenly became "Jews." At least one Jewish researcher, Arthur Koestler, suggests that the Ashkenazi (European) Jews are descended from the Khazars rather than from ancient Israel, though it is likely that they have intermarried with other Jews over the centuries.[25]

These and other factors have led Patai to conclude that there have been

> substantial modifications in the racial identity of the original biblical Children of Israel, which itself is still overshadowed by a great question mark. The Jewish sojourn in a constantly expanding global Diaspora for some two and a half millennia resulted in an increasing diversification that, by the outgoing Middle Ages, reached a stage at which the Jewish people, whatever their historical antecedents and the power of their cultural and religious traditions that sustained them, could no longer be considered members of a single race. In a word: to be a Jew has for long not been a question of genes, but of a mind-set.[26]

It is important to remember that most Jews today represent that part of Israel that has retained a knowledge of its identity, while the greater part of the tribes of ancient Israel, as indicated above, have lost a knowledge of who they once were as they were scattered among all nations. In light of the above observations, it is clear that the identity of an "Israelite" or a "Jew" in genetic terms is far more complex than is often appreciated.

The Lord promised Abraham that he would have posterity as numerous "as the stars of the heaven, and as the sand which is upon the sea shore" (Genesis 22:17). Among modern peoples who claim descent from Abraham are more than thirteen million Jews worldwide[27] and hundreds of millions of Arabs. Because of intermarriage, however, none of these can claim exclusive Abrahamic ancestry. During the nearly two millennia since the Romans expelled them from Jerusalem, Jews have intermarried with non-Jews on every continent. Following expansion out of the Arabian peninsula in the seventh century AD and since then, Arabs have similarly integrated with people from the Middle East all across North Africa and into other parts of the world in more recent times. So one can safely say that most, if not all, of Abraham's descendants have mixed ancestry.

## The Lemba and the Lehites

If mtDNA is not a promising avenue for tracing Israelite heritage among Native Americans, there is at least the possibility of seeking out another distinctive genetic trait and testing specifically for it among Native American populations. One such candidate is the Y-chromosome haplotype that uniquely identifies the heritage of a Jewish *cohen* (priest). In arguing that scientists should be able to find evidence of Israelite DNA among Native Americans if the Book of Mormon is true, critics note the example of the African Lemba tribe, which claims Jewish origins. Several recent studies of Lemba Y-chromosome DNA have found evidence supporting a Jewish origin, indicating that many Lemba carry the distinctive *cohen* haplotype found among some Jews, especially among those claiming to be *cohanim*—that is, descendants of Moses' brother, Aaron, of the tribe of Levi.[28] Some researchers "date the origin of the Cohen haplotype to 2,100 to 3,250 years ago, putting it within the historical range of the alleged Lehite and Mulekite migrations to the New World."[29] Presumably, if the Book of Mormon is historical, it should be possible to find similar evidence in Native American DNA, but "DNA tests of the Lemba yielded a strikingly different outcome than for Native Americans."[30]

There are, however, several problems with this line of reasoning. The assumption that researchers should be able to find the *cohen* marker in Amerindian populations, if any Native Americans were truly Israelite, fails because there is no indication in the Book of Mormon that the Nephites had Levites among them. Lehi was from the tribe of Joseph (1 Nephi 5:14; Alma 10:3). The priesthood mentioned in the Book of Mormon is the Melchizedek Priesthood (Alma 13).[31] With no record of *cohanim* or even Levites among pre-Columbian Americans, researchers are currently at a loss to know what DNA markers to use in determining whether or not a Native American is a descendant of Israel. Second, it is not certain that the *cohen* haplotype was even present in preexilic Israelites, although that is possible. Third, the Lemba retained a memory of their connection with the Jews, which is why researchers were interested in studying them in the first place. In contrast to the Lemba, however, the people of Lehi, like the lost tribes, did not retain a memory of Israelite origins after Moroni had buried the plates. With no living tradition of an Israelite connection to direct his choice of a study group, a modern researcher is left with the daunting prospect of testing all Amerindian groups for a marker that may never have been manifested among the Book of Mormon peoples and, indeed, may not even have existed at the time of their separation from the rest of Israel.

### Jewish Diseases

Considering the problems attendant on mtDNA and Y-chromosome studies of Native Americans that might reveal Israelite genetic connections, the question remains of what other marker a researcher could use. Some critics have asserted that other biological characteristics found in modern Jews and passed down genetically should be used as markers with which to compare modern Native Americans.[32] Various hereditary ailments such as Tay-Sachs disease occur rarely in the general population but are common among some groups of Jews. Since these particular diseases are not currently found in Native American populations, critics suggest that this disproves the idea that Native Americans may have Israelite ancestry.

This argument faces two major hurdles when applied to the Book of Mormon. First, before making such comparisons, one would need to establish whether such diseases were common among preexilic

Israelites. As noted above, ancient Israel was genetically diverse and may have differed in significant ways from modern Jewish populations. It needs to be established that such characteristics are representative of the people from which Lehi and Mulek and their companions came before one can compare them with Amerindian populations, ancient or modern. Some scientists believe that Tay-Sachs disease could be a relatively recent ailment among Jews "that may have resulted from only a single mutation hundreds of years ago."[33] Before one could use this disease as a biological marker, it would be necessary, at the very least, to establish the presence of this malady in the ancient Judaic population from which Lehi and his companions came.

Second, the argument assumes that these rare diseases are common to all Jews, but this is not the case. Tay-Sachs disease, for example, tends to be common among Ashkenazi Jews but is as rare in Jews of non-Ashkenazi descent as it is among non-Jews. Similarly, other diseases that may be found in one Jewish group tend to be rare or absent in another. After reviewing the literature relating to Jewish diseases, Patai concludes, "When certain diseases appear to be more or less common in Jews than non-Jews, closer inspection usually reveals that the high or low incidence of the disease is in fact a feature of only one group of Jews. The group may consist of Middle Eastern Jews, Sephardic Jews, or even Ashkenazi Jews originating from a small area in Eastern Europe. None of the diseases described is characteristic of Jews in general."[34] Consequently, "the distribution of particular diseases cannot be used to differentiate Jews in general from non-Jews."[35] The bottom line is that scientists currently do not have an ancient Israelite marker of any kind with which to compare Native American populations.

## Who Are Lehites? Lineage-Related Terms in the Book of Mormon Text

If their arguments are to have any validity, critics of the Book of Mormon must assume that lineage-related terms in the Book of

Mormon—such as *descendant, seed, children, Nephite,* and *Lamanite*—are exclusively genetic in their meaning. As noted already, however, the term *house of Israel* as used in the Bible has always included both literal descendants and others who became part of the family through intermarriage, alliance, conversion, or other means. The same was apparently true for Lehite Israel—while familial terms in the Book of Mormon include a genetic component, the more common usage of such terms in the text is ideological, social, and political. Just as the concept of *Israel* embraced many who were not actual descendants of Jacob, the concepts of *Nephite* and *Lamanite* included within those designations both literal descendants and others who were adopted in. An examination of how these terms are used in the scriptural texts of Latter-day Saints is revealing.

*Descendant.* The number of appearances of the term *descendant* is impressive in itself. Apparently, among the Book of Mormon peoples, being the descendant of some notable figure was considered meaningful enough to be recorded and invoked for its prestige through the centuries. Some examples of these usages follow.

• Jaredite descendants were mentioned in Ether's genealogy (Ether 1:6, 16, 23; 10:1, 8–9; 11:11).

• Lehi discovered that he was a descendant of Joseph (1 Nephi 5:14; 6:2; 2 Nephi 3:4).

• Ammon and the Nephite dissenter Coriantumr were both said to be descendants of Zarahemla (Mosiah 7:3, 13; Helaman 1:15), who was a descendant of Mulek (Mosiah 25:2).

• Descendants of Nephi were not as numerous as the people of Zarahemla (Mosiah 25:2).

• The elder Alma was a descendant of Nephi (Mosiah 17:2).

• Those who kept the Nephite record were also descendants of Nephi (Mormon's introduction to 3 Nephi), and the kingdom was conferred only upon descendants of Nephi (Mosiah 25:13).

• The Nephite dissenter Ammoron, who became a Lamanite king, was a descendant of Zoram (Alma 54:23).

- Another Lamanite king was a descendant of Ishmael (Alma 17:21).
- Lamanites included descendants of the priests of Noah and other dissenters from the Nephites (Alma 43:13).
- Actual descendants of Laman and Lemuel and Ishmael joined the church through the ministry of the sons of Mosiah (Alma 24:29; 17:21).
- Amulek emphasized his descent from Nephi in order to persuade the people of Ammonihah to listen to Alma's teachings (Alma 10:2–3).
- Helaman's army of two thousand were said to have been descendants of Laman, son of Lehi (Alma 56:3).
- Moroni had to search among his men to find one who was a descendant of Laman (Alma 55:4).
- At one time the Gadianton robbers included "real descendants of the Lamanites" (Helaman 11:24).
- Mormon described himself as a descendant of Nephi (Mormon 1:5; 8:13) and "a pure descendant of Lehi" (3 Nephi 5:20).

While it seems that something genetic was often implied by the use of the term *descendant,* such references usually occur in a context in which this is thought to be noteworthy or exceptional. Such distinctions would be meaningless if all or a large part of the total population could claim the same genetic heritage.

*Seed.* One might assume that the term *seed* refers to literal descendants of Israel or Lehi. While some passages seem to refer to literal descendants, that usage is not exclusive and can include other groups as well. In this context, Abinadi's discussion of Christ is noteworthy.

> And now what say ye? And who shall be his seed? Behold I say unto you, that whosoever has heard the words of the prophets, yea, all the holy prophets who have prophesied concerning the coming of the Lord—I say unto you, that all those who have hearkened unto their words, and believed

that the Lord would redeem his people, and have looked forward to that day for a remission of their sins, I say unto you,
that these are his seed, or they are the heirs of the kingdom
of God. For these are they whose sins he has borne; these
are they for whom he has died, to redeem them from their
transgressions. And now, are they not his seed? Yea, and are
not the prophets, every one that has opened his mouth to
prophesy, that has not fallen into transgression, I mean all
the holy prophets ever since the world began? I say unto you
that they are his seed. (Mosiah 15:10–13)

Abinadi, then, defines the *seed of Christ* as the prophets and
everyone else who hears their words, hearkens to them, believes in
and looks forward to Christ's redemption, and has not subsequently
fallen away. In this passage, *seed* refers to a covenantal relationship
rather than a genetic one. They are considered the seed or children of
Christ, and he becomes their covenant father. The Abrahamic covenant is based upon this same concept. The Lord promised Abraham:

And I will make of thee a great nation, and I will bless
thee above measure, and make thy name great among all
nations, and thou shalt be a blessing unto thy seed after
thee, that in their hands they shall bear this ministry and
Priesthood unto all nations; And I will bless them through
thy name; for *as many as receive this Gospel shall be called
after thy name, and shall be accounted thy seed, and shall rise
up and bless thee, as their father.* (Abraham 2:9–10)

Abraham's "seed," then, includes not only his literal descendants,
but also all those who enter the covenant or receive the gospel. In
terms of blessings, there appears to be no difference between the
two. Through the covenant all may become Abraham's seed, and he
becomes their father.

Similarly, the Lord told Lehi's family, "Wherefore, I will con-
secrate this land unto thy seed, *and them who shall be numbered*

*among thy seed,* forever, for the land of their inheritance; for it is a choice land, saith God unto me, above all other lands, wherefore I will have all men that dwell thereon that they shall worship me, saith God" (2 Nephi 10:19). Mormon noted that "whosoever did mingle his seed with that of the Lamanites did bring the same curse upon his seed. Therefore, *whosoever suffered himself to be led away by the Lamanites was called under that head"*—that is, *Lamanites* (Alma 3:9–10). Also, "whosoever *would not believe* in the tradition of the Lamanites, but *believed* those records which were brought out of the land of Jerusalem, and also in the tradition of their fathers, which were correct, who believed in the commandments of God and kept them, were *called* the Nephites, or the people of Nephi, from that time forth" (Alma 3:11). Those who rejected Nephite traditions and intermarried with unbelieving Lamanites, those who fought against the Nephites, and those who departed from the Nephites were *called* Lamanites, just as those who accepted Nephite teachings were *called* Nephites. "I will bless thee, and *whomsoever shall be called thy seed, henceforth and forever;* and these were the promises of the Lord unto Nephi and to his seed" (Alma 3:17). The Nephites were "destroyed" not by being genetically extinguished but by ceasing to exist as an identifiable cultural group; those Nephites who elected to abandon their cultural ties—including both literal descendants of Nephi and other people who had once been called Nephites—were thereafter numbered with the Lamanites.

> And when that great day cometh, behold, the time very soon cometh that those who are now, or the seed of those who are now *numbered among* the people of Nephi, shall no more be *numbered among* the people of Nephi. But whosoever remaineth, and is not destroyed in that great and dreadful day, shall be *numbered among* the Lamanites, and shall become like unto them, all, save it be a few who shall be called the disciples of the Lord; and them shall the Lamanites pursue even until they shall become extinct. And

now, because of iniquity, this prophecy shall be fulfilled. (Alma 45:13–14)

*Children.* One can see a similar pattern in the usage of the term *children.* Men and women become the children of Christ through covenant. "And now, because of the covenant which ye have made ye shall be called the children of Christ, his sons, and his daughters; for behold, this day he hath spiritually begotten you; for ye say that your hearts are changed through faith on his name; therefore, ye are born of him and have become his sons and his daughters" (Mosiah 5:7; see also 4 Nephi 1:17; Ether 3:14). This can also be seen in the example of the children of Amulon: "And it came to pass that those who were the children of Amulon and his brethren, who had taken to wife the daughters of the Lamanites, were displeased with the conduct of their fathers, and they would no longer be called by the names of their fathers, therefore they took upon themselves the name of Nephi, that they might be called the children of Nephi and be numbered among those who were called Nephites" (Mosiah 25:12). The Book of Mormon text plainly indicates that the terms *seed* and *children* did not apply exclusively to genetic descendants but also included those who were called *or* numbered among such descendants. Similarly, Christ, Abraham, Nephi, Laman, or anybody else could be called someone's father even if the relationship was not a literal one.

Accordingly, non-Israelites who receive gospel covenants are numbered among not only the children of Israel, but also the children of Lehi. As the angel of the Lord explained to Nephi, in the last days the Gentiles who repent "and harden not their hearts against the Lamb of God . . . shall be numbered among the seed of thy father; yea, they shall be numbered among the house of Israel; and they shall be a blessed people upon the promised land forever" (1 Nephi 14:1–2). Repentant Gentiles become children of Lehi and Israel. Nephi further explained, "For behold, I say unto you that as many of the Gentiles as will repent are the covenant people of the Lord; and as many of the Jews [among which he includes his own people] as will not repent shall be cast off; for the Lord covenanteth with none save it be with them that repent and believe in his Son, who is the Holy One of Israel" (2 Nephi 30:2). The Lamanites also must repent and come to a knowledge of the "great and true shepherd, and be *numbered* among his sheep" (Helaman 15:13).

*Nephite.* While the term *Nephite,* as it appears in the Book of Mormon, can refer to actual descendants of Nephi, the son of Lehi (Mormon 1:5; 8:13), it is more commonly used in a political and ideological sense to mean anybody under the rule of Nephi or his descendants. It can also include those of at least partial Israelite origin, like the Mulekites, who united with the Nephites (Mosiah 25:1–4); those originally of some other name who took upon themselves the name of Nephi and were called Nephites (Mosiah 25:12); those friendly to Nephi or the Nephites (Jacob 1:14); those numbered with the Nephites (Alma 3:17); those who kept the commandments of God and believed in the records and tradition of the Nephites (Alma 3:11); and those who accepted and sought to follow the teachings of Christ (4 Nephi 1:36). Throughout the Nephites' thousand-year history as a people, many of their literal descendants defected to, intermarried with, or were numbered among the Lamanites. Modern revelation indicates that among Native American peoples today are some, yet to be revealed, who are descendants of the Nephites, Jacobites, Josephites, and Zoramites and that one day they will receive a knowledge of the gospel (D&C 3:16–17).

*Lamanite.* Like the term *Nephite,* the term *Lamanite* has a number of different meanings in scripture.[36] It can refer to the following:

- Actual descendants of Laman, Lemuel, and the sons of Ishmael who followed Laman's leadership after the death of Lehi (2 Nephi 5:1–6). Modern revelation indicates that among Lamanites today are some, yet to be revealed, who are descendants of Laman, Lemuel, and the sons of Ishmael and that they will one day receive a knowledge of the gospel (D&C 3:18).

- Those who did not believe in the warnings and revelations of God through Nephi (2 Nephi 5:6).
- Those not friendly to Nephi or the Nephites (2 Nephi 5:14; Jacob 1:13–14).
- Those who rejected and did not believe in the records and traditions of the Nephites (Alma 3:11).
- Those who intermarried with the Lamanites (Alma 3:9, 15).
- Those who fought against the Nephites (Alma 3:16).
- Any who dissented from the Nephites (Alma 3:17).
- Any led away by the Lamanites (Alma 3:10).
- Those who rejected the teachings of Christ, together with their children and ideological sympathizers (4 Nephi 1:38).
- After the destruction of the Nephites as a cohesive group, the seed of anyone who at any time had once been numbered with the "people of Nephi" (Alma 45:13; cf. 45:14).

From the perspective of the "record of the Nephites," one could justifiably consider any pre-Columbian unbelievers whose ancestors were once blessed on the land to be Lamanites (2 Nephi 10:10–11, 18–19). Whether one is a literal descendant of Lehi or not, the Book of Mormon clarifies that being numbered among the covenant people of God is of primary importance to one's identity (2 Nephi 30:2).

After the appearance of Jesus in the New World, the conversion of the people ushered in an era of peace. In describing this time, the prophet Mormon said: "And they were married, and given in marriage, and were blessed according to the multitude of the promises which the Lord had made unto them. . . . There were no robbers, nor murderers, neither were there Lamanites, nor any manner of -ites; but they were in one, the children of Christ, and heirs to the kingdom of God" (4 Nephi 1:11, 17). Previous tribal and ethnic distinctions—including, apparently, prohibitions against intermarriage— were abolished until sometime between 110 and 194 years after Christ, at which time "a small part of the people . . . had revolted from the church and *taken upon them the name of Lamanites;* therefore there began to be Lamanites again in the land" (4 Nephi 1:20). In about the year 231 after Christ's birth, Mormon described a great division among the people:

> And it came to pass that in this year there arose a people who were *called* the Nephites, and they were true believers in Christ; and among them there were those who were *called* by the Lamanites—Jacobites, and Josephites, and Zoramites; therefore the true believers in Christ, and the true worshipers of Christ, . . . were *called* Nephites, and Jacobites, and Josephites, and Zoramites. And it came to pass that they who rejected the gospel were *called* Lamanites, and Lemuelites, and Ishmaelites; and they did not dwindle in unbelief, but they did wilfully rebel against the gospel of Christ; and they did teach their children that they should not believe, even as their fathers, from the beginning, did dwindle. And it was because of the wickedness and abomination of their fathers, even as it was in the beginning. And they were taught to hate the children of God, even as the Lamanites were taught to hate the children of Nephi from the beginning. (4 Nephi 1:36–39)

This language is important in understanding the term *Lamanite* as it is used thereafter. Those who became Lamanites were *called* Lamanites whether they were actually descended from Laman or not. One's standing in relationship to the gospel covenant became the primary distinction between a Nephite and a Lamanite, not one's genetic heritage. While it is likely that there was a hereditary component to these tribal identifications, they were, like Israelite identity, primarily ideological, describing how these groups viewed themselves in relation to each other and using the names of Nephi and Laman as proclamations of allegiance rather than kinship. This complicates the work of anyone who might wish to use contemporary genetic studies to prove or disprove Native American ancestral affiliation with Lehi.

Early revelations to the Prophet Joseph Smith found in the Doctrine and Covenants associate Native American groups with the Lamanites of the Book of Mormon. In Doctrine and Covenants 3:17–20 we read that the Book of Mormon is intended to bring the Nephites, Jacobites, Josephites, Zoramites, Lamanites, Lemuelites, and Ishmaelites "to the knowledge of their fathers" (v. 20). Similar ideas are found in Doctrine and Covenants 10:45–51 and 19:27. The Lord instructed Oliver Cowdery and others to "go unto the Lamanites" and teach them (D&C 28:8–9; see D&C 28:14; 30:6; 32:2) and told Newel Knight and others to "take [their] journey into the regions westward, unto the land of Missouri, unto the borders of the Lamanites" (D&C 54:8; see also 28:9). The land west of Missouri was then known as the "Indian Territories," so the passage connects at least some Native Americans of that region to the Lamanites. However, the nature of this association is not entirely clear, since the term *Lamanite* is, as demonstrated, not exclusively genetic in its meaning. It is certainly possible that North American Indian groups visited by early Latter-day Saint missionaries included within their number at least some who were actual descendants of Book of Mormon peoples.[37] There is archaeological evidence that in pre-Columbian times some Mesoamerican peoples interacted with those in the Mississippi and Ohio River valleys and the American Southwest, settling among and perhaps intermarrying with people who were already in those regions, and that others migrated from Mesoamerica into parts of South America.[38] It is reasonable to suppose that at least some of these migrants were actual descendants of Lehi or Mulek, but their modern descendants—"Lamanites," in our terms—would likely have had many other ancestors in their genealogy who would not necessarily have been Israelite; consequently, it could be very difficult to detect evidence for a few Israelite ancestors in the DNA of individual Native Americans today.

Recently, some critics, lacking support for their arguments in the Book of Mormon text, have taken to quoting the introduction to the current edition of the Book of Mormon, which describes the Lamanites as "the principal ancestors of the American Indians."[39] These words first appeared in the 1981 edition and were not found in any previous edition, but these critics tend to cite them as if they are, and always have been, of scriptural stature. Such an argument reflects a misunderstanding of Latter-day Saint beliefs about scripture and revelation. Simply put, chapter headings, introductions, and footnotes do not carry any canonical authority. The term *principal ancestors* is not scriptural, nor does such language appear to have ever been used by Joseph Smith, who never detailed or quantified the nature of the Native Americans' Israelite heritage.[40] Though written in good faith, study helps like these are supplemental to scripture and can neither replace nor override it. The fact that some Latter-day Saints may have *assumed* a uniquely or predominantly Israelite heritage for Native Americans is irrelevant, since tradition and popular assumption are not revelation.[41] Elder Bruce R. McConkie explained this view as follows: "The books, writings, explanations, expositions, views, and theories of even the wisest and greatest men, either in or out of the Church, do not rank with the standard works. Even the writings, teachings, and opinions of the prophets of God are acceptable only to the extent that they are in harmony with what God has revealed and what is recorded in the standard works."[42] Elder Charles W. Penrose of the Quorum of the Twelve Apostles explained, "The Saints believe in divine revelation to-day. At the head of this Church stands a man who is a Prophet, Seer and Revelator, sustained in that position by the vote of the whole body of its members. When the Lord wishes to speak to His Church, as a body, He does so through that individual, His servant."[43] Elder Penrose further observed that the president of the church "is a man of wisdom and experience, and we respect and venerate him; but we do not believe his personal views or utterances are revelations from God." Of course, Latter-day Saints are always open to additional revelation through appointed channels, but even then, "when 'Thus saith the

Lord' comes from him [the president of the church], the Saints investigate it; they do not shut their eyes and take it down like a pill. When he brings forth light they want to comprehend it."[44] If the ordained prophet's words are open to investigation, certainly the words of the 1981 introduction to the Book of Mormon are as well.

Although the idea of Lamanites being "the principal ancestors of the American Indians" is not scriptural, it may still be helpful, for the sake of clarity, to note what the current introduction actually says and does not say. While it specifically mentions the Jaredite and Lehite migrations, the statement does not say that these colonists were the only pre-Columbian peoples that ever came to the Americas.[45] Second, the statement does not say that the Nephites and Lamanites in the Book of Mormon consisted *only* of people descended from Lehi. This is an important point, since the Book of Mormon allows for the presence of people in the Americas other than those descended from the Jaredite, Lehite, and Mulekite colonies.[46] The covenants concerning the land of promise in the Book of Mormon were always open-ended, allowing other peoples and groups to be numbered with Lehi's family and partake of all the blessings of the land. As already shown, once so numbered, they *became* Israel, regardless of their genetic origin.

Alma prophesied that the Lamanites who remained in the land after the Nephites were destroyed would be a composite of all those who had once been numbered with both the Lamanites and the people of Nephi; anyone who remained in the land after the Nephite destruction was to be numbered—from the Nephite perspective, at least—with the Lamanites (Alma 45:13–14). Even if Latter-day Saints were to accept the assertion that these Lamanites are the "principal ancestors of American Indians," there is no way to know which Native Americans are literal descendants of Lehi and which descend from those who were once *numbered* with Lehi's people. We cannot know whether all or even most Native Americans would even carry any of Lehi's genes, even if one could determine what marker could be used to identify a gene as "Lehite."

In short, the critics' reliance on the term *principal ancestors* really amounts to a nonargument. Latter-day Saints are not bound by unscriptural assumptions, and many readers of the Book of Mormon—including many Latter-day Saint leaders—have suggested that Native American ancestry was not confined to Book of Mormon peoples and may have been quite diverse.

## Genetics and Population Studies

The Book of Mormon, then, does not require the view that all Native Americans must be literal descendants of Lehi, although all could still be quite properly considered "Lamanite." Is it possible, however, that all or most Native Americans *could* be literal descendants of Lehi? Surprisingly enough, it is. In 1999, Joseph T. Chang, a statistician at Yale University, published a study in which he demonstrated the statistical likelihood that all human beings are descended from common ancestors in the not-so-distant past.[47] His findings were restated three years later by Steve Olson in an *Atlantic Monthly* article aimed at a popular audience. In summarizing Chang's study, Olson reports that

> the most recent common ancestor of every European today (except for recent immigrants to the Continent) was someone who lived in Europe in the surprisingly recent past—only about 600 years ago. In other words, all Europeans alive today have among their ancestors the same man or woman who lived around 1400. Before that date, according to Chang's model, the number of ancestors common to all Europeans today increased, until, about a thousand years ago, a peculiar situation prevailed: 20 percent of the adult Europeans alive in 1000 would turn out to be the ancestors of no one living today (that is, they had no children or all

their descendants eventually died childless); each of the remaining 80 percent would turn out to be a direct ancestor of
every European living today.[48]

While Chang's statistical analysis holds, there would be exceptions because of endogamy (in-group marriage) in some societies. For example, Arabs have traditionally preferred to marry a first
parallel cousin, meaning that a man would marry the daughter of a
paternal uncle. But even in endogamous societies, the rule is not so
strict as to prevent mating, if not marriage, with outsiders. (Neither
conquerors nor slaves always married the women with whom they
had sexual relations.) Other scientists, in evaluating Chang's work,
note: "In the real world, the selection of parents . . . is, of course,
not random. Geography, race, religion and class have always played
strong roles in biasing mate selection. Even so, the models are telling
us something important: In subpopulations where random mating
can take place, a common ancestor pool emerges with startling rapidity, in hundreds rather than hundreds of thousands of years."[49]

In the modern era, with improved transportation and the break-
ing down of "racial" barriers, Olson remarks:

> Chang's model has even more dramatic implications.
> Because people are always migrating from continent to con-
> tinent, networks of descent quickly interconnect. This means
> that the most recent common ancestor of all six billion peo-
> ple on earth today probably lived just a couple of thousand
> years ago. And not long before that the majority of the peo-
> ple on the planet were the direct ancestors of everyone alive
> today. Confucius, Nefertiti, and just about any other ancient
> historical figure who was even moderately prolific must to-
> day be counted among everyone's ancestors.[50]

Chang showed that everyone alive today would be descended,
not just from one ancestor, but from an entire ancestral population.
In reference to Chang's study, Olson observes: "If a historical figure

who lived more than 1,600 years ago had children who themselves had children, that person is almost certainly among our ancestors. . . . One need go back only a couple of millennia to connect everyone alive today to a common pool of ancestors." However, "being descended from someone doesn't necessarily mean that you have any DNA from that person." For example, "The amount of DNA each of us gets from any one of our 1,024 ancestors ten generations back is minuscule—and we might not get any DNA from that person, given the way the chromosomes rearrange themselves every generation."[51] So the reality of one's descent from any given notable historical figure is not at all unlikely, but proving the ancestral connection in one's own genealogy—or through analysis of one's own genetic code—is another matter entirely.

> Mitochondrial DNA is a powerful tool because it cuts through this thicket and highlights a single vine—but for the very same reason, it misrepresents the complexity of our past. To understand the full story of human ancestry, the way that genes and lineages evolve over tens and hundreds of generations, we have to use mathematical models and computer simulations, because we do not have genealogical records that extend so far back into the past. These *biparental* models show that mitochondrial DNA actually underestimates how quickly human populations become homogeneous in ancestry.[52]

In short, contemporary scientific studies in genetics at present permit only a very finite peek at the panoramic mosaic of an individual's ancestry.

> The analysis of mitochondrial DNA has allowed scientists to obtain many spectacular results regarding human evolution. MtDNA represents a small, though essential, piece of our whole genome. Its relevance to the origin of and relationships among human groups lies in its peculiar mode

of transmission through the maternal line, analogous to sur-
names. However, our genetic ancestry is much broader. . . .
Our surname, like mtDNA, is only one small piece of information about our origins.

Mitochondrial genes contain information largely about
energy production. But most of the information that charac-
terizes us as human beings resides in our so-called nuclear
genes, which constitute more than 99.99 percent of the human genome. . . .

The next time you hear someone boasting of being descended from royalty, take heart: There is a very good probability that you have noble ancestors too. The rapid mixing
of genealogical branches, within only a few tens of generations, almost guarantees it. The real doubt is how much
"royal blood" your friend (or you) still carry in your genes.
Genealogy does not mean genes. And how similar we are genetically remains an issue of current research.[53]

## A Universal Covenant

The Lord told Abraham, "And in thy seed shall *all* the nations
of the earth be blessed" (Genesis 22:18, emphasis added). A similar
promise was made to Isaac: "In thy seed shall *all* the nations of the
earth be blessed" (Genesis 26:4, emphasis added). To Jacob he said:
"And thy seed shall be as the dust of the earth, and thou shalt spread
abroad to the west, and to the east, and to the north, and to the
south: and in thee and in thy seed shall *all* the *families* of the earth
be blessed" (Genesis 28:14, emphasis added). Chang's model suggests
that Abraham, Isaac, and Jacob could indeed be ancestors of every-
body now living. "The forces of genetic mixing are so powerful that
everyone in the world has Jewish ancestors, though the amount of
DNA from those ancestors in a given individual may be small. In
fact, everyone on earth is by now a descendant of Abraham, Moses,
and Aaron—if indeed they existed."[54]

Of course, contemporary scientists are unable to verify or refute definitively such distant genealogical connections. Abraham was not our only ancestor, but one among a multiplicity of others, and any distinctive markers from his DNA signature may have long been lost to time. The same could be said of Lehi. However, the loss of genetic evidence readily identifiable through current scientific tools does not affect the connection between these men and their *seed,* using that term in its scriptural sense as explained above. Latter-day Saints understand both Abraham and Lehi to be real, historical personages and ancient prophets of God, and both number among their descendants millions of literal progeny and millions whose affiliation was or is ideological or sociocultural rather than genetic. Nevertheless, they are all heirs of the covenant as it was made with their fathers, or the men they choose as their fathers. The scriptures remind us that ultimately, whom we *choose* to follow tells more about who we are than our genes do (Matthew 3:9; John 8:53–59). Abraham, Lehi, and others made and kept their covenants with God, and all who follow in their footsteps are their seed. That is a heritage worth knowing.

# Notes

1. Thomas W. Murphy, "Lamanite Genesis, Genealogy, and Genetics," in *American Apocrypha: Essays on the Book of Mormon,* ed. Dan Vogel and Brent Lee Metcalfe (Salt Lake City: Signature Books, 2002), 68. For a specific response to this charge, see John Tvedtnes, "The Charge of 'Racism' in the Book of Mormon," *FARMS Review* 15/2 (2003): 183–97.

2. See Brian Stubbs, "Elusive Israel and the Numerical Dynamics of Population Mixing," *FARMS Review* 15/2 (2003): 165–82.

3. See studies referred to by Murphy, "Lamanite Genesis, Genealogy, and Genetics," 59–61.

4. For a full description of the uses of mitochondrial DNA in genetic identification, see McClellan, "Detecting Lehi's Genetic Signature," *FARMS Review* 15/2 (2003): 42–43, 69–71.

5. See Matthew Roper, "Nephi's Neighbors: Book of Mormon Peoples and Pre-Columbian Populations," *FARMS Review* 15/2 (2003): 91–128.

6. Lehi was "a descendant of Manasseh" (Alma 10:3), so he had partial Egyptian heritage.

7. The Bible notes that Rebekah's nurse, Deborah, accompanied Jacob and his family during their return to his homeland (Genesis 35:8).

8. The term *mixed multitude* denotes non-Israelites in Nehemiah 13:3.

9. John Bright, *A History of Israel*, 3rd ed. (Philadelphia: Westminster, 1981), 134.

10. Raphael Patai, *The Myth of the Jewish Race*, rev. ed. (Detroit: Wayne State University Press, 1989), 94.

11. Roger W. Uitti, "Jerahmeel," in *The Anchor Bible Dictionary* (New York: Doubleday, 1992), 3:683; J. Kenneth Kuntz, "Kenaz," in *Anchor Bible Dictionary*, 4:17; Mark J. Fretz and Raphael I. Panitz, "Caleb," in *Anchor Bible Dictionary*, 1:808–10; and Bright, *History of Israel*, 134. In the Bible, see Judges 4:11 and 1 Samuel 15:6; 27:10; 30:29; cf. Genesis 15:19.

12. See Judges 1:19, 21, 27–35; 2:1–3, 11–14, 20–23; 3:5–7; 10:6. I noted earlier that the family of Rahab of Jericho was saved.

13. Patai, *Myth of the Jewish Race*, 96.

14. C. H. J. de Geus, "Manasseh," in *Anchor Bible Dictionary*, 4:495.

15. For a brief look at the problem of tracing Lehi's genetic signature through mtDNA or Y-chromosome DNA, see John M. Butler, "A Few Thoughts from a Believing DNA Scientist," *Journal of Book of Mormon Studies* 12/1 (2003): 36–37. For a more extensive look, see McClellan, "Detecting Lehi's Genetic Signature," in this volume.

16. Patai, *Myth of the Jewish Race*, 96.

17. Ibid., 96–97.

18. Ibid., 97.

19. Ziony Zevit, *The Religions of Ancient Israel: A Synthesis of Parallactic Approaches* (London: Continuum, 2000), 642.

20. Bright, *History of Israel*, 163.

21. From the Annals of Sargon II, quoted in James B. Pritchard, ed., *The Ancient Near East*, vol. 1, *An Anthology of Texts and Pictures* (Princeton: Princeton University Press, 1958), 195.

22. From the Prism of Sennacherib, quoted in Pritchard, *Ancient Near East*, 200.

23. See Jeffrey R. Chadwick, "Lehi's House at Jerusalem and the Land of His Inheritance," in *Glimpses of Lehi's Jerusalem* (Provo, Utah: FARMS, 2004), 81–130.

24. See McClellan, "Detecting Lehi's Genetic Signature," in this volume.

25. Arthur Koestler, *The Thirteenth Tribe: The Khazar Empire and Its Heritage* (London: Hutchinson, 1976).

26. Patai, *Myth of the Jewish Race*, xiv.

27. Estimates of the Jewish Agency from "Map of Jewish Population Worldwide," posted at www.jfed.org/jewishmap.htm (accessed 14 October 2003).

28. Karl Skorecki et al., "Y Chromosomes of Jewish Priests," *Nature*, 2 January 1997, 32; James S. Boster et al., "High Paternity Certainties of Jewish Priests," *American Anthropologist* 100/4 (1998): 967–71; Mark G. Thomas et al., "Origins of Old Testament Priests," *Nature*, 9 July 1998, 138–39; Tudor Parfitt, *Journey to the Vanished City: The Search for a Lost Tribe of Israel* (New York: Vintage, 1999); Amanda B. Spurdle and Trefor Jenkins, "The Origins of the Lemba 'Black Jews' of Southern Africa: Evidence from p12F2 and Other Y-Chromosome Markers," *American Journal of Human Genetics* 59 (1996):

1126–33; Mark G. Thomas et al., "Y Chromosomes Traveling South: The Cohen Modal Haplotype and the Origins of the Lemba—the 'Black Jews of Southern Africa,'" *American Journal of Human Genetics* 66 (2000): 674–86; Avshalom Zoossmann-Diskin, "Are Today's Jewish Priests Descended from the Old Ones?" *HOMO: Journal of Comparative Human Biology/Zeitschrift für vergleichende Biologie des Menschen* 51/2–3 (2000): 156–62.

Although Lemba folklore indicates an ancient Israelite migration to southern Africa, researchers are not agreed that the presence of the *cohen* haplotype alone is sufficient evidence to verify the legend; some of those listed above believe that the marker was introduced into the region by Jews serving on Portuguese ships that frequented the area in the sixteenth century AD.

29. Murphy, "Lamanite Genesis, Genealogy, and Genetics," 60. See Neil Bradman, Mark Thomas, and David Goldstein, "The Genetic Origins of Old Testament Priests," in *America Past, America Present: Genes and Languages in the Americas and Beyond,* ed. Colin Renfrew (Cambridge: McDonald Institute for Archaeological Research, 2000), 31–44.

30. Murphy, "Lamanite Genesis, Genealogy, and Genetics," 61.

31. See Joseph Fielding Smith, "The Priesthood of the Nephites," in *Answers to Gospel Questions* (Salt Lake City: Deseret Book, 1957), 1:123–26.

32. See, for example, *DNA vs. the Book of Mormon,* videocassette (Brigham City, Utah: Living Hope Ministries, 2003).

33. Patai, *Myth of the Jewish Race,* 231.

34. Ibid., 325. For an extended discussion of Jewish diseases, see ibid., 295–326.

35. Ibid., 326.

36. See John L. Sorenson and Matthew Roper, "Before DNA," *Journal of Book of Mormon Studies* 12/1 (2003): 11; D. Jeffrey Meldrum and Trent D. Stephens, "Who Are the Children of Lehi?" *Journal of Book of Mormon Studies* 12/1 (2003): 38–51.

37. See Stubbs, "Elusive Israel," in this volume.

38. Sorenson and Roper, "Before DNA," 8–9. For a discussion of northward migrations of Mesoamerican peoples, see John L. Sorenson, "Mesoamericans in Pre-Columbian North America," in *Reexploring the Book of Mormon,* ed. John W. Welch (Salt Lake City: Deseret Book and FARMS, 1992), 218–20. In the same volume, see his "Mesoamericans in Pre-Spanish South America," 215–17. See Sorenson's footnotes for references to intercultural studies performed by such non–Latter-day Saint archaeologists as Michael Coe, Allison C. Paulsen, Charles R. Wicke, and James B. Griffin.

39. See Murphy, "Lamanite Genesis, Genealogy, and Genetics," 53, who refers to Michael Crawford, *The Origins of Native Americans: Evidence from Anthropological Genetics* (New York: Cambridge University Press, 1998), 3–4.

40. See Roper, "Nephi's Neighbors," in this volume. A legitimate question is what we should understand by the term *principal.* Does this mean "chief" or "primary," "most important," or "most significant"? Is this to be taken in a numerical sense, or does it refer to some other noteworthy attribute of the subject in question? In his letter to John Wentworth, Joseph Smith briefly summarized the Book of Mormon account by noting the destruction of the Jaredites, who were then followed by Israelites who came from Jerusalem. Interestingly, he described the Nephites as "the principal nation"

of that second group. *The Papers of Joseph Smith,* ed. Dean C. Jessee (Salt Lake City: Deseret Book, 1989), 1:432. Since the Nephites, we are told, were clearly less numerous than the Lamanites (Mosiah 25:1–3), a condition that prevailed throughout most of the Book of Mormon narrative, it is difficult to see how the term *principal* can be taken in this instance to mean the most numerous group. In this context, the term seems best to refer to that which was the most important to the Book of Mormon writers. One can with some justification interpret "principal ancestors" in the 1981 introduction as referring to Lamanite importance in relation to the Book of Mormon and the covenants described there, rather than to the size of their genetic contribution to the Native American gene pool.

41.   President Harold B. Lee stated this clearly on at least two occasions: "If anyone, regardless of his position in the Church, were to advance a doctrine that is not substantiated by the standard Church works, meaning the Bible, the Book of Mormon, the Doctrine and Covenants, and the Pearl of Great Price, you may know that his statement is merely his private opinion. The only one authorized to bring forth any new doctrine is the President of the Church, who, when he does, will declare it as a revelation from God, and it will be so accepted by the Council of the Twelve and sustained by the body of the Church. And if any man speak a doctrine which contradicts what is in the standard Church works, you may know by that same token that it is false and you are not bound to accept it as truth." Harold B. Lee, "Measure Truth by Standard Works," in *The First Area General Conference of The Church of Jesus Christ of Latter-day Saints for Germany, Austria, Holland, Italy, Switzerland, France, Belgium, and Spain* [held in Munich, Germany, 24–26 August 1973] (Salt Lake City: The Church of Jesus Christ of Latter-day Saints, 1974), 70–71. Elsewhere he said: "If it is not in the standard works, you may well assume that it is speculation. It is man's own personal opinion, to put it another way; and if it contradicts what is in the scriptures, you may know by that same token that it is not true. This is the standard by which you measure all truth. But if you do not know the standards, you have no adequate measure of truth." Clyde J. Williams, ed., *Teachings of Harold B. Lee, Eleventh President of The Church of Jesus Christ of Latter-day Saints* (Salt Lake City: Bookcraft, 1996), 149.

42.   Bruce R. McConkie, *Mormon Doctrine* (Salt Lake City: Bookcraft, 1973), 765.

43.   Charles W. Penrose, "The Doctrine of Revelation," *Millennial Star,* 21 March 1892, 191.

44.   Ibid.

45.   For example, the introduction makes no mention of the Mulekites, who are said in the Book of Mormon to have been more numerous than the Nephites (Mosiah 25:2). The very notion of principal ancestors inescapably implies *secondary* ones.

46.   See, for example, Roper, "Nephi's Neighbors," in this volume. For an overview of archaeological and other scientific evidence for Old World peoples in the pre-Columbian New World, see Sorenson and Roper, "Before DNA," 18–23.

47.   Joseph T. Chang, "Recent Common Ancestors of All Present-Day Individuals," *Advanced Applied Probability* 31 (1999): 1002–26. For a simpler, more specialized, independently derived numerical study that supports Chang's hypothesis, see Stubbs, "Elusive Israel," in this volume. For the scientific approach to population studies, see

McClellan, "Detecting Lehi's Genetic Signature," in this volume; Michael F. Whiting, "DNA and the Book of Mormon: A Phylogenetic Perspective," *Journal of Book of Mormon Studies* 12/1 (2003): 24–35 (also this volume pp. 111–30).

48. Steve Olson, "The Royal We," *Atlantic Monthly,* May 2002, 63–64.

49. Susanna C. Manrubia, Bernard Derrida, and Damián H. Zanette, "Genealogy in the Era of Genomics," *American Scientist* 91/2 (2003): 164.

50. Olson, "Royal We," 64.

51. Steve Olson, *Mapping Human History: Genes, Race, and Our Common Origins* (Boston: Houghton Mifflin, 2002), 47.

52. Manrubia, Derrida, and Zanette, "Genealogy in the Era of Genomics," 158, 160.

53. Ibid., 165. Some of that current research was announced early in 2003. A survey of 2,123 males from the Caucasus to China suggested that the Y chromosomes of up to 8 percent of all men living within the area formerly controlled by the Mongol empire indicated their descent from the ruling house of the Mongols; this means that about 16 million men—about 1 in 200 of the world's total male population—are probably descendants of Genghis Khan. Chris Tyler-Smith et al., "The Genetic Legacy of the Mongols," *American Journal of Human Genetics* 72 (March 2003): 717–21.

54. Olson, *Mapping Human History,* 114.

# Elusive Israel and the Numerical Dynamics of Population Mixing

*Brian D. Stubbs*

Ethnic mixing viewed through the glimpse of a single lifetime can seem negligible. However, a detailed examination of the mathematics of population mixing over a few lifetimes reveals how quickly and thoroughly populations mix over time. Even scholars seldom realize how dynamic the cumulative effect of this mixing is upon a pedigree. The passage of only five hundred years can result in 98 percent of a tribe's or community's posterity not being pure- or full-blooded. This article examines the numerical dynamics of population mixing and their significance for Book of Mormon peoples in the New World and for Israel generally throughout the world.

As a potential candidate for being in an ethnically mixed marriage, I have given the matter of mixing considerable thought: my wife is from Argentina, while my known/recorded ancestry comes out of the British Isles. I call myself a *potential* candidate because the common views used to determine this sort of distinction are oversimplified, if not erroneous, so I have doubts that my wife and I qualify any more than most others would. The lineage of most persons and groups consists of genetic contributions from several ethnic varieties. The three numerically prominent population groups in the history of Western Europe are the Celts, the Germanic peoples, and the Romans. Everyone with roots out of Western Europe would have all three well represented in his or her ancestry, whether verifiable or not. As I look at my pedigree from 1700 to 1850, half the marriages are unions between a Germanic spouse (English) and a Celtic spouse

(Welsh, Scottish, or Irish), though each of those individuals would already have been a thorough Germanic-Celtic mix.

The Romans ruled Britain from the middle of the first century AD to the year 410[1] and during that time undoubtedly bestowed a considerable genetic contribution upon the island population. Whatever islanders missed out on Roman genes through that episode probably picked up some from their pre-English Germanic ancestors on the continent, who also mixed with and were ruled by the Romans through the same centuries before crossing the channel in the middle of the fifth century AD. And if those two episodes didn't make enough of a genetic impact, a third opportunity came in the centuries after 1066 during the rule of the Norman French, who were themselves at least a four-way mix of Norsemen (hence the name *Norman*), Germanic Franks, Celtic Gauls, and (of course) Romans, whose Latin was largely the progenitor of the French language. So I—and everyone from the British Isles—would have quite a thorough mix of Germanic, Celtic, and Roman ancestors.

My wife's ancestors are primarily from Spain and Italy, with a probable, though unverifiable, Native American line or two. (Of course, I may have one, too.) In areas now labeled Spain and Italy, the Celtiberians (a Celtic-Iberian mix) in Spain and other Celtic groups lived in or bordered and mixed with the populations of both areas more centuries than they did not. Similarly, the Visigoths and other Germanic peoples were also prominent in the histories and pedigrees of those areas; and, of course, the Romans came out of Italy and ruled Spain for some time. So if I am 40 percent Germanic, 30 percent Celtic, 20 percent Roman, and 10 percent other, and if my wife is 20 percent Germanic, 30 percent Celtic, 40 percent Roman, and 10 percent other, are we more different than most random couples of Western European extraction? She and I are distant cousins three ways! Even the geneticists find national identities in Europe rather indistinguishable.[2]

## Israel Disseminated

According to mathematical probabilities that will be detailed below, Israel's permeation of world populations affects the genetic heritage of at least a hundred times more people than is obvious or known—in the Old World and the New. The linguistic variety in the Americas[3] and John Sorenson's population analysis[4] both suggest that many other peoples dwelt in ancient America in addition to Book of Mormon groups.[5] After the Book of Mormon groups arrived in the New World, the diffusion of Israel in the New World would in many ways have paralleled that in the Old World. In both hemispheres, many persons, families, and groups regularly left the several main bodies to seek perceived "greener pastures" of land, opportunity, or marriage. For example, even before Christ's time, enough Jews had left Palestine that the Jewish population outside of Palestine was likely greater than the Jewish population in Palestine.[6]

Similar diffusions of Lehites and Mulekites into surrounding populations of the New World (or assimilations of outside populations into Lehite and Mulekite groups) were undoubtedly occurring throughout Book of Mormon history and since.[7] For example, the Mulekite group that the Nephites found in Zarahemla may have been only one of many groups splintered off since their original disembarkment, just as the Nephites who found them were but a fraction of Lehi's posterity in the Americas at that time. Then the several splinter groups would subsequently have mixed with other pre-Columbian populations.

Besides revealing a magnified extent of population mixing, an understanding of the numerical dynamics behind it also discourages the common oversimplification that a person is either "of Israel" or is "not of Israel." The likelihood of a person having a high percentage of Israelite blood these days is improbable to impossible, yet in many areas the likelihood of high percentages of people having some Israelite ancestry is probable. No one has a lot, but a lot have a little.

No one is a "pure Israelite," nor ever has been, except Israel (Jacob) himself. Jacob's twelve sons—who were only half Israelite— presumably did not marry sisters, so Jacob's grandchildren, who made the trek into Egypt to meet their uncle Joseph, were already only one-quarter Israelite, Israel (Jacob) being only one of the four grandparents of each of his son's children. How many of those grandchildren married cousins and how many married outside the group is not known. Some of Jacob's posterity probably married into the ethnic group to which Joseph's wife and children belonged. Regardless, by the time Jacob died in Egypt, most of his posterity were probably from a quarter to one thirty-second Israelite, geneti- cally speaking. Those proportions diminished through succeeding centuries as Israelites married Midianites, Moabites, Hittites, and so on. Following the various dispersions, the percentages of Israelite an- cestry within each person would diminish at more accelerated rates.[8]

As a result, few, if any, could be as much as 25 percent Israelite (even in Jewish communities), yet the numerical dynamics of popu- lation mixing suggest that smaller percentages of the literal "blood of Israel" are likely to be in many more persons than ever suspected. However, the thoroughness, extent, and rapidity of the spread and diffusion of Israel in both hemispheres cannot be fully appreciated without a careful consideration of the actual mathematics involved.

### Tracking the Numbers

Neighboring populations mix whether they are comparable or different in size, but small populations mix even faster because the smaller the group, the greater the percentage that marries outside the group. For example, in an Amerindian tribe or Jewish community of 1,000 to 2,000, there may be 50 to 100 unmarried persons of mar- riageable age at any given time. Therefore, about 25 to 50 potential partners of the opposite gender exist within one's own group, which is not a wide selection. Even though a certain number will marry one of those 25 to 50 within the group, it is likely that others will marry outside the group. So the percentage of a small population that will marry outside its group, due simply to a lack of prospective partners within the group, is much higher than the percentage of a large population that will marry into an outside or neighboring group.[9]

Consider a hypothetical and simplified but realistic scenario for a tribe, a Jewish community, or some other minority population living among a larger population of "outsiders." Jewish families or communities are as cohesive as any, yet they, too, naturally diffuse into neighboring populations—and they allow incursions by genetic outsiders through conversions. This is apparent by the facts that many Jews in Africa are black, that the Jews in China look oriental,[10] that the Jews in Europe look more European than Mediterranean, and so on. Suppose that a small percentage of the children born into a Jewish community marries outside the group. Even if the "outsider" spouse was not a convert to Judaism, the children of this marriage would likely know of their Jewish heritage and might be acquainted with their Jewish grandparents, aunts, uncles, and cousins. But the children of these children—that is, the great-grandchildren of the last regular reader of the Torah—may or may not know that they are of Jewish descent, that their great-grandfather was the last orthodox observer in their line, and that their second cousins and their parents' cousins are Jewish. I know my thirty aunts and uncles and my eighty first cousins well, but I knew none of my parents' cousins or my second cousins until I moved to a small town three hundred miles away, made new friends, and after several years of acquaintance discovered that three of them were my second cousins. In other words, the passage of a few generations often obscures ancestral identities.

Returning to the example, it is instructive to chart the numerical impact over several generations of even a fraction of the community's young people marrying outside the community, as I have done in table 1 (next page). To facilitate the math, I have calculated the ratio of those who marry outside the community at 10 percent; the

## Table 1. The Numerical Dynamics of Population Mixing

| generation | those with ancestry exclusively from within the ethnic group | | | | those with ancestry from outside the group | | | | total adults descended from group ($a_i + a_o = a_x$) |
|---|---|---|---|---|---|---|---|---|---|
| | adults ($a_i$) | % of $a_x$ | couples ($c_i$) | offspring* ($c_i \times 2.5$) | adults ($a_o$) | % of $a_x$ | couples ($c_o$) | offspring ($c_o \times 2.5$) | |
| 1 | 900 | 90% | 450 | 1,125 = 1,013 + 112 | 100 | 10% | 100 | 250 | 1,000 |
| | | | | 112 + 250 = 362 adults with mixed ancestry in the 2nd generation | | | | | |
| 2 | 1,013 | 74% | 506 | 1,265 = 1,139 + 126 | 362 | 26% | 362 | 905 | 1,375 |
| | | | | 126 + 905 = 1,031 adults with mixed ancestry in the 3rd generation | | | | | |
| 3 | 1,139 | 52% | 570 | 1,425 = 1,283 + 142 | 1,031 | 48% | 1,031 | 2,577 | 2,170 |
| | | | | 142 + 2,577 = 2,577 adults with mixed ancestry in the 4th generation | | | | | |
| 4 | 1,283 | 32% | 640 | 1,600 = 1,440 + 160 | 2,719 | 68% | 2,719 | 6,797 | 4,002 |
| 5 | 1,440 | 17% | 720 | 1,800 = 1,620 + 180 | 6,957 | 83% | 6,957 | 17,392 | 8,397 |
| 6 | 1,620 | 8% | 810 | 2,025 = 1,823 + 202 | 17,572 | 92% | 17,572 | 43,930 | 19,192 |
| 7 | 1,823 | 4% | 911 | 2,277 = 2,050 + 227 | 44,132 | 96% | 44,132 | 110,330 | 45,955 |
| 8 | 2,050 | 2% | 1025 | 2,562 = 2,306 + 256 | 110,557 | 98% | 110,557 | 276,392 | 112,607 |

*In this column, the total number of offspring with ancestry exclusively from within the group is broken into figures representing 90 percent and 10 percent of that total. The 90-percent figure becomes the $a_i$ figure for the next generation, while the 10-percent figure is added to the $c_o \times 2.5$ figure of the same generation to yield the $a_o$ figure of the next generation.

number of discrete generations per century as three—or 33 years per generation, which is actually longer than the average; and a constant population growth rate of 2.5 children per couple. This latter figure might be slightly high considering the infant mortality rate of past centuries, but the percentages shown on the table would be valid regardless. I have also assumed equal gender ratios and a constant rate of diffusion in each generation. These are simplifications, certainly, but they do not diminish the value of the illustration.

On the table, the generation number is on the left. The next four numbers then follow for those whose ancestry comes exclusively from within the ethnic group: the number of adults with ancestry from exclusively within the group, the percentage they represent of the total number of adults in that generation that are related to the group, the number of couples that those adults would form if everyone married, and the number of offspring of those couples if couples averaged 2.5 children who reached adulthood. In the next four columns to the right are parallel figures for those marrying partners with ancestry from outside the group; the fourth of these columns, labeled "offspring," represents those born to these marriages, having ancestry partly from outside the original group and partly from within it. The last column shows the total number of adults of that generation, of whatever ancestry, who are descended from it.

Let's walk through the first few generations. From a community including, say, 1,000 adults of one generation, 900, or 90 percent, marry within the group to form 450 couples ($c_i$)—half the number of individuals, since both spouses come from within the group. The other 10 percent, or 100, marry outside the group to form 100 couples ($c_o$), since the partner of each member of the group comes from outside the group. This factor alone accounts for a phenomenal geometric growth of posterity with ancestry from outside the group that increases much faster than the number of posterity with ancestry from exclusively within the group.

However, each succeeding generation with ancestry from outside the group will have ever smaller fractions of their ancestry from within the group.

At a population growth rate of 2.5 children per couple, the 450 couples that marry within the ethnic group would have 1,125 children ($c_i$ x 2.5), 90 percent of whom (1,013) marry within the group and 10 percent of whom (112) marry outside the group—meaning that they marry someone whose ancestors were not exclusively from within the group, even if some of them were. The 112 marrying outside the group in this second generation combine with the 250 born to those with one parent from outside the group for a total of 362 persons descended from the group but with ancestry from outside of it in the second generation. Those 362 comprise 26 percent of the total 1,375 (that is, 1,013 + 362, or $a_x$) descended from the group in the second generation. Those 362 persons marry an equal number with ancestry from outside the group to form 362 couples who in turn have 905 children, while the 1,013 who marry within the group form 506 couples (assuming that one did not marry) and have 1,265 children. Of those 1,265 children, 10 percent, or 126, marry partners with ancestry from outside the group in the third generation, combining with their 905 relatives with ancestry from outside the group for a total of 1,031 adults with ancestry from outside the group in the third generation. Keep in mind that the number of related adults with ancestry from outside the group for any given generation ($a_o$) is the 10 percent of the previous generation that married outsiders or partners of mixed ancestry added to the offspring with mixed ancestry born in that generation. The related adults with ancestry from outside the group in the fifth generation, for example, is 6,957, adding the numbers 160 + 6,797 from the fourth generation. The percentage figure to the right of each figure in the "adults" columns is the percentage that number of adults comprises of the total adult population related to the group, of whatever ancestry ($a_x$). For example, in the fifth generation, 1,440 adults with ancestry from exclusively within the group comprise 17 percent of the total 8,397 adults related to the group, while the remaining 83 percent are the 6,957 adults of mixed ancestry.

After only eight generations (approximately 267 years), only 2 percent of the group's posterity still has ancestry exclusively from within the group and 98 percent of those related to the group have mixed ancestry. In actuality, the numbers of individuals with ancestry from outside the group will not multiply quite as rapidly as table 1 portrays because, as indicated, many in surrounding areas will be distant relatives with some ancestry from within the group; that is, not every person who marries outside the group will marry a person totally unrelated to the group. Some would marry outside partners who themselves are 1/8 or 1/64 Jewish, Hopi, Zuñi, or whatever; thus, after the first generation, the number of marriageable adults with some ancestry from outside the group ($a_o$) will not quite equal that same number of new couples ($c_o$), as portrayed in the table. The argument that Jews or other groups are more strictly cohesive than to allow 10 percent to leave may occasionally apply, but even 3 percent would yield the same result, though this would come about in 800 years instead of 267: 2 to 10 percent with ancestry from exclusively within the group versus 90 to 98 percent with ancestry from outside the group.

The dynamics of this phenomenon also explain why thousands of the present descendants of the Cherokee look Caucasian. The Cherokee may have mixed with Europeans more than any tribe; thus, claims of Cherokee ancestry made by people who do not look remotely Amerindian are not necessarily fictitious but may simply reflect these figures—that 2 to 10 percent of Cherokee descendants are still in the group and look Amerindian, while 90 to 98 percent of Cherokee descendants are Caucasian-looking Americans.[11] Continuing the math over a millennium or two would leave less than 1 percent of today's literal descendants of the Cherokee, Hopi, Kiowa, Jews, or whatever minority population knowing about that heritage, while more than 99 percent would not know about it and would label themselves according to their most recent ancestry, since a knowledge of one's ancestors beyond great-grandparents is often lost.

For example, I once told a Navaho friend that he looked Hopi to me. As a fluent speaker of Navaho, born and raised by two Navaho parents, he replied confidently, "I'm full-blooded Navaho." I asked where his family was from originally, and it was an area not far from Hopi land. Two years later he reminded me of my previous observation and told me that he had recently learned from a grandparent that some of his ancestral lines were Hopi. As I told him, it is probable that many Navahos and Hopis near the joint-use area are about half-Hopi and half-Navaho and are thus blood brothers who feud only according to most recent ancestry. The same would be true of ethnic groups in many parts of the world. Some studies find Jews and Palestinians nearly indistinguishable genetically.[12]

Some may claim that in former, less-mobile times, peoples and places were more homogenous than they are today. However, many historical accounts (such as Acts 2:5–12) show that international travel was as common and ethnic variety in many places as diverse as they are today. Historical records of pre-Columbian American life are rare, but what sixteenth- to nineteenth-century accounts we do have suggest a "melting-pot" effect in Native Americans at least as dynamic as today.[13]

Let us use a different method to figure how many persons and families of Europe, for example, could have traces of Jewish or Israelite ancestry. It will use simplifications similar to those in the previous hypothetical scenario, but again, they do not lessen its value as an illustration. Ralph Marcus writes that at the time of Christ, 10 percent of the Roman Empire was Jewish, comprising about 6 million of a total population of 60 million. They were identified in two hundred communities around the Mediterranean besides Palestine, and their numbers appear to have been significant in Spain, Italy, and Greek-speaking areas.[14] Because such estimates could be high—although it should be borne in mind that they reflect only those *known* to be Jewish—we will cut them in half to be conservative and estimate the total Jewish population at 3 million instead of 6 million. Most Jewish emigrations occurred between the destructions of the First and Second Temples—586 BC to AD 70. The destinations of choice were Africa, Arabia, Europe, or deeper into Asia. But of the four possible areas, let us not assume that a full fourth of the Jewish population immigrated to Europe—let's assume a total of perhaps 120,000, representing only 4 percent of the 3 million.

Estimates of Europe's population in those times usually range from 30 to 40 million.[15] For mathematical convenience, let's select an intermediate estimate of 36 million. Calculating about 4.5 people per family, 36 million would yield 8 million families in Europe. The 120,000 Jews living in Europe at a given time would represent about three generations, so if one in 20 of the 40,000 in the generation of marriageable age married a non-Jew at a constant rate of diffusion, then 2,000 "gentile," or non-Jewish, families would receive a new member having Jewish ancestry in the first generation. If each of those mixed couples had two children that reached adulthood and married (which represents zero population growth, again for the sake of mathematical simplicity), then in the second generation, 4,000 families would receive some Jewish heritage through them, plus another 2,000 families who would receive from among the next generation of Jews a new member—the one in 20 that would marry outside their Jewish community—for a total of 6,000 families with some Jewish heritage. The two offspring from each of those 6,000 families would unite with offspring from 12,000 gentile families, and an additional 2,000 of the next Jewish generation would marry outside their community, for a total of 14,000 families containing a member with some Jewish heritage. This pattern would continue as follows:

Table 2. Jewish Diffusions into the Families of Europe

| generation | Jews marrying into outside families | part-Jewish persons creating families | total families affected |
|---|---|---|---|
| 1 | 2,000 | none | 2,000 |
| 2 | 2,000 | 4,000 | 6,000 |
| 3 | 2,000 | 12,000 | 14,000 |
| 4 | 2,000 | 28,000 | 30,000 |
| 5 | 2,000 | 60,000 | 62,000 |
| 6 | 2,000 | 124,000 | 126,000 |
| 7 | 2,000 | 252,000 | 254,000 |
| 8 | 2,000 | 508,000 | 510,000 |
| 9 | 2,000 | 1,020,000 | 1,022,000 |
| 10 | 2,000 | 2,044,000 | 2,046,000 |
| 11 | 2,000 | 4,092,000 | 4,094,000 |
| 12 | 2,000 | 8,188,000 | 8,190,000 |

In 12 generations—only 400 years—the total number of affected families has already surpassed the approximate total number of families in Europe, according to our population estimate. Even if the number of families were actually double our estimate, it would take only one more generation for all to be affected; if quadruple that, only two more generations. In other words, whether our initial estimates are entirely accurate or not hardly matters, since the passage of time would fill out the established pattern very rapidly in any case.

However, the numbers in table 2 do not mean that all the families of Europe would be affected in 400 years, because families nearer the Jewish communities would be impacted several times during these centuries, while other families further away would not be affected at all in the early generations. That is, certain areas would receive higher proportions of the total "offshoots" or available "diffusions" from each Jewish generation, while other areas would receive few to none, early in the process at least. From the twelfth generation on, the 2,000 "pure" Jews leaving the main groups each generation is so minuscule

compared to the number who are part Jewish and producing posterity that one could leave out that part of the calculation, to simplify the
math even further, and merely double the number of those who are
part Jewish each generation for an approximation of the number of
diffusional branches sent out each generation. Rounding our twelfth-
generation number off to 8 million and doubling that for 33 more generations, for a total time period of 1,500 years or 45 generations—say,
from the time of Christ to AD 1500—we would reach a billion familial
contributions at the nineteenth generation, a trillion at the twenty-
ninth, and about 64 quadrillion after 45 generations,[16] which exceeds
by many times the population of the earth, let alone the number of
families in Europe. However, once again, the numbers would not grow
as rapidly as the tables portray because many of these part-Jewish people would be marrying each other, creating only one new family instead of two. Said differently, many persons, families, or areas would
be receiving dozens to hundreds of these infusions into their ancestry over the generations and may have surprisingly high percentages
of Jewish ancestry; others, of course, would have less. However, with
even a fraction of that number of diffusional branches being sent out
over 1,500 years, how many persons in Europe would *not* have Jewish
ancestry? Probably very few.

So, as mentioned, it may be misleading to think of persons as
either "of Israel" or "not of Israel." Even Jacob's grandchildren were
only one-quarter (25 percent) "of Israel," and the percentages among
Israelites can only have decreased since. On the other hand, a surprisingly high percentage of the world's present population may have
traces of Israelite ancestry, and Abraham's descendants may indeed
be numbered as the stars in the sky and the sands of the seashore
(Genesis 22:17).

## The Meaning of It All

So what is the significance of all this to the Amerindians in the
New World and to peoples in the Old World and to you and me?

It means that no one is "pure" Israelite but that very many are part Israelite. In the Old World, it probably means that if Joseph Smith, whose known and more recent ancestry is out of the British Isles, was as much Ephraimite as any on earth, as has been said of him,[17] and if the roots of most early church leaders came out of the same areas, then it stands to reason that a migration of Ephraimites entered northwestern Europe and the British Isles in the distant past. As for other places in the Old World, we have mentioned the large numbers of Jews living in Rome and Spain even before Christ was born, and the substantial Jewish and Yiddish-speaking presence in central and eastern Europe speaks for the probability that significant numbers throughout Europe and Asia have Israelite ancestry. The same is possible for much of the world.

In the New World, the numerical dynamics of population mixing make easily feasible the views of Mark E. Petersen and Ted E. Brewerton that most Amerindians are descended from Book of Mormon peoples,[18] even if Book of Mormon peoples were originally a minority of ancient American populations and are thus only a part of the ancestry of most individuals. Exact numbers and percentages must await more sophisticated and accurate measures, but the pattern makes such views easily possible, if not probable.

The latest sensation for Book of Mormon critics is DNA. A video produced by Living Hope Ministries entitled *DNA vs. the Book of Mormon* discusses both Native American DNA and linguistic data in an attempt to discount the Book of Mormon. I am not a microbiologist, but I am a linguist, and for scholarship's sake, I hope that the treatment of the genetic data was more credible than the comments on the linguistic data. In that poorly documented "documentary," Thomas Murphy, listed as an anthropologist and scholar, claimed that the linguistic data of Amerindian languages generally show a link with Asia.[19] That is 2 percent true and 98 percent false. Of some hundred-plus Amerindian language families,[20] one (Eskimo-Aleut) still straddles the Bering Strait and one other (Na-

Dene, or at least Athapaskan) shows promise for demonstrable language origins from Asia.[21] However, the other ninety-eight or so language families show no demonstrable linguistic tie with Asia. Most linguists, like most scholars, assume that those languages came from Asia, but too long ago to have retained a verifiable link due to too much change over too many centuries. But that is an assumption. Any credible linguist would agree that no one has identified a linguistic connection between East Asian languages and any of the other language families except the two mentioned.

Even the film's claim that 99 percent of Amerindian DNA is of Asian origin, with no sign of Jewish DNA, raised many questions in my mind: (1) First, in the European gene pool, have microbiologists been able to identify Celtic DNA as opposed to Germanic or Roman? Even if Celtic DNA could be isolated, to say that 99 percent of Europeans have Celtic DNA would be misleading, since similarly high percentages would also have Germanic, Roman, Greek, Basque, Jewish, and several other kinds of DNA—that is, most individuals in Europe would have those several kinds of DNA—if the science were advanced enough to identify the DNA supplied by all the varied people who filled an individual's billion ancestral slots eight hundred years ago.[22] (2) Bering Strait DNA will, of course, exist throughout the Americas, just like Celtic DNA exists throughout Europe. So if Celtic DNA cannot be isolated, given the well-documented history of Europe, what can definitively be said of the varieties of DNA (besides East Asian) that may exist in the Americas? Though 99 percent of samples from Amerindians may show Asian DNA, 75 percent could also show Lehite DNA, as soon as, or if, it is ever identified—because it will not be the same as Jewish DNA.[23] Lehi and Ishmael were Josephites, not Jewish; though the two tribes are distantly related, the genetic compositions of both have been highly diluted in the millennia since Judah and Joseph were born to the same father through different mothers. (3) Is it even possible to identify Josephite DNA? Are there any Israelite human remains from northern Palestine dating between 1000 and 600 BC that might be used for a test? (4) Even if a comparison with Jewish DNA is allowed, what Jewish DNA have the studies dealt with—the Jews in Europe, or the black Jews in Africa, or the Jews in China, or whatever DNA all these groups have in common? (5) Has molecular science been sufficiently refined to measure dates or amounts of change over a given time period or for a given number of generations? (6) Of the trillion-plus ancestral slots on anyone's pedigree chart forty generations back (ca. 1,200 years), how many individual ancestors could the science presently identify?

I understand that the science of DNA identification is still in its infancy, that only small percentages of the DNA strands have been dealt with successfully, and that even though tremendous potential exists, most of that potential remains to be realized.[24] I am excited about the potential, but I am less than overwhelmed by the premature shots in the dark and unfounded assumptions based upon perhaps the first 5 percent of that potential. It may be only a matter of time until evidence for multitudes of Lehite posterity in the Americas becomes clear. The numerical dynamics of population mixing would undoubtedly be involved; for in both the Old World and the New, the parable of the olive tree in Jacob 5, with its grafts being transplanted into populations the world over, is profoundly significant.

## Notes

1. Albert C. Baugh and Thomas Cable, *A History of the English Language,* 3rd ed. (Englewood Cliffs, N.J.: Prentice-Hall, 1978), 44–46; Winston L. S. Churchill, *Churchill's History of the English-Speaking Peoples,* originally published as four volumes in 1955, arranged for one volume by Henry S. Commager (New York: Barnes and Noble, 1995), 3–12. Although Julius Caesar mounted invasions of Britain in 55 and 54 BC, Roman influence was neither widespread nor lasting until the conquest begun by Claudius in AD 43.

2. Nancy Shute, "Where We Come From," *U.S. News and World Report,* 29 January 2001, 36, states that "most people of European origin are so genetically mixed that it's impossible to tell German from Frenchman, Bosnian from Serb."

Of course, this line of thinking concerns biology more than culture, the other dimension of ethnicity, but culture preservation has been an elusive ideal among civilized peoples ever since they decided what culture is. I know nothing about the culture(s) of my Celtic ancestors except that they played bagpipes instead of CDs. Even the more recent pioneer culture from which so many Latter-day Saints in the western United States spring is becoming a poorly comprehended past for most youth. The only culture those youth and I know very well is the present U.S. culture, with its valued visitation rights to Wal-Mart and McDonalds—our favorite Celtic restaurant.

3. Lyle Campbell, *Historical Linguistics: An Introduction* (Cambridge, Mass.: MIT Press, 1999), 163; Johanna Nichols, *Linguistic Diversity in Space and Time* (Chicago: University of Chicago Press, 1992), 233. Campbell and Nichols are among the foremost specialists in Amerindian languages. Campbell sets the number of Amerindian language families at over 150; Nichols offers a number of 157; I have seen other counts around 100 and as low as 80. A language family is a group of languages that linguists can demonstrate to be related to one another and descended from a common parent language spoken anciently. In size, language families can range from a small number of languages, or an isolate not verifiably related to anything else, to large numbers, like the Algonkian and the Uto-Aztecan language families, which consist of about 30 languages each.

4. John L. Sorenson, "When Lehi's Party Arrived in the Land, Did They Find Others There?" *Journal of Book of Mormon Studies* 1/1 (1992): 1–34.

5. See Matthew Roper, "Nephi's Neighbors: Book of Mormon Peoples and Pre-Columbian Populations," *FARMS Review* 15/2 (2003): 91–128 (also this volume 217–56); John L. Sorenson and Matthew Roper, "Before DNA," *Journal of Book of Mormon Studies* 12/1 (2003): 13–23 (also this volume pp. 27–70).

6. Ralph Marcus, "The Challenge of Greco-Roman Culture," in *Great Ages and Ideas of the Jewish People,* ed. Leo W. Schwarz (New York: Random, 1956), 114–15, states that by the time of Christ, the Jewish population comprised 10 percent of the Roman Empire and was found in two hundred communities throughout southern Europe, western Asia, and northern Africa.

7. See Matthew Roper, "Swimming in the Gene Pool: Israelite Kinship Relations, Genes, and Genealogy," in this volume, 257–94.

8. See ibid.

9. For example, about half of the small population of Utes on the White Mesa Ute Reservation in southeastern Utah (about 250 persons) marry another Ute; the other half marry non-Utes. That pattern over the last five or ten generations would result in few if any of them being "pure Ute."

10. *The Jewish Encyclopedia* (New York: Funk and Wagnalls, 1907), 4:33–38, s.v. "China," discusses customs of Jewish groups in China that point to the possibility that they left Palestine before rabbinic Judaism developed, eventually arriving in China about 2,000 years ago. A photo in the article shows Chinese Jews to be indistinguishable from Chinese non-Jews. See also the photographic essay depicting Jews with a wide range of physical features in "The Problematic Role of DNA Testing in Unraveling Human History," *Journal of Book of Mormon Studies* 9/2 (2000): 66–74.

11. It has been reported to me by part-Cherokee persons that these ratios are apparent at tribal reunions, where the majority of Cherokee descendants look Caucasian.

12. Shute, "Where We Come From," 39, cites a study by Michael Hammer and states that "although Palestinian and Jewish men may be political foes, they are also brethren, so closely related as to be genetically indistinguishable."

13. My monograph "Athapaskans, Puebloans, and the Prehistory of the Navaho People," a manuscript in process, cites several examples of eighteenth- and nineteenth-century historical accounts addressing the frequency of intertribal mixing, especially as it applies to the Puebloan ancestry of the Navaho people.

14. Marcus, "Challenge of Greco-Roman Culture," 114–15; Haim Beinart, *Atlas of Medieval Jewish History* (New York: Simon and Schuster, 1992), 80–82; Cecil Roth, ed., *The Standard Jewish Encyclopedia*, new rev. ed. (Garden City, N.Y.: Doubleday, 1966), 791, 1608, 1744–46, and 1753–56.

15. J. M. Roberts, *History of the World* (New York: Oxford University Press, 1993), 334, 409, suggests a population of about 40 million in AD 1000; "Medieval Sourcebook: Tables on Population in Medieval Europe," online at www.fordham.edu/halsall/source/pop-in-eur.html (accessed 3 October 2003), offers population figures of 27.5 million in AD 500, 18 million in AD 650, and 38.5 million in AD 1000; several other sources in similar ranges are not cited.

16. For doubters, I shall complete the chart: 12th generation = 8 million; 13th = 16 million; 14th = 32 million; 15th = 64 million; 16th = 128 million; 17th = 256 million; 18th = 512 million; 19th = 1 billion (rounded off); 20th = 2 billion; 21st = 4 billion; 22nd = 8 billion; 23rd = 16 billion; 24th = 32 billion; 25th = 64 billion; 26th = 128 billion; 27th = 256 billion; 28th = 512 billion; 29th = 1 trillion (rounded off); 30th = 2 trillion; 31st = 4 trillion; 32nd = 8 trillion; 33rd = 16 trillion; 34th = 32 trillion; 35th = 64 trillion; 36th = 128 trillion; 37th = 256 trillion; 38th = 512 trillion; 39th = 1 quadrillion (rounded off); 40th = 2 quadrillion; 41st = 4 quadrillion; 42nd = 8 quadrillion; 43rd = 16 quadrillion; 44th = 32 quadrillion; 45th = 64 quadrillion. In numerals, a quadrillion is written as a 1 followed by 15 zeros.

17. In addition to 2 Nephi 3:11, several other sources assert the literal descent of Joseph Smith Jr. from Joseph in Egypt and his son Ephraim, though the term *pure* is used loosely in some of them: Brigham Young, in *Journal of Discourses*, 2:269 (8 April 1855); Joseph Fielding McConkie, "Joseph, Son of Jacob," in *Encyclopedia of Mormonism* (New York: Macmillan, 1992), 2:760–61; W. Cleon Skousen, *The Fourth Thousand Years* (Salt Lake City: Bookcraft, 1966), 584–85.

18. Mark E. Petersen, *Children of Promise: The Lamanites, Yesterday and Today* (Salt Lake City: Bookcraft, 1981), 31; Ted E. Brewerton, "The Book of Mormon: A Sacred Ancient Record," *Ensign*, November 1995, 30.

19. *DNA vs. The Book of Mormon*, videocassette (Brigham City, Utah: Living Hope Ministries, 2003).

20. See note 3 above.

21. Robert Shafer, "Athapaskan and Sino-Tibetan," *International Journal of American Linguistics* 18/1 (1952): 12–19. Before becoming aware of Shafer's article, I served a Navaho-speaking mission and found enough semantic similarity between Athapas-

kan and Asian languages to convince me of a probable connection between the two; but even if their language is largely from across the Bering Strait, the Navaho are genetically an Athapaskan-Puebloan mix. I will address this issue in "Athapaskans, Puebloans, and the Prehistory of the Navaho People."

22.  One's ancestral slots double each generation back: 2 parents; 4 grandparents; 8; 16; 32; 64; 128; 256; 512; 1,024 (only 10 generations back, or 267 years ago). One can continue doubling or else calculate that each of those 1,024 have 1,024 progenitors of their own 10 generations back, totaling over a million slots 20 generations back, or 533 years ago. Each 10 generations, or 267 years, adds three more digits to the number of ancestral slots—though it does not add that number of ancestors, since the number of one's ancestral slots would soon exceed the population of the earth; instead, the same persons begin appearing several times in one's pedigree.

23.  See Roper, "Swimming in the Gene Pool," in this volume.

24.  See Martin Jones, *The Molecule Hunt: Archaeology and the Search for Ancient DNA* (New York: Arcade, 2001).

# Index